GUIDE TO GPS POSITIONING

Prepared under the leadership of

David Wells

by

Norman Beck
Demitris Delikaraoglou
Alfred Kleusberg
Edward J. Krakiwsky
Gérard Lachapelle
Richard B. Langley
Mete Nakiboglu
Klaus-Peter Schwarz
James M. Tranquilla
Petr Vaníček
David Wells

First printing, December 1986
Second printing, with corrections, May 1987

CANADIAN GPS ASSOCIATES

© CANADIAN GPS ASSOCIATES 1986, 1987

ISBN: 0-920-114-73-3

Orders: Additional copies may be obtained from
Canadian Institute of Surveying and Mapping
Box 5378
Postal Station F
Ottawa, Ontario
Canada
K2C 3J1
Telephone: (613) 224-9851
Price: $35.00 in Canadian funds (shipping extra)

Questions and correspondence:
Canadian GPS Associates
Box 3184
Postal Station B
Fredericton, New Brunswick
Canada
E3A 5G9

Recommended citation and reference:
Citation: [Wells et al., 1986]
Reference: Wells, D.E., N. Beck, D. Delikaraoglou, A. Kleusberg, E.J. Krakiwsky, G. Lachapelle, R.B. Langley, M. Nakiboglu, K.P. Schwarz, J.M. Tranquilla and P. Vaníček (1986). *Guide to GPS Positioning*. Canadian GPS Associates, Fredericton, N.B., Canada.

Printed in Fredericton, New Brunswick, Canada
by the University of New Brunswick Graphic Services.
Cover designed by Richard B. Langley.

INTRODUCTION

Goals, content, and format

The Guide to GPS Positioning is a self-contained introduction to the Global Positioning System, designed to be used in any of the following three ways:
- as a self-study guide,
- as lecture notes for formal post-secondary education courses, or
- as hand-out material to support short-course and seminar presentations on GPS.

The intended audience includes practicing surveyors, hydrographers, engineers, geophysicists, geologists, geographers, oceanographers, space scientists, and professionals in information management, transportation, forestry, and agriculture. In short, anyone interested in the potential of GPS to provide accurate, inexpensive, consistent positioning.

The content has been intentionally kept on the conceptual level as much as possible. The Guide is primarily an introduction, rather than an explication of the details of the latest research results concerning GPS. A minimum of mathematics is used, with each term hopefully fully explained. On the other hand, we attempt to describe all the concepts required to understand and use GPS, and we believe that even those actively using GPS will find this Guide to be of value.

The structure of this guide is modular in both a macro and a micro sense. At the macro level the fifteen chapters in this Guide can be grouped into four units:
- A description of GPS (chapters 1 to 5)
- GPS data collection and processing (chapters 6 to 10)
- GPS applications (chapters 11 to 15)
- GPS receivers (Appendix A).
These four units can be used together to provide a complete overview of GPS, or can be used independently from each other for more specialized audiences.

At the micro level, within each chapter, each topic is dealt with in two pages: a graphic or summary page illustrating the concept or listing the main points, and a text page providing a detailed description of the topic. In adopting this format, we followed two earlier GPS publications, *Everyman's Guide to Satellite Navigation*, by Steven D. Thompson, and *The WM GPS Primer*, by René Scherrer (see Appendix C for details). Our 2-page topic modules are designed to be as independent from each other as possible, so that a specialized presentation on GPS can be assembled by selecting only the appropriate topic modules required.

Canadian GPS Associates

The preparation of this Guide has been an experiment in collaborative desktop publishing, and very much a learning experience. Canadian GPS Associates is a partnership of the authors listed on the title page, formed to pursue joint projects, the first of which was the production and distribution of this Guide. Several of the authors had organized and presented a series of one-day tutorials on GPS in the spring of 1985, for which the handout material left much to be desired. It was clear to us that the need for an introductory, but complete, description of GPS concepts was not met by the available reference material (see Appendix C for our recommendations on material to supplement this Guide). This Guide is our response to that need.

After exploring several possibilities for financing the production of this Guide, we resolved in early 1986 to produce it ourselves, and formed Canadian GPS Associates, hoping to recover our costs after it is published. The times were with us — during 1986 desktop publishing became feasible even for neophytes like us. We decided in January to use the word processing and graphics capabilities of the Apple Macintosh computer and the Apple Laserwriter to produce camera-ready copy. Our inexperience showed, however: the initial estimates of completion during the second, and then the third quarter of 1986 were optimistic, due to three reasons.

- Our preconceptions that we had a pretty good handle on the concepts we wanted to explain in this Guide were shattered when we got down to the hard business of attempting to explain them in an easily understood form. We have learned a lot ourselves during the past year, and believe the Guide is better for the delay.
- Desktop publishing isn't easy. Author-produced graphics may have advantages of flexibility and control over draftsman-produced graphics, but they are surely very time consuming. Initially not all the authors were familiar with, or had access to, a Macintosh, so there was a learning curve.
- The authors live and work in three Canadian cities (Fredericton, Ottawa, and Calgary) which are separated by baseline distances of 575 km, 3010 km, and 3490 km. This made communications and discussions difficult.

Acknowledgements

The process of preparing this Guide has been a 'collegial' one. Preparation of the initial draft of each chapter was assigned to teams of one to five of the authors. This draft was reviewed by all the authors, but one author not on the initial team had the primary responsibility for review and revision. Some chapters, more contentious than others, have undergone several complex iterations of review and revision. The final Guide is a collective product of all the authors, rather than an edited version of each individual contribution, a fact which is indicated on the cover by the phrase *prepared under the leadership of*, rather than *edited by*. This in no way lessens the overall responsibility I bear for this final product, but indicates that my relationship to the other authors has been particularly unique and rewarding.

Nevertheless, each chapter has benefitted mainly from the efforts of a subset of the authors, and it is appropriate to acknowledge this here:

- Vaníček prepared Chapter 1, with contributions from Langley and Wells.
- Kleusberg prepared Chapter 2, with a contribution from Tranquilla.
- Langley prepared Chapter 3, with a contribution from Wells.
- Wells, Vaníček, Langley, and Tranquilla contributed to Chapter 4.
- Wells, Delikaraoglou, Nakiboglu, Kleusberg and Langley contributed to Chapter 5.
- Wells prepared Chapter 6, with contributions from Langley.
- Langley prepared Chapter 7, with contributions from Tranquilla and Wells.
- Delikaraoglou, Kleusberg, Tranquilla, and Vaníček contributed to Chapter 8.
- Delikaraoglou, Wells, Vaníček, Kleusberg and Tranquilla contributed to Chapter 9.
- Krakiwsky prepared Chapter 10, with contributions from Wells and Kleusberg.
- Lachapelle, Wells, Langley, Vaníček, and Kleusberg contributed to Chapter 11.
- Schwarz prepared Chapter 12, and Kleusberg, Lachapelle and Wells contributed.
- Tranquilla prepared Chapter 13, with a contribution from Kleusberg.
- Vaníček prepared Chapter 14, and Kleusberg, Wells, and Langley contributed.
- Beck prepared Chapter 15, with a contribution from Wells.
- Beck prepared Appendix A, with a contribution from Langley.
- Wells had prepared Appendix B for an earlier publication.
- Wells and Langley prepared Appendix C.
- Wendy Wells prepared Appendix D.

We have benefitted from advice from colleagues, and assistance from our students and research assistants. In particular, we thank See Hean Quek. During preparation of the Guide, Canadian GPS Associates was asked to prepare and present two series of GPS tutorials: 3, two-day seminars for the Alberta Bureau of Surveying and Mapping, and five presentations of a one-day GPS tutorial for the various regional offices of the Canadian Hydrographic Service. These tutorials were essentially a field test of the material in the Guide. Feedback from participants in both these tutorial series improved the content of our final product.

While most of the graphics and text were produced originally by the authors, maintenance of the over 300 documents (or 4 megabytes) which comprise this Guide; rendering each of them into accurate and consistent grammar and notational conventions; and preparation of the bibliography in Appendix D, have all been the responsibility of Wendy Wells, my very special sister, without whose help this Guide would have been even more extensively delayed.

We welcome comments, criticisms, and suggestions, so that we may improve future editions of the Guide. As noted in Appendix A, we would appreciate hearing from manufacturers and software developers about new GPS products.

David Wells
Fredericton
December 31, 1986

NOTATION

$\mathbf{R} = (X, Y, Z)^T$ position of receiver

$\mathbf{r} = (x, y, z)^T$ position of satellite

$\rho = \| \mathbf{r} - \mathbf{R} \|$ distance between satellite and receiver

c vacuum speed of light

f carrier frequency

$\lambda = c/f$ carrier wavelength

ϕ carrier phase observation (in cycles)

$\Phi = -\lambda\,\phi$ carrier phase observation (in length units)

$d\tau$ time delay observation

$p = c\,d\tau$ pseudo-range observation (in length units)

$d\rho$ range error due to inaccurate ephemerides

dt satellite clock error

dT receiver clock error

d_{ion} range error due to ionospheric refraction

d_{trop} range error due to tropospheric refraction

N integer carrier phase ambiguity

$$\Phi = \rho + c(dt - dT) + \lambda N - d_{ion} + d_{trop}$$

$$p = \rho + c(dt - dT) \qquad\qquad + d_{ion} + d_{trop}$$

Δ between-receiver difference

∇ between-satellite difference

δ between-epoch difference

TABLE OF CONTENTS

Chapter 4   Global Positioning System basic concepts

Chapter 5   Orbit description, determination, and dissemination

Chapter 6   Signal structure

Chapter 9   Biases and errors

Chapter 10   Solutions

Appendix A Characteristics of various GPS receivers

Appendix B Glossary of GPS Terminology

Appendix C GPS Information Sources

Appendix D Bibliography

CHAPTER ONE

CONCEPTS OF POSITIONING FROM SPACE

Guide to GPS Positioning
© Canadian GPS Associates, April 1986

CONCEPTS OF
POSITIONING FROM SPACE

POSITIONING:

- Point positioning
- Relative positioning
- Network of points
- Confidence regions and relative errors

POSITIONING FROM SPACE

- Astronomical positioning
- Basic concept of satellite point positioning
- Ranges and directions to satellites
- Ranges to satellites
- Relative satellite positioning

CONCEPTS OF POSITIONING FROM SPACE

Positions can be determined in different ways and using different instruments or systems of instruments. Depending on what the position is determined with respect to defines the positioning mode. The position can be determined with respect to a coordinate system, usually geocentric, with respect to another point, or within the context of several points.

Here we concentrate on the concepts involved in determining positions from space by means of satellites. For comparison, the basic idea of positioning using optical astronomy is also shown. Even though GPS is limited to the use of range measurements only, the more general approach taken here should help to place this technique in the context of other existing possibilities.

POINT POSITIONING

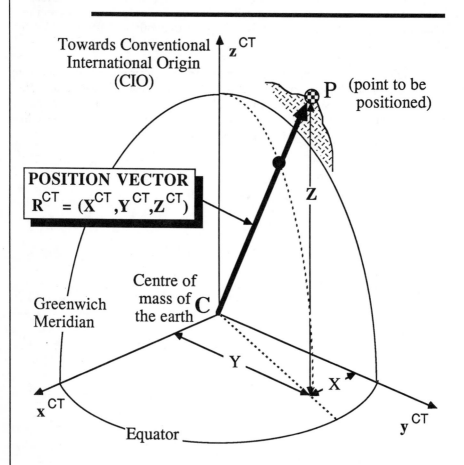

This particular coordinate system is the
CONVENTIONAL TERRESTRIAL SYSTEM (CT)

POINT POSITIONING

By *positioning* we understand the determination of positions of stationary or moving objects [Vaníček and Krakiwsky, 1986]. These positions can be determined:

(1) With respect to a well-defined coordinate system usually by three coordinate values. (Here we assume that the 'well-defined' coordinate system is itself positioned and oriented with respect to the earth.)

(2) With respect to another point, taking one point as the origin of a local coordinate system.

The first mode of positioning is known as *point positioning*, the second as *relative positioning*. (Some people call relative positioning, differential positioning.) It does not matter, conceptually, which coordinate system is used for point positioning. Nevertheless, it is usual to employ a geocentric system, i.e., a system whose origin coincides with the centre of mass (C) of the earth, as shown here. Therefore, the term *absolute positioning* is sometimes used instead of point positioning, especially in kinematic applications.

If the object to be positioned is stationary, we speak of *static positioning*. When the object is moving, we speak of *kinematic positioning*. Both positioning modes can be and are being used for either kind of positioning. Both modes and both kinds are dealt with in this guide. We note that static positioning is used in surveying; kinematic in navigation. They differ in some important aspects, as we shall see later.

RELATIVE POSITIONING

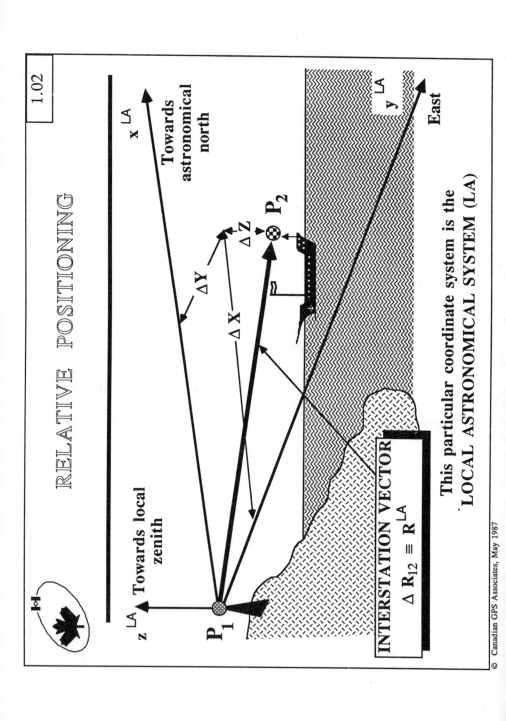

INTERSTATION VECTOR

$\Delta R_{12} \equiv R^{LA}$

This particular coordinate system is the
LOCAL ASTRONOMICAL SYSTEM (LA)

RELATIVE POSITIONING

Relative positioning using terrestrial methods is simpler than point positioning, particularly if the two points are intervisible. Many relative positioning techniques exist, based on a variety of physical and geometrical concepts. Relative positioning is the basic mode used in surveying practice.

Any local coordinate system may be used for relative positioning. When survey instruments are used for relative positioning, it is then natural to use the Local Astronomical (LA) system, shown here. As we shall see later for relative positioning from space, other systems are being used.

Suppose now that the position R_1 of point P_1 is known in one coordinate system and the interstation vector ΔR_{12} (ΔX, ΔY, ΔZ) is determined in the same coordinate system. Then the vector equation

$$R_2 = R_1 + \Delta R_{12}$$

gives us the position of P_2 in the same coordinate system. If ΔR_{12} has been determined in a different coordinate system (*) then it has to be transformed into the same (as R_1) system by the following transformation:

$$\Delta R_{12} = R(\omega_x, \omega_y, \omega_z) \, \Delta R_{12}{}^* \ ,$$

where R is a rotation matrix and ω_x, ω_y, ω_z are the appropriate misalignment angles between the two systems. We note that if this mode is used for kinematic positioning, both ΔR_{12} and R_2 are functions of time.

NETWORK OF POINTS

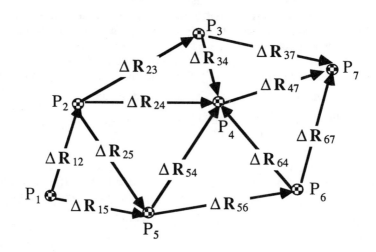

Provided all ΔR_{ij} are in the same coordinate system as R_1 we have (for example):

$$R_7 = R_1 + \Delta R_{12} + \Delta R_{24} + \Delta R_{47}$$

© Canadian GPS Associates, April 1986

NETWORK OF POINTS

Often it is advantageous to connect a whole family of points into a **network**. This mode is normally used for stationary, properly-monumented points. This is because of the necessity to re-occupy the individual points of the network. When these points are positioned together, connected together by means of redundant links, they make a geometrically stronger configuration.

In a network, each link may be considered as an interstation vector and each pair of adjacent points as a pair of points to be positioned relatively with respect to each other. If all the interstation vectors are known — derived from observations — then the network can serve as a medium for transmitting positions from one end to the other, as shown here. From this point of view, the network mode can be regarded as an incremental mode. As such, it naturally suffers from error accumulation, and care must be taken to curb the systematic error propagation. In surveying practice, networks are the most common mode of positioning. The points linked together by a network are called *control points*.

For accurate positioning, we have always relied on relative positioning techniques. Relative positioning in the network mode has served as the basic mode of geodetic positioning. Since terrestrially-based optical instruments (transit, theodolite, level, electro-optical distance measuring device, etc.) have been used exclusively to observe the interstation vectors, the links between (adjacent) points have been confined to lines of sight. A *horizontal geodetic network* is a network for which the horizontal coordinates, latitude and longitude, of the control points in the network are determined as accurately as possible, whereas heights are known only approximately. A *geodetic levelling network* is comprised of vertical control points (bench marks) whose heights are known as accurately as possible and whose horizontal positions are only very weak.

CONFIDENCE REGIONS AND RELATIVE ERRORS

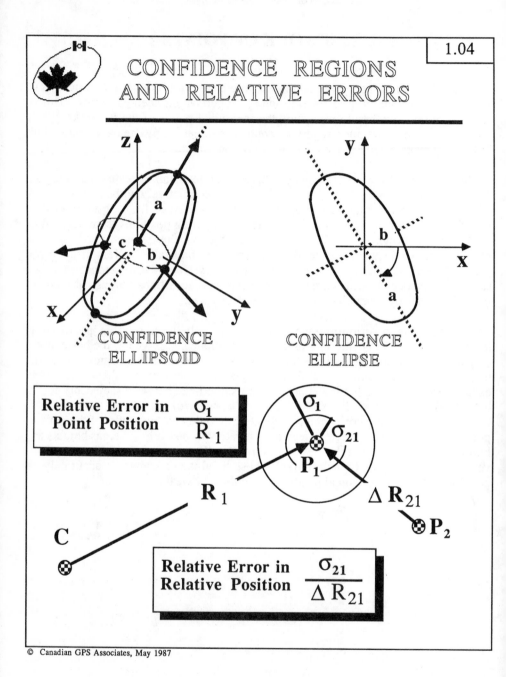

CONFIDENCE ELLIPSOID

CONFIDENCE ELLIPSE

Relative Error in Point Position $\dfrac{\sigma_1}{R_1}$

Relative Error in Relative Position $\dfrac{\sigma_{21}}{\Delta R_{21}}$

CONFIDENCE REGIONS AND RELATIVE ERRORS

In theory as well as in practice, it is very important to be able to quantify the **goodness** of positions, i.e., their accuracy. This can be done in many different ways, the most reasonable being by means of **confidence regions**. In this figure a, b, and c are the semi-axes of the confidence regions. The confidence regions are either ellipsoids, for three-dimensional cases, or ellipses, for two-dimensional cases. They are formulated in such a way that their volume or area contains a preselected level of probability (that the true value lies within the figure), e.g., 99%, 95%.

It is customary among some people to use a proportional error presentation instead of confidence regions. This representation is obtained by dividing the standard (position) error in the desired direction by the distance from the origin of the coordinate system used. Proportional accuracy can be defined for point positioning as well as for relative positioning: one metre error in the geocentric position of a point represents a relative error of 1 m divided by the radius of the earth $(6.371 \times 10^6 m)$ and is equal to 0.16 parts per million (0.16 ppm). To get a proportional accuracy of 0.16 ppm in a relative position of two points 10 km apart, their relative position would have to be known with $\sigma = 1.6$ mm.

The proportional errors of relative positions of adjacent points in the present horizontal networks in Canada are at best about 10 ppm (first-order control). For levelling networks, the relative accuracy is about one order of magnitude higher. Both horizontal and levelling networks are now being redefined, re-adjusted, and generally improved to become more compatible with new positioning capabilities. In North America, the new horizontal network contains many Transit (Doppler) satellite-determined positions that have been included to strengthen the geometry, location, and orientation of the network.

Another concept which has been frequently used to describe accuracy is the concept of Dilution of Precision (DOP). The DOP is, in essence, a root-sum-squared measure of the size of the confidence region.

Both the DOP as well as confidence regions stem from a more general concept of a covariance matrix, which in this context is an assembly of variances (squares of standard deviations) and covariances of individual coordinates of a set of points of simultaneous interest. These coordinates may be one or several dimensional. For example, a set consisting of one point in three dimensions has a 3 by 3 covariance matrix associated with it. Different kinds of DOPS are nothing but the square roots of the traces of different submatrices of the covariance matrix, divided by the measurement standard deviation, whereas the semi-axes of the confidence regions are related to the eigenvalues of this matrix [Vaníček and Krakiwsky, 1986].

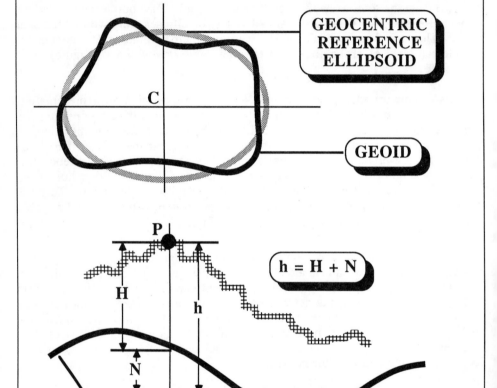

HORIZONTAL AND VERTICAL DATUMS

GEOCENTRIC REFERENCE ELLIPSOID

C

GEOID

P

$h = H + N$

H

h

N

GEOID (VERTICAL DATUM)

REFERENCE ELLIPSOID (HORIZONTAL DATUM)

HORIZONTAL AND VERTICAL DATUMS

The concept of datums is very important in classical positioning. A *datum* is a surface of constant coordinate values. Two kinds of datums, vertical and horizontal, are used in practice. A *vertical datum*, a surface of zero height, is usually chosen to be the *geoid*, which is the equipotential surface of the earth's gravity field that best approximates mean sea level. Heights referred to the geoid, called *orthometric heights* H, are the heights one usually finds plotted on topographical maps. Orthometric heights are the heights used almost exclusively in surveying practice and elsewhere.

If the geoid is replaced with a biaxial ellipsoid, one can define *geometrical heights* h, also called heights above the (reference) ellipsoid, which have very little use in practice. However, their attraction is that they can be obtained directly from three-dimensional Cartesian coordinates of the point of interest, provided the location and orientation of the reference ellipsoid in the Cartesian coordinate system is known [Vaníček and Krakiwsky, 1986]. The equation that links the two kinds of heights is shown in the figure, where the elevation N of the geoid above the reference ellipsoid is usually called the *geoidal height*. Globally, the absolute value of N with respect to the best fitting geocentric reference ellipsoid is almost everywhere smaller than 100 metres.

Whereas the use of the ellipsoid as a reference for heights is impractical for many tasks, its use as a reference for horizontal coordinates, latitude φ and longitude λ, is widespread. This is why such reference ellipsoids are commonly called *horizontal datums*. Many horizontal datums (both geocentric and non-geocentric) are used throughout the world.

Clearly, if we were happy describing positions by Cartesian coordinates in a system such as, for example, the Conventional Terrestrial system, the use of both vertical and horizontal datums could be abandoned. This is, conceptually, the case with positioning by satellites. However, in practice, satellite-determined Cartesian coordinates must usually be transformed to φ, λ, and H. This transformation, as stated above, requires knowledge of:
• the location and orientation with respect to the Cartesian coordinate system of the horizontal datum selected,
• the height of the geoid above the horizontal datum.

ASTRONOMICAL POSITIONING

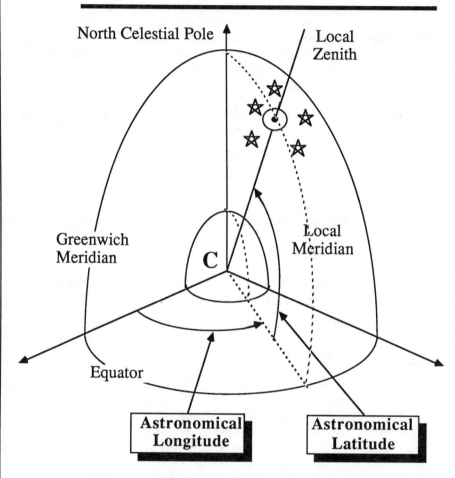

North Celestial Pole

Local Zenith

Greenwich Meridian

C

Local Meridian

Equator

Astronomical Longitude

Astronomical Latitude

This figure does not illustrate a coordinate system in the strict sense, only a concept

ASTRONOMICAL POSITIONING

To accurately measure point positions on the surface of the earth has been a human endeavour since time immemorial. The only technique available before the advent of satellites was optical astronomy. The basic idea of *astronomical positioning* is to find the position of local zenith among stars, as shown here. From the relative position of local zenith with respect to the surrounding stars (whose positions, in turn, are already known), the *astronomical latitude* and *astronomical longitude* are derived. The equations for doing it can be found in Vaníček and Krakiwsky [1986].

The main problem with astronomically-determined 'positions' is that they have to be transformed into a well-defined coordinate system, to be useful for accurate positioning. This task requires a good knowledge of the earth's gravity field. Without this knowledge, the distortions in astronomically derived 'positions' may reach many hundreds of metres. Nevertheless, such 'positions' may still be quite useful for rough positioning or navigation on land, in the air, or at sea. With good knowledge of the gravity field, the errors in positions after the transformation are of the order of 10 metres, i.e., the proportional accuracy of those positions is of the order of 1 ppm.

Today, astronomical positioning is not used much for precise positioning. Rather, the astronomical 'positions' are used to study the earth's gravity field; they provide an easy tool to evaluate the *deflection of the vertical*, the slope of the geoid with respect to the selected reference ellipsoid.

BASIC CONCEPT OF SATELLITE POINT POSITIONING

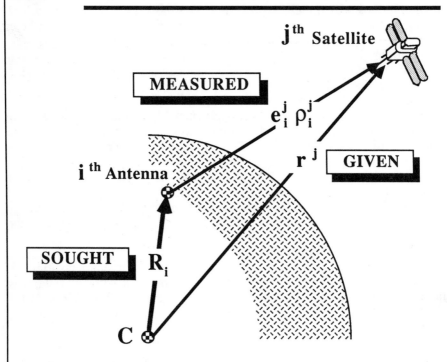

j^{th} Satellite

MEASURED

$e_i^j \, \rho_i^j$

r^j **GIVEN**

i^{th} Antenna

SOUGHT R_i

C

$$R_i = r^j - e_i^j \, \rho_i^j$$

R_i is the position vector of the ith antenna

r^j is the position vector of the jth satellite

$e_i^j \, \rho_i^j$ is the range vector between the two.

BASIC CONCEPT
OF SATELLITE POINT POSITIONING

In this guide, satellite positioning refers to positioning by means of satellites; it does **not** mean positioning of satellites. ready to

The basic concept of point positioning by means of satellites is shown here. In a nutshell: we wish to determine the position (R_i) of the ith *antenna* (the device that receives the satellite signal and is then positioned). We know the position (r^j) of the jth *satellite* (emitting the signal) and have thus to measure the *range vector* $e_i^j \rho_i^j$ between the two. Depending on how the range vector is measured, we get different satellite positioning techniques.

To predict accurately the position of the satellite $r^j(t)$ in time is a rather difficult proposition. The task of predicting the *ephemeris* — which is the proper name of r^j as a function of time — calls for a specialized knowledge of satellite dynamics which historically belongs in the field of celestial mechanics. The ephemerides are usually determined and predicted (in time) by the operators of the satellite system. It is, however, possible for the user of the system to improve the given ephemerides. It is also possible for the users to establish an independent network of tracking stations, preferably a global one, and compute the ephemerides in a postmission mode.

It should be clear that if the antenna changes its position R_i in time (kinematic positioning), then R_i has to be continuously re-evaluated. If the antenna is stationary, then the re-evaluation should always lead to the same result, and we will have a redundancy of results.

In many applications the position of the antenna itself is not of primary interest. It is the position of the survey marker, the centre of a hydrographic launch, etc., that is to be determined. For this reason, the offset (eccentricity) of the antenna with respect to the derived point must be established or monitored.

RANGING AND
DIRECTIONS TO SATELLITES

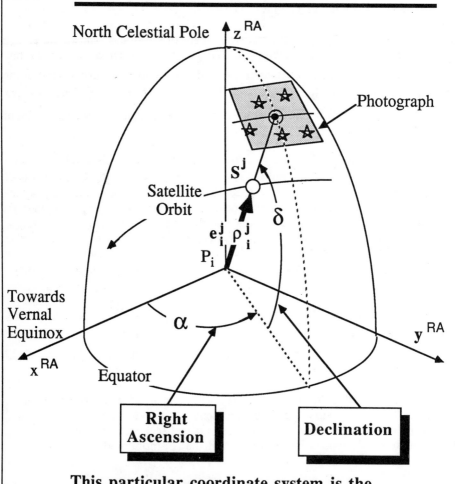

North Celestial Pole z^{RA}

Photograph

S^j

Satellite
Orbit

δ

$e_i^j \quad \rho_i^j$

P_i

Towards
Vernal
Equinox

α

y^{RA}

x^{RA}

Equator

**Right
Ascension**

Declination

This particular coordinate system is the
RIGHT ASCENSION SYSTEM (RA)

RANGING AND DIRECTIONS TO SATELLITES

Ideally, we would like to measure both the length of the range vector, i.e., the *range*, and its direction. It is theoretically possible to do this: for instance, we could simultaneously photograph the satellite against the star background and electronically measure the range. The two angles that define the direction of the range vector are called *right ascension* (α) and *declination* (δ). They can be measured from known positions of surrounding stars on the photograph and are considered to be coordinates (angular) in a coordinate system known as the *Right Ascension* (RA) system. (The version of the RA-system shown in this figure is centred at a point on the surface of the earth. A version which is geocentric is often used as well.) The direction angles cannot be determined directly (in real time) if reasonably high accuracy is required. This seems to rule out this technique as an accurate real-time positioning tool.

The question then is: Can directions to satellites be used in satellite positioning? They can, and they have been used in several campaigns. However, the accuracy of these directions is not very high; in addition to other problems, optical refraction (bending) is quite strong and very difficult to model. Therefore, at present, this satellite positioning mode is only of historical value.

It is worth noting, however, that optical direction measurements remain an important means of determining the positions of satellites (satellite tracking). Catalogues of the thousands of objects in orbit around the earth are maintained by NASA, and other agencies, based in part on photographs of these objects from **known** ground stations, against the star background.

RANGING TO SATELLITES

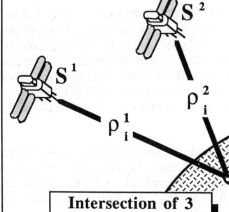

Intersection of 3 spheres with radii

$$\rho_i^1, \rho_i^2, \rho_i^3$$

KNOWN:	r^1, r^2, r^3
OBSERVED:	$\rho_i^1, \rho_i^2, \rho_i^3$
SOUGHT:	R_i

$$\left\| r^j - R_i \right\| = \rho_i^j \qquad j = 1,2,3$$

RANGING TO SATELLITES

Much better results have been obtained from observing ranges. When all three components of the vector $e\rho$ are not observed simultaneously, a minimum of three non-coplanar ranges have to be observed to get the required position, as shown here.

If R_i is the position vector of a stationary antenna, then the three (or more) non-coplanar ranges can be measured at different times and hence may (or may not) pertain to one and the same satellite. If the antenna is moving, then to get a position at any instant of time, often called the *fix*, the three (or more) ranges have to be measured simultaneously. This infers that, for ranging in a kinematic point positioning mode, at least three satellites have to be 'visible' to the antenna at the same time.

Ranging can be done using different parts of the electromagnetic spectrum. The visible part of the spectrum is used in *laser ranging;* NAVSTAR/GPS uses L-band frequencies (1.2 to 1.6 GHz), whereas the Transit (Doppler) system uses VHF and UHF radio frequencies (150 and 400 MHz). Generally, laser ranging is more accurate than *radio ranging,* but it is less practical because of its limitations due to visibility, portability, and excessive cost of equipment. Laser ranging has an accuracy of about 5 cm (one sigma level) from three month's worth of ranging [Smith et al., 1985]. The corresponding accuracy from GPS cannot be assessed because no such experiment has yet been conducted, to the best of our knowledge. It is thought, however, that an accuracy of a few decimetres could be eventually achieved.

RELATIVE
SATELLITE POSITIONING

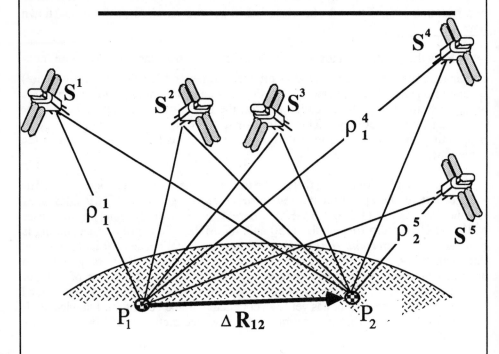

Conceptually: $R_1 = r^j - e_1^j \rho_1^j$

$R_2 = r^j - e_2^j \rho_2^j$

$\Delta R_{12} = R_2 - R_1 = e_1^j \rho_1^j - e_2^j \rho_2^j = \Delta e_{12}^j \rho_{12}^j$

RELATIVE SATELLITE POSITIONING

It should be mentioned here that range differencing may be considered a technique akin to ranging. Range differencing, based on integrated Doppler shifted frequency of the incoming signal, is used in the Navy Navigation Satellite System, also known as the Transit system.

The effects limiting the accuracy of radio positioning are: the atmospheric propagation delay, drift in the satellite and possibly the receiver clocks, and error in satellite ephemerides. Some of these effects can be suppressed, or even eliminated, if relative positions, rather than point positions, are sought. Put in other words: it is possible to determine relative positions, and thus also geometrical configurations of points, much more accurately than it is to locate these points on the earth's surface.

This is true for both ranging and range differencing. It is even more the case when simultaneous, rather than sequential, observations to each satellite are used. The relative positioning mode was used extensively with the Transit system under the name of *translocation*. The best proportional accuracies currently obtainable in relative positioning are 5 to 10 ppm, when using the Transit system, and 0.1 to 2.0 ppm, when using GPS. The relative positioning ranging mode can be used for both static and kinematic kinds of positioning.

RELATIVE SATELLITE POSITIONING

CHAPTER TWO

APPLICATIONS OF POSITIONING FROM SPACE

Guide to GPS Positioning
© Canadian GPS Associates, April 1986

APPLICATIONS OF POSITIONING FROM SPACE

LAND APPLICATIONS

Surveying and geodesy

Transportation and communication

MARINE APPLICATIONS

Surveying and geodesy

Transportation and marine sciences

AIR APPLICATIONS

Surveying and geodesy

Transportation

SPACE APPLICATIONS

RECREATIONAL APPLICATIONS

MILITARY APPLICATIONS

APPLICATIONS OF POSITIONING FROM SPACE

One of the most significant and unique features of space-based positioning systems, such as GPS, is the fact that the positioning signals are available to users at any position world-wide at any time. It can thus be reasonably expected that such a system, when fully operational, will generate a large community of users.

Provided that large enough markets for GPS receivers develop, then competition and the economies of scale will lead to very low-cost receivers. It must be stressed that there is no technological barrier to low-cost receivers — it is purely a question of how many units over which the development costs must be spread. Several GPS manufacturers have already claimed large-scale production costs of $US 1000 per unit or less.

In this chapter, we look at the many applications of positioning from space, in several cases assuming low-cost receivers. GPS is mentioned extensively throughout, because it is the system most likely to first provide world-wide positioning coverage from space. However, as we will see in the next chapter, there are alternatives to GPS which may be better suited to many of these applications.

LAND APPLICATIONS IN
SURVEYING AND MAPPING

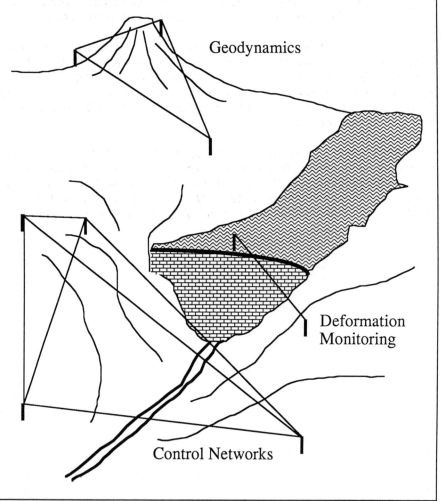

Geodynamics

Deformation
Monitoring

Control Networks

LAND APPLICATIONS
IN SURVEYING AND MAPPING

The high precision of GPS carrier phase measurements, together with appropriate adjustment algorithms, provide an adequate tool for a variety of tasks in surveying and mapping. We may distinguish between applications for:

- cadastral surveying
- geodetic control
- local deformation monitoring
- global deformation monitoring.

Surveying for cadastral purposes normally requires an accuracy in relative position of 10^{-4}. This accuracy can be easily achieved utilizing GPS observations. However, for a wide application of GPS in this field, completely automated processing, if possible on site, is required. It is expected that this feature will be available in GPS receivers within the next few years.

Geodetic control can involve high accuracy networks, from which lower order networks are established. The required accuracies in relative positioning are of the order of 5×10^{-6} to 1×10^{-6} for distances of 20 to 100 km. This accuracy level is routinely achieved by postprocessing GPS carrier phase observations with standard software. Lower order geodetic control (for mapping, for example) can also be established economically by GPS.

Local deformation monitoring (mining subsidence, structural deformation) requires accuracies of 1 mm to 1 cm over distances of up to a few kilometres. The presently achievable accuracy for these applications is limited by uncertainties in the variation of the electrical centre of the GPS antennas and signal distortions due to the reflective environment of the antennas. Further problems arise from limited satellite visibility due to signal shadowing in a typical industrial environment.

Global deformation monitoring (plate tectonics, etc.) requires accuracies of 10^{-7} to 10^{-8} over intercontinental distances. The main differences compared with the previously discussed applications lie in the necessity for an elaborate modelling of the GPS satellite orbits, atmospheric signal propagation delays, and other biases.

LAND APPLICATIONS IN TRANSPORTATION AND COMMUNICATION

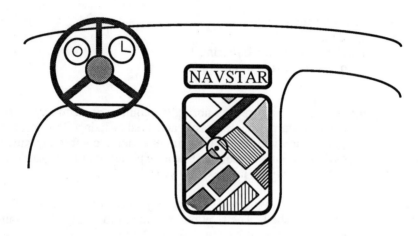

NAVIGATION

- Emergency vehicles
- Law enforcement
- Search and rescue

MONITORING

- Truck fleets
- Boxcars
- Taxi fleets

LAND APPLICATIONS
IN TRANSPORTATION AND COMMUNICATION

Wide popularity of GPS positioning and navigation in civil transportation will follow a significant decrease in the price level of GPS receivers. As this cost reduction probably will be achieved in the years to come, GPS can assume tasks now performed by conventional methods. In land navigation, an automated display of the vehicle position (obtained by GPS) on an electronic chart may replace the 'manual' comparison of the surroundings of the vehicle with a conventional map. This application will be of particular importance for emergency vehicles, law enforcement vehicles, search and rescue missions, etc.

Monitoring the location and movement of vehicles can be achieved if they are equipped with automated transmitters in addition to the GPS receiver. The position determined by the GPS receiver/processor can be transmitted to a central site for display. This application can be of significant importance for controlling and dispatching boxcars, taxi fleets, truck fleets, etc.

MARINE APPLICATIONS IN SURVEYING AND MAPPING

Drill rig positioning

Marine gravity surveys

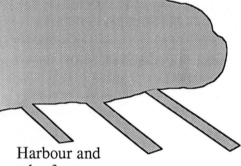

Buoy surveying

Harbour and wharf surveys

Shoal surveying

MARINE APPLICATIONS
IN SURVEYING AND MAPPING

GPS is ideally suited for inshore and offshore positioning because of its high accuracy and the short observation time required for a position fix. The horizontal position requirements for marine surveys vary between a few decimetres and several tens of metres. To meet these requirements, different observation and processing techniques using pseudo-ranges and/or carrier phases must be employed. Marine applications include the mapping of navigational hazards (shoal surveying, buoy surveying) and the survey of wharfs and harbours. Positioning requirements in marine geophysical exploration (e.g., seismic surveys) can be met as well as requirements for drilling positioning.

In marine geodesy (ocean bottom topography, earth's gravity field, etc.), GPS can serve as a positioning tool. For gravity field determination, the receiver velocity is required in addition to the receiver position.

MARINE APPLICATIONS IN TRANSPORTATION AND MARINE SCIENCES

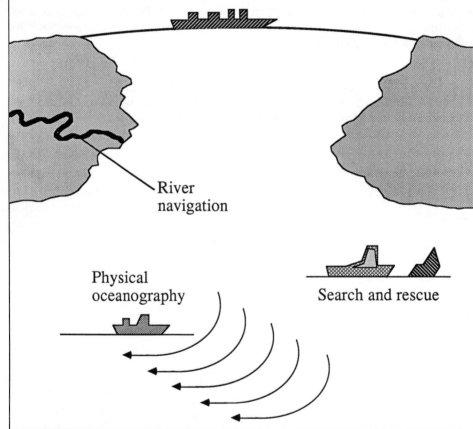

En route
navigation

River
navigation

Physical
oceanography

Search and rescue

MARINE APPLICATIONS
IN TRANSPORTATION AND MARINE SCIENCES

GPS will become the ideal marine navigation tool once the satellite constellation is complete enough to provide continuous two-dimensional positioning. Marine navigation accuracy requirements vary between several metres (inshore, harbour, and river navigation) and several hundred metres (en route navigation). The capability to provide sufficient navigation accuracy for all different phases of marine travel by a single radio positioning system is a primary advantage of GPS. Precise GPS procedures utilizing both pseudo-ranges and carrier phases may lead to inshore and river navigation without buoys. Offshore search and rescue missions will become more efficient due to improved navigation accuracy.

The positioning requirements for field work in physical oceanography can be met by GPS. Carrier phase measurements provide additionally precise ship's velocity, which is needed in ocean current studies.

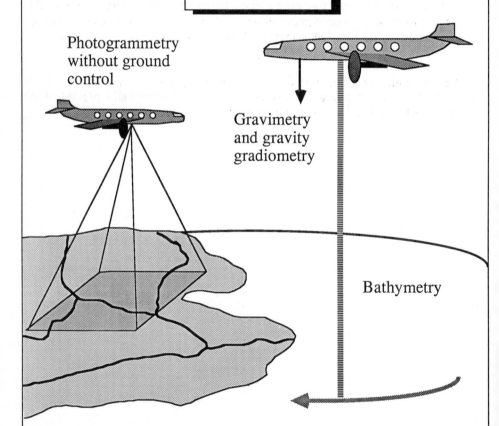

Sensor positioning and navigation

Photogrammetry without ground control

Gravimetry and gravity gradiometry

Bathymetry

AIRBORNE APPLICATIONS
IN SURVEYING AND MAPPING

In airborne applications in surveying and mapping, GPS can provide mainly **sensor navigation and positioning.**

In **aerial photogrammetry,** sensor (camera) navigation accuracy requirements of several tens of metres can be met easily by GPS. High precision postmission sensor positioning (and sensor orientation) by GPS can replace aerotriangulation and thus render ground control points superfluous. Positioning accuracy requirements for this application vary between 0.5 m and 25 m for different mapping scales.

Airborne laser profiling can be used for direct digital mapping of the topography (digital terrain model) if the sensor (laser) position is known with an accuracy of 0.5 to 1 m vertically and several metres horizontally. GPS is expected to provide this position accuracy in postmission analysis.

Roughly the same positioning requirements have to be met for **airborne gravity and gravity gradiometry.** In these applications, GPS measurements can additionally determine the sensor velocity needed for the Eötvös reduction of the gravity data.

Airborne laser bathymetry and **radar imaging** require less accurate sensor positions which can be easily determined by GPS measurements.

AIRBORNE APPLICATIONS
IN TRANSPORTATION

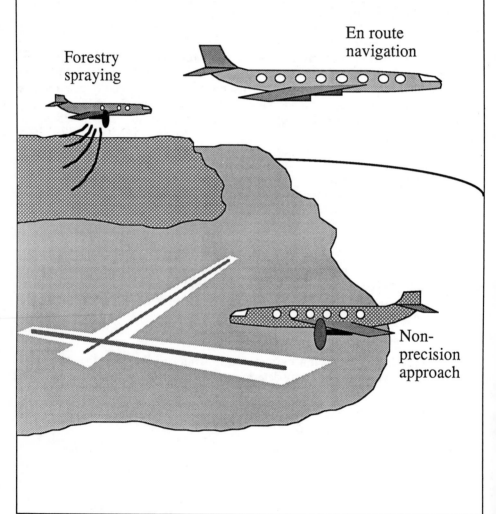

En route
navigation

Forestry
spraying

Non-
precision
approach

AIRBORNE APPLICATIONS IN TRANSPORTATION

The usefulness of GPS as a stand-alone **en route navigation** system in civil aviation depends critically on whether it can provide truly continuous positioning with full redundancy. In the presently-planned GPS configuration, 'outages' due to bad satellite geometry will occur in different areas. During an 'outage,' safe navigation by means of GPS measurements alone becomes impossible. However, GPS can be utilized as part of an integrated navigation system. Position updates obtained by GPS during non-outage periods are far superior in accuracy to any other radio positioning system.

Differential GPS techniques can be employed for **non-precision approach navigation** provided the airport is outside the above-mentioned outage zones.

In other airborne applications (forestry and crop spraying, etc.), where navigation is not required for aviation safety but for the deployment of freight, GPS can easily meet the navigation accuracy requirements.

SPACE APPLICATIONS

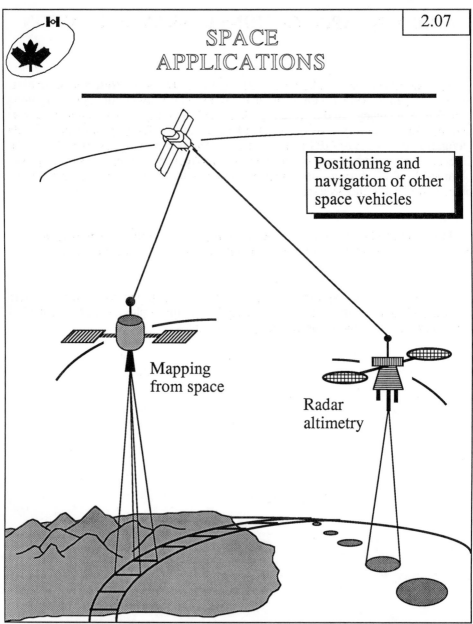

Positioning and navigation of other space vehicles

Mapping from space

Radar altimetry

SPACE APPLICATIONS

Space applications of GPS consist mainly of positioning and navigation of other space vehicles carrying geophysical and/or geodetic sensors. Usually, these satellites have low orbits and, therefore, the measurement geometry is similar to terrestrial applications. Typical examples are satellite remote sensing and radar altimetry. Satellite positions obtained from GPS measurements can be used to improve and/or simplify the orbit computations for these space vehicles or even replace the orbit integration by discrete orbit positions.

RECREATIONAL APPLICATIONS

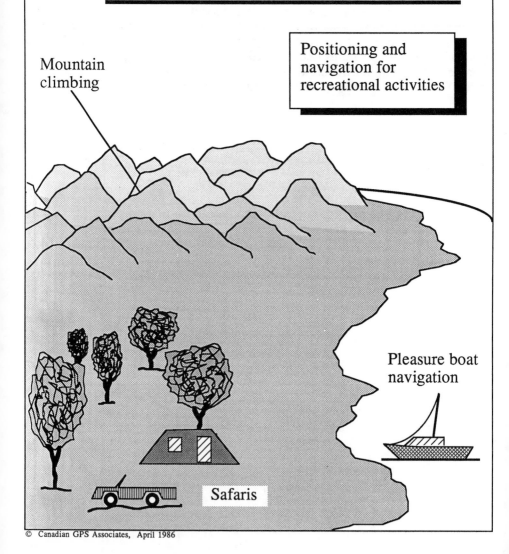

Positioning and navigation for recreational activities

Mountain climbing

Pleasure boat navigation

Safaris

RECREATIONAL APPLICATIONS

It is expected that the cost of GPS receivers will continue to decrease. At a price level of several hundred dollars, a GPS receiver will be affordable for non-professional users. At the same time, advances in microelectronics will have reduced the volume, weight, and complexity of receivers.

In this case, recreational activities will provide a huge market for these low cost, portable, and easy-to-use receivers.

Low to medium accuracy positions (tens to hundreds of metres) will be used by yacht and boat owners, hikers and bikers, safari participants, and many others.

MILITARY
APPLICATIONS

POSITIONING AND NAVIGATION

- en route navigation

- low-level navigation

- target acquisition

- photo reconnaissance

- remotely operated vehicles

- updating inertial navigation systems

- sensor emplacement

- missile guidance

- command and control

MONITORING
NUCLEAR DETONATIONS

MILITARY APPLICATONS

The Global Positioning System is primarily designed for real-time military positioning. Military applications encompass airborne, marine, and land navigation. GPS will serve as a stand-alone system and as a part of integrated navigation systems. This figure shows a list of the main military applications. In addition, the GPS satellites carry sensors to detect and monitor nuclear detonations.

CHAPTER THREE

EXTRATERRESTRIAL POSITIONING SYSTEMS

Guide to GPS Positioning
© Canadian GPS Associates, April 1986

EXTRATERRESTRIAL POSITIONING SYSTEMS

TECHNIQUES USED IN EXTRATERRESTRIAL POSITIONING

THE PAST

Optical Systems
Early Radio Ranging and Direction Finding Systems

THE PRESENT

Transit Satellite Positioning
Principle of Doppler Positioning
Transit Doppler Measurements
ARGOS
Global Positioning System
Satellite Laser Ranging
Very Long Baseline Interferometry
New Technology Accuracy vs. Distance
GPS and Other Systems

THE FUTURE

Geostar
NAVSAT
The Future of Satellite Positioning

EXTRATERRESTRIAL POSITIONING SYSTEMS

In the last twenty years or so, geodetic positioning accuracy has increased by over two orders of magnitude. A similar improvement has been seen in navigation capability. These improvements are chiefly attributable to the development of systems based on the so-called 'extraterrestrial' instrumentation techniques. In this chapter, we briefly review these techniques. We include some techniques that are no longer used for positioning purposes in order to give a historical perspective and also describe two systems, Geostar and NAVSAT, that have been proposed but have not yet been implemented. We concentrate on the physical principles and the instrumentation used in these techniques but also include details on the accuracies of the techniques and their applicabilty to the range of positioning needs. We conclude this chapter with some 'crystal-ball gazing' on future concepts of satellite positioning.

TECHNIQUES USED IN EXTRATERRESTRIAL POSITIONING

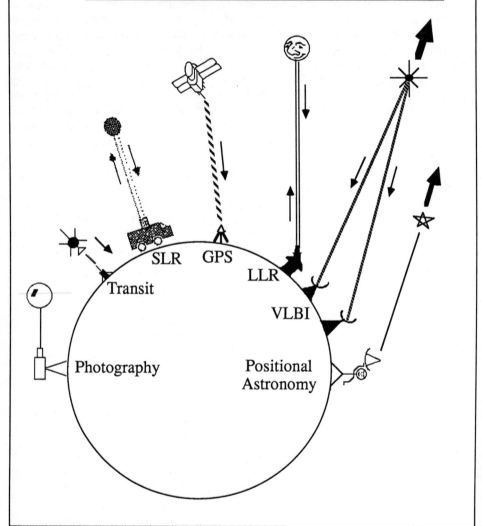

SLR GPS

Transit

LLR

VLBI

Photography

Positional
Astronomy

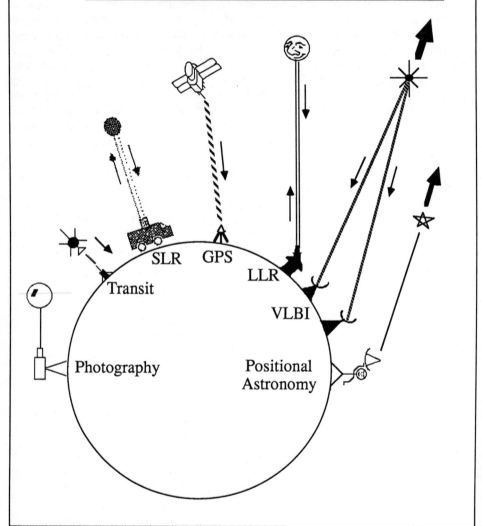

3.01

TECHNIQUES USED IN EXTRATERRESTRIAL POSITIONING

An *extraterrestrial positioning system* is a system for establishing positions of points on or near the surface of the earth which utilizes electromagnetic radiation either emitted or reflected from an object in orbit about the earth or at some greater distance. Included under this definition is traditional *positional astronomy* (Chapter 1) used for both geodetic and navigational purposes. All other extraterrestrial techniques rely on space technology and have been developed since 1957. Currently used space techniques include the **Transit, Argos,** and **GPS** radio positioning systems, **satellite** and **lunar laser ranging,** and **very long baseline interferometry.** In addition to providing positional information, these techniques contribute a variety of useful geodetic and geophysical information, including the coefficients describing the earth's gravity field and the orientation of the earth's crust with respect to its rotation axis.

Other space techniques have been used in the past to obtain useful positions. These techniques include **satellite photography, C-** and **S-band radar systems,** and the **GRARR (Goddard Range and Range Rate), SECOR (Sequential Collation of Range),** and **Minitrack** systems. Some of these latter techniques, although not presently achieving useful terrestrial positions, are still utilized for spacecraft tracking and orbit determination.

Although not directly providing terrestrial coordinates, the techniques of **satellite altimetry** and **satellite-to-satellite tracking** should also be mentioned. These techniques provide useful information about the sea surface, the geoid, and the external gravity field of the earth.

OPTICAL SYSTEMS

INSTRUMENT	APERTURE (cm)	TIMING ACCURACY (msec)	DIRECTIONAL ACCURACY (arc seconds)	FAINTEST SATELLITE (magnitude)
Baker-Nunn tracking camera	50	0.1	2	12
Hewitt camera	63	0.2	1	7.5
BC-4 camera	12	0.1	2	6
PC-1000 camera	20	0.1	2	6
NAFA 3c/25 camera	10	2	5	4.5
MOTS-40 camera	20	2	2	5
Kinetheodolite photo-graphic	20	10	20	4
Kinetheodolite photo-visual	10	10	40	8
70-mm theodolite	7	100	110	8
7 x 50 binoculars	5	100	110	8
11 x 80 binoculars	8	100	70	9.5
20-cm telescope	20	100	70	11

© Canadian GPS Associates, April 1986

OPTICAL SYSTEMS

Optical systems are those systems which utilize the visible part of the electromagnetic spectrum. This definition would encompass astronomical positioning using a theodolite or sextant and also laser ranging. However, we will not consider these techniques in this section. Conventional astronomical positioning has been discussed in Chapter 1, and laser ranging will be discussed later in this chapter.

Optical systems range in accuracy and complexity from simple binoculars to 60 cm tracking cameras. They have been used in the past for both satellite tracking (i.e., orbit determination) and terrestrial positioning but only the tracking cameras provided geodetically-useful results [Henriksen, 1977]. A tracking camera records a photographic image or a series of images of a satellite, either from a flashing beacon or via reflected sunlight, together with the images of background stars. The time of exposure is also precisely recorded. The positions of the satellite images on the processed film are subsequently measured with respect to stars in the field of view. If the positions of the stars are known, then the topocentric right ascension and declination of the satellite can be determined. Three such determinations combined with the known coordinates of the camera are sufficient for determining the orbit of the satellite. Additional observations can be used to improve the orbit's accuracy.

Alternatively, if the orbit of the satellite is known, it is possible to determine the geocentric coordinates of the camera. Two techniques have been used. In the *geometric* method, two or more cameras simultaneously record satellite images and the camera positions are then determined by triangulation. In the *dynamic* method, observations are not necessarily synchronized but precise knowledge of the satellite orbit is required. Several three-dimensional networks were established using these techniques [Henriksen, 1977]. One of them was the BC-4 worldwide satellite triangulation network, a network of 45 stations whose coordinates were established through observations of the balloon satellite PAGEOS, using Wild BC-4 cameras. The relative positions of the stations were determined with an estimated accuracy of about 5 m. Greater accuracy in position determination using satellite photography is not readily achievable due to a number of error sources. Chief among these are scintillations of the satellite due to atmospheric turbulence and distortions in the photographic emulsion. Consequently, in geodesy, satellite photography has been superseded by other techniques.

Optical systems are still an important source of information for satellite orbit determination and surveillance. They figure prominently, for example, in the U.S. Air Force's Spacetrack System and its Ground-based Electro-Optical Deep Space Surveillance (GEODSS) System.

EARLY RADIO RANGING AND
DIRECTION FINDING SYSTEMS

SYSTEM (Operators)	FREQUENCY (MHz)	OBSERVABLE	ACCURACY Range (m)	Direction (")
C- and S-band radar (U.S. DoD, NASA)	5400-5900 2100-2300	phase	2-5	20
GRARR (Goddard Space Flight Center)	S-band (e.g. 2270 up 1705 down)	phase and phase rate	5	
SECOR (DoD)	420.9 up 449, 224.5 down	phase	3-10	
Minitrack (NASA)	108; 136-138	interferometric phase		20

EARLY RADIO RANGING AND DIRECTION FINDING SYSTEMS

The radio portion of the electromagnetic spectrum also found early use in satellite geodesy. It was the study of the Doppler shift of the radio beacons in the early satellites that led to the first real improvement in the determination of the shape of the earth in over 100 years. Several radio systems were developed for satellite tracking and orbit determination. In the United States, these systems included **C- and S-band radar**, the **Goddard Space Flight Center Range and Range Rate (GRARR) system**, and NASA's **Minitrack system**. In addition to their role in orbit determination, the systems were utilized for tracking camera calibration and directly for geodetic positioning. The U.S. Army's **Sequential Collation of Range (SECOR) system**, on the other hand, was developed specifically for positioning purposes.

The C- and S-band radars are operated by the U.S. Department of Defense and by NASA. Radar pulses directed at a satellite are returned by skin reflection or via a transponder, and the two-way pulse travel time is measured. Range accuracies of 2 to 5 m can be obtained. Radars can also provide angular position to about 20".

The GRARR system relies on a transponder in the satellite to respond to an S-band signal transmitted from an antenna on the ground. Superimposed on the carriers by phase modulation are 6 to 8 frequencies between 8 Hz and 500 kHz. The relative phases of the transmitted and received modulations are used to infer the range to the satellite. The multiple modulation frequencies are used to remove the inherent cycle ambiguity. The phase rate or Doppler shift of the received carrier is also measured. The range accuracy of GRARR is about 5 m.

Minitrack, or more fully Prime Minitrack, was NASA's first tracking system. It consists of a pair of crossed interferometers which measure the relative phase of a nominally 136 (formerly 108) MHz signal transmitted by suitably-equipped satellites as received at the two ends of the interferometer. The same principle is used in the U.S. Naval Space Surveillance System and in very long baseline interferometry (see later in this chapter). With Minitrack, the altitude and azimuth of a satellite can be determined to about 20".

The SECOR system, which was operated between 1962 and 1970, consisted of four ground stations each transmitting modulated signals on 420.9 MHz to a transponder on certain satellites. The transponders returned the signal on 449 and 224.5 MHz. By measuring the relative phase of the transmitted and received 585.533 kHz modulation, the range to the satellite could be determined. An additional three modulation frequencies provided ambiguity resolution. Range accuracies of 3 to 10 m were obtained.

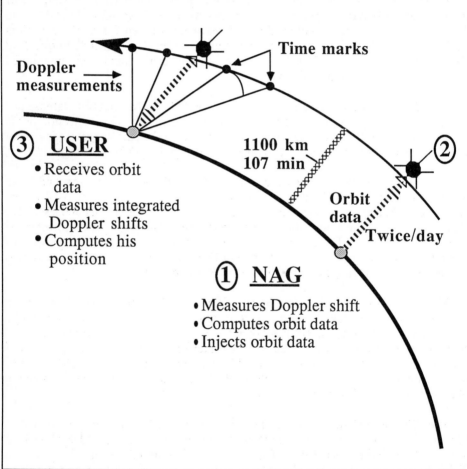

TRANSIT SATELLITE POSITIONING

Doppler measurements

Time marks

③ <u>USER</u>
- Receives orbit data
- Measures integrated Doppler shifts
- Computes his position

1100 km
107 min

Orbit data

Twice/day

②

① <u>NAG</u>
- Measures Doppler shift
- Computes orbit data
- Injects orbit data

TRANSIT SATELLITE POSITIONING

Experiments performed by scientists at the Johns Hopkins University Applied Physics Laboratory (ARL) following the launch of Sputnik 1 showed that it was possible to determine the satellite's orbit by analysing the Doppler shift of the satellite's radio transmissions. It was subsequently realized that if the position of a satellite could be determined by measuring the Doppler shift at a station of known position, then it should be possible to determine the position of the station if the position of the satellite is known. This realization led to the development by ARL of the U.S. Navy Navigation Satellite System, commonly known as Transit.

The first prototype Transit satellite was launched in 1961. Following deployment of a number of test satellites, the system was declared operational in 1964 and became classified. However, in 1967 Transit was declassified and became available for civilian use.

The Transit system consists of three components: the satellite tracking and control facilities, the satellites themselves, and the users. The Transit satellites are controlled by the U.S. Naval Astronautics Group (NAG) at Point Mugu, California. Four tracking stations in the U.S. record Doppler measurements on each pass of every operational satellite. These data are sent to Point Mugu where the orbit of each satellite is determined and extrapolated into the future. Twice a day, this ephemeris is transmitted by one of two injection stations to the satellite where it is stored in memory for subsequent rebroadcast.

Six Transit satellites are presently fully operational, including one launched in May 1967. Of these six, four are of the older Oscar type and two are of the advanced NOVA class. Another Oscar has been stored in orbit for future use. The satellites are in circular, polar orbits with altitudes of roughly 1100 km and their nodes more or less evenly spaced around the equator. Their corresponding orbital period is about 107 minutes. Each satellite transmits two harmonically related carrier frequencies, one at 400 MHz, the other at 150 MHz. Both frequencies are actually offset from these nominal values by -80 ppm to make receiver operation simpler. The use of two frequencies permits correction for the dispersive effect of the ionosphere (see Chapter 9). Superimposed on both carriers by balanced phase modulation is a broadcast message containing the orbit information previously injected into the satellite by the NAG. The message is continuously transmitted as a series of two-minute paragraphs, each paragraph consisting of 6103 binary bits. From the message, a new instantaneous orbit can be computed every two minutes.

The received signals are compared with the local oscillator frequency generated in the user's receiver and the Doppler shift, or frequency difference, is integrated to yield the observable. By combining these Doppler counts with the satellite orbit data, accurate coordinates of the receiver can be determined.

The Soviet Union operates a system similar to Transit, called Tsicada.

PRINCIPLE OF
DOPPLER POSITIONING

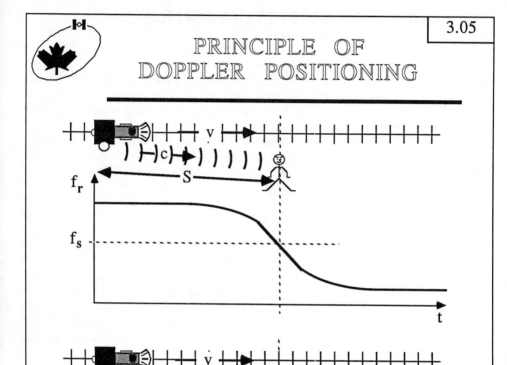

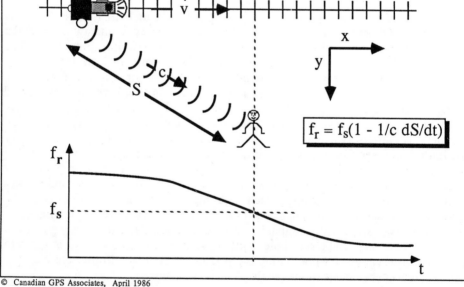

$$f_r = f_s(1 - 1/c \; dS/dt)$$

PRINCIPLE OF DOPPLER POSITIONING

The Doppler effect, discovered by Christian Doppler a nineteenth century Austrian physicist, is familiar to anyone who has waited patiently at a railway level crossing for a train to pass. The pitch of the train's horn or whistle changes as the train passes. It starts out high, changing imperceptibly as the train approaches, then drops noticeably as the train goes through the crossing, and maintains a lower pitch as the train recedes in the distance. This same phenomenon which is so readily apparent at audio frequencies also affects electromagnetic waves. The frequencies of both radio and light waves are shifted if the source (transmitter) and the observer (receiver) are in relative motion.

The classical explanation of the effect is that the observer receives more wave crests per second, i.e., the frequency is increased if the source and the observer are moving closer together, whereas fewer wave crests per second are received, i.e., the frequency is decreased, if the source and the observer are moving farther apart. If the relative speed of the source and observer is much less than the speed of light, then the received frequency is given approximately as

$$f_r \approx f_s (1 - 1/c \; dS/dt)$$

where f_s is the frequency at the source, c is the speed of light, and S the distance or *range* between the source and the observer; dS/dt is the *range rate*.

Returning to the train at the level crossing, you may have noticed that the closer you are to the track, the faster the change in pitch of the horn. And even if you could not see or feel the train, you can tell when it passes the crossing (*the point of closest approach*) by noting the instant when the pitch of the horn is mid-way between the high and low extremes (f_s). Therefore by monitoring the frequency of the received sound as the train passes and knowing its assumed constant speed, you can establish your position in a two-dimensional coordinate system where the x-axis, say, runs along the track and the y-axis runs perpendicular to it. The origin may be assigned arbitrarily. This is the principle of Doppler positioning.

In the case of a Transit satellite (or any other satellite for that matter), the position of a receiver can be established by continuously recording the Doppler shift of the received signals (or the number of cycles of the Doppler frequency which is a more precisely obtained observable). Subsequently these data are combined with accurate coordinates of the satellite to determine the position of the receiver. As with the passage of a train, a single satellite pass can provide at most only two coordinates of the receiver's position. Whereas this may be satisfactory for navigation at sea where the height above the reference ellipsoid is approximately known, three-dimensional positioning requires observing multiple satellite passes.

TRANSIT DOPPLER MEASUREMENTS

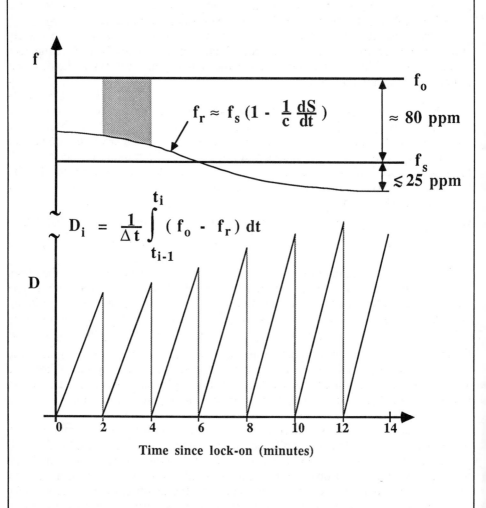

$$f_r \approx f_s \left(1 - \frac{1}{c}\frac{dS}{dt}\right)$$

f_o

≈ 80 ppm

f_s

$\lesssim 25$ ppm

$$D_i = \frac{1}{\Delta t}\int_{t_{i-1}}^{t_i}(f_o - f_r)\,dt$$

Time since lock-on (minutes)

TRANSIT DOPPLER MEASUREMENTS

The approximate frequency of a received satellite radio signal (ignoring relativistic effects) is given by

$$f_r \approx f_s (1 - 1/c \, dS/dt) ,$$

where f_s is the frequency of the signal measured at the satéllite, c is the speed of light, and dS/dt is the range rate. The *Doppler shift frequency*, $f_r - f_s$, is approximately proportional to the range rate, the component of the satellite's velocity vector along the line of sight from the receiver. The maximum range rate of a Transit satellite is about 7.4 km s^{-1} implying a maximum Doppler shift when the satellite rises or sets of 25 ppm of the transmitted frequency. This corresponds to 8.4 kHz at a frequency of 400 MHz.

The Doppler shifts may be measured by differencing the received frequencies from constant reference frequencies in the receiver. For most Transit receivers, these frequencies are 400 MHz and 150 MHz precisely. The satellite transmitter frequencies are approximately 80 ppm lower than the receiver reference frequencies in order that the Doppler shift does not go through zero. If the transmitter frequencies were not offset, the receiver would have difficulty distinguishing between positive and negative Doppler shifts. A record of the Doppler shift of a Transit signal during a typical pass is shown in the upper part of this figure. The point of closest approach of the satellite, when the Doppler shift is zero, occurred 6 minutes after the receiver locked onto the signal.

Most Transit Doppler receivers count the number of accumulated cycles of the Doppler frequency (actually, $f_o - f_r$) rather than measure the instantaneous Doppler frequency itself, since counting cycles can be carried out more precisely than measuring the instantaneous frequency. The counter is read out at intervals and the data stored. The counter is reset either after each two minute paragraph or at the end of the pass. Sequential differences in counter readings actually constitute a series of biased range differences.

The curves in this figure are based on actual data collected from Oscar 19 by a Canadian Marconi CMA-722B receiver near Ottawa, Canada, on 30 July 1983.

Suggested further readings:
Bomford, G. (1980). *Geodesy*. 4th ed., Oxford University Press, Oxford, Ch. 7, Section 7.
Stansell, T.A. (1978). *The Transit Navigation Satellite System*. Magnavox Government and Industrial Electronics Company, Torrence, Ca, U.S.A.

ARGOS

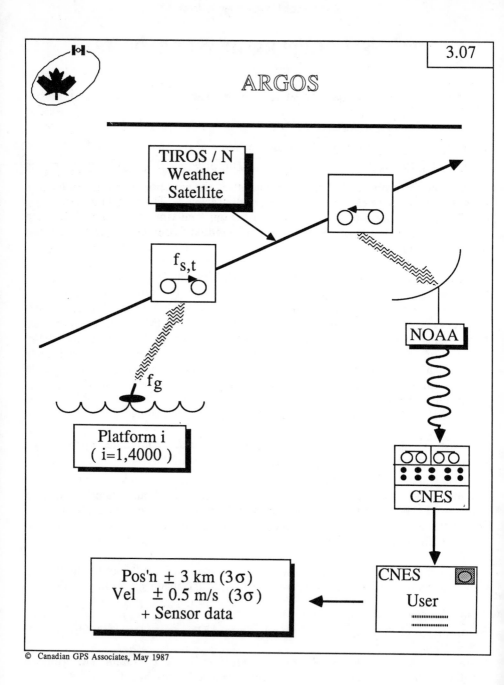

TIROS / N
Weather
Satellite

$f_{s,t}$

f_g

Platform i
(i=1,4000)

NOAA

CNES

Pos'n ± 3 km (3σ)
Vel ± 0.5 m/s (3σ)
+ Sensor data

CNES
User

ARGOS

Another satellite system which uses the Doppler effect for positioning is Argos [Service Argos, 1978], a cooperative project of the French Centre National d'Etudes Spatiales (CNES), NASA, and the U.S. National Oceanic and Atmospheric Administration (NOAA). However, in contrast to the Transit system, the transmitters are operated by the users and the receivers are in the satellites. An Argos transmitter on an instrumented 'platform' of some sort (oceanographic or navigation buoy, radiosonde balloon, remote weather station, etc.), periodically emits a 401.65 MHz signal carrying information from the platform's sensors. One of two passing U.S. TIROS/N-class weather satellites picks up this signal and records its Doppler shift along with the sensor data. These data are subsequently played back when the satellite is in range of one of three tracking stations: Wallops Island, Virginia; Gilmore Creek, Alaska; or Lannion, France. The tracking stations relay their data to NOAA's National Environmental Satellite Service in Suitland, Maryland, where they are sorted and then passed on to the Argos Data Processing Centre at CNES in Toulouse, France. CNES computes the position and velocity of the platform from the recorded Doppler shifts. This information along with the sensor data is conveyed to the operator of the platform by telex or letter. The two-dimensional (latitude and longitude) positions and velocities are claimed to be accurate to ± 3 km and ± 0.5 m s^{-1} (3σ), respectively. Up to 4000 platforms requiring location service can be handled by the Argos system, assuming these are uniformly distributed over the earth's surface.

The Argos receiving system was first implemented on the prototype TIROS/N spacecraft, orbited in 1978. Subsequent TIROS/N satellites, NOAA-6 through NOAA-10, have also carried the Argos Data Collection System.

Position determination from signals uplinked to a satellite is also utilized in the COSPAS-SARSAT search and rescue system [McPherson, 1981].

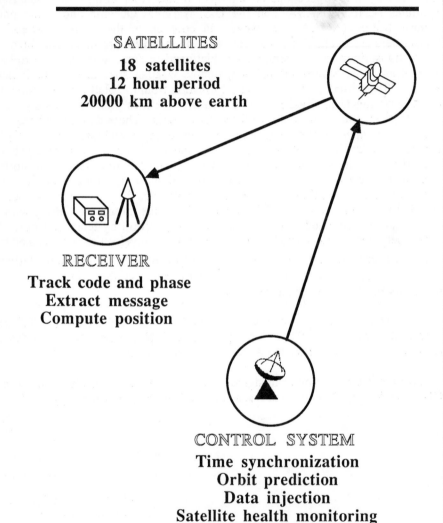

GLOBAL POSITIONING SYSTEM

SATELLITES

18 satellites
12 hour period
20000 km above earth

RECEIVER

Track code and phase
Extract message
Compute position

CONTROL SYSTEM

Time synchronization
Orbit prediction
Data injection
Satellite health monitoring

GLOBAL POSITIONING SYSTEM

Although GPS will be dealt with at length in the succeeding chapters of this manual, a brief introduction to the system will be given here to put it in context with the other extraterrestrial positioning techniques.

The NAVSTAR (NAVigation Satellite Time And Ranging) Global Positioning System (GPS) is a satellite-based positioning system currently under development by the United States Department of Defense. Work on the system began in 1973 as a result of the merger of the U.S. Navy's TIMATION Program and the U.S. Air Force's 621B Project. Both of these programs had been established in the mid-1960s to develop a passive navigation system using measured ranges.

GPS consists of three segments: the satellites, the control system, and the users. When fully deployed in the early 1990s, the satellite segment will consist of a constellation of 18 operational (Block II) satellites plus 3 in-orbit spares. The satellites are arrayed in 6 orbital planes inclined 55° to the equator. Each orbit is circular with a nominal altitude of 20 183 km. The corresponding orbital period is 12 sidereal hours, one half of the earth's period of rotation. Each satellite transmits two radio frequencies for positioning purposes; L_1 on 1575.42 MHz, and L_2 on 1227.6 MHz. The carrier frequencies are modulated by two pseudo-random noise codes and a navigation message. The carrier frequencies and the modulations are controlled by on-board atomic clocks.

The control system consists of monitor stations on Diego Garcia, Ascension Island, Kwajalein, and Hawaii, and a master control station at the Consolidated Space Operations Center at Colorado Springs, Colorado. The purpose of the control system is to monitor the health of the satellites, determine their orbits and the behaviour of their atomic clocks, and inject the broadcast message into the satellites.

The user segment consists of all military and civilian users. Appropriate receivers track the codes or the phase of the carriers (or both) and in most cases also extract the broadcast message. By aligning a receiver-generated replica of the code with the arriving signal, the range to the satellite can be determined. If the ranges to four satellites are combined with the orbit descriptions (see Chapter 1; the fourth range is required to account for the behaviour of the receiver's clock), the receiver can determine its three-dimensional geocentric coordinates. For precise geodetic work, carrier or code frequency phase is measured and recorded for future processing.

As of the date of writing this manual, 10 prototype (Block I) GPS satellites have been launched. Extensive civilian positioning tests and even production work have been carried out. Although the primary goal of GPS is to provide ground, sea, and air units of the U.S. and its NATO allies with a unified, high-precision, all-weather, instantaneous positioning capability, in its present test phase GPS is freely available to anyone to use. GPS will continue to be available to civilians, perhaps with certain restrictions (see Chapter 4), once the system is declared operational.

SATELLITE LASER RANGING

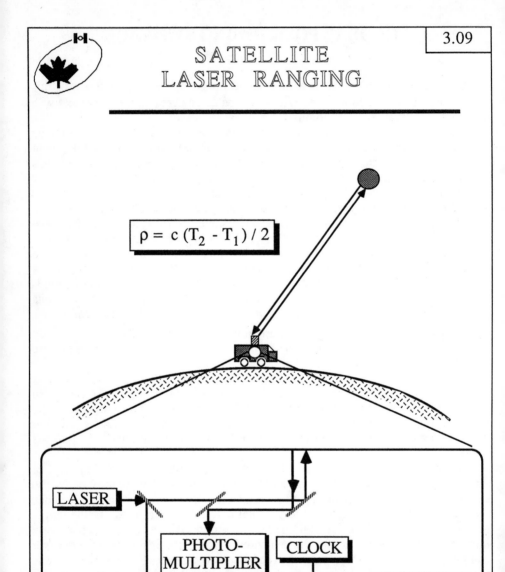

$$\rho = c\,(T_2 - T_1)\,/\,2$$

LASER

PHOTO-MULTIPLIER

CLOCK

PHOTODIODE

STOP

COUNTER

TAPE RECORDER

START

© Canadian GPS Associates, April 1986

SATELLITE LASER RANGING

The principle of satellite laser ranging (SLR) is illustrated in this figure. A short pulse of intense laser light is directed via a fully-steerable telescope to a satellite carrying a corner-cube retroreflector. The reflector directs the light back to the SLR system where the returning photons are collected by a telescope and detected by a sensitive photomultiplier tube. By measuring the elapsed time between transmission and reception of the laser pulse, the range to the satellite can be determined.

The first SLR systems began operating in the early 1960s. At the present time there are over 25 fixed, precision SLR systems worldwide. In addition, NASA has developed and deployed 8 MOBLAS-class mobile systems and 4 TLRS easily transportable systems; a further two transportable systems, MTLRS-1 and -2, have been built in Europe.

Most SLR systems now use short pulse length (100 ps) neodymium YAG lasers with an output at 532 nm and a power of a few mJ per pulse. Some systems still use the more powerful (several joules per pulse) but wider pulse width (several nanoseconds) ruby lasers with output at 694 nm. Most SLR systems have separate telescopes for transmitting and receiving; some use a single telescope. The receiving telescopes used range in size from 28 cm diameter to a metre or more. The receiving sensitivities of systems range from a single photon to more than 100 photons. The best single shot range accuracy is about 2 cm r.m.s.

SLR data are usually analysed using the dynamical approach in which data from many stations spanning periods from about 5 to 30 days are combined. Station positions, orbital elements, and various biases are determined simultaneously. The lengths of global intersite baselines have been determined to precisions of 3 to 5 cm. The SLR networks also provide accurate values of the earth rotation parameters.

Over 15 retroreflector-equipped satellites have been placed in earth orbit. Of these, the most fruitful have been the dedicated LAGEOS and Starlette satellites. Recently, Japan launched the third fully reflecting satellite, the Experimental Geodetic Payload, 'Ajisi.'

Laser ranging to the earth's natural satellite, the moon, is also carried out by a few specially equipped stations. Reflectors were deployed on the lunar surface by the crews of Apollo 11, 14, and 15 and remotely by two Soviet Luna landers.

Suggested further reading:
Degnan, J.J. (1985). "Satellite laser ranging: Current status and future prospects." *IEEE Transactions on Geoscience and Remote Sensing*, Special Issue on satellite geodynamics, Vol. GE-23, No. 4, pp. 398-413.

VERY LONG BASELINE INTERFEROMETRY

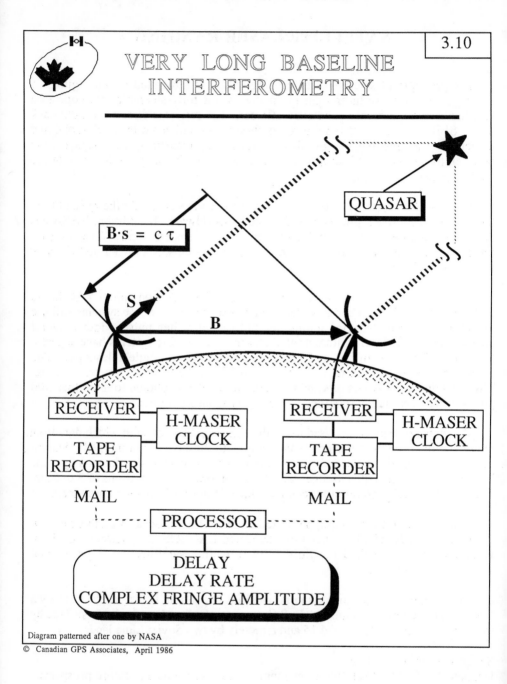

Diagram patterned after one by NASA

VERY LONG BASELINE INTERFEROMETRY

Very long baseline interferometry (VLBI) is the most accurate of all the extraterrestrial positioning techniques. It was initially developed by astronomers as a tool to improve the resolution of radio telescopes. However, it was realized even before the first successful tests of the concept in 1967 by independent teams of Canadian and American astronomers that it would be an ideal geodetic instrument.

VLBI uses the principle of wave interference and is analogous to the familiar Young's double slit experiment of classical optics. Signals from a radio source, usually the random noise signals of a quasar or other compact extragalactic object, are received at the antennas of two or more radio telescopes. These signals are amplified and translated to a lower frequency band under control of a hydrogen maser frequency standard (see Chapter 7). The translated signals are digitized, time-tagged, and recorded on wide bandwidth magnetic tape. Subsequently the tape recordings are played back at a central processing site. The processor is a computer-controlled cross-correlator which delays and multiplies the signals from the tapes recorded at a pair of radio telescopes. The output of the processor is a sampled cross-correlation function equivalent to the fringes of Young's experiment.

The primary observable of geodetic VLBI is the *group delay*, the difference in arrival times of the quasar signal wavefronts at the radio telescopes. In principle, the delay can be measured in the correlation process by noting the time offset between a pair of tape recordings required to achieve maximum correlation. The *phase (delay)* of the correlation function and its time rate of change, the *delay rate*, are also measured. In practice, the group delay is obtained from measurements of the phase delay at different frequencies.

The primary component of the measured group delays is the *geometric delay*, $\tau = (\mathbf{B \cdot s}) / c$, where $\mathbf{B}$ is the baseline vector connecting two radio telescopes, s is the unit vector in the direction of the radio source, and c is the speed of light. From observations of a dozen or more radio sources during a nominal 24-hour session, the three components of the baseline vector can be retrieved. A number of biases in the data must be carefully measured or modelled.

The radio frequencies used for geodetic VLBI are in the microwave portion of the electromagnetic spectrum. The Mark-III VLBI system [Clark et al., 1985] uses 14 frequencies at S band (2.2 - 2.3 GHz) and X band (8.2 - 8.6 GHz); the two bands being used in order to correct for ionospheric delay (see Chapter 9).

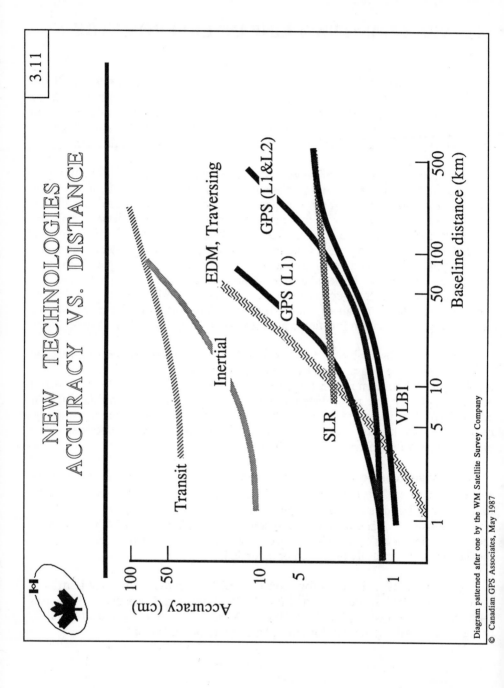

NEW TECHNOLOGIES
ACCURACY VS. DISTANCE

3.11

Transit

Inertial

EDM, Traversing

GPS (L1)

GPS (L1&L2)

SLR

VLBI

Accuracy (cm)

100
50
10
5
1

Baseline distance (km)

1   5   10   50   100   500

Diagram patterned after one by the WM Satellite Survey Company

© Canadian GPS Associates, May 1987

NEW TECHNOLOGIES: ACCURACY VS. DISTANCE

The relative positioning accuracy of extraterrestrial techniques has improved by over two orders of magnitude during the past twenty years or so. Centimetre-level accuracy is available from SLR and VLBI, and from GPS when dual-frequency receivers are used. For baselines longer than about 5 km, these techniques exceed the capabilities of the conventional techniques of EDM and traversing. Although not an extraterrestrial technique, inertial surveying systems are also capable of relatively high accuracy. Routine accuracies approaching 10 cm over very short baslines have now been obtained. Even the venerable Transit system is capable of achieving relative position accuracies of better than 50 cm on baselines shorter than 100 km. In general, the accuracy of all these techniques falls off with increasing baseline distance due to incomplete modelling of the particular biases that affect each technique. Only the techniques of SLR and VLBI have accuracies which are almost independent of baseline length.

The accuracies shown in this figure refer to the length of the baseline between points, after accounting for any scale differences between the coordinate systems employed. The accuracies of the *components* of a three-dimensional vector baseline will in general not be the same as the length accuracy due to the way errors in bias modelling map into the components. For example, relative heights determined by VLBI or GPS are not as accurate as the relative horizontal components because of incomplete modelling of atmospheric delays. In addition, there may be difficulty in accessing the desired coordinate system. Accurately positioning a baseline in the conventional terrestrial (CT) system using one of the extraterrestrial techniques, requires accurate knowledge of the variations in the spin of the earth and the motion of the pole of rotation. Uncertainties in these parameters will map into components of a baseline vector purported to be in the CT-system. Global networks of VLBI and SLR stations are being used to monitor the rotation of the earth and to establish fiducial points in the CT-system.

GPS AND OTHER SYSTEMS

ONE - WAY SYSTEMS   (military)

GPS = NAVSTAR
- Proposed in the early 1970s
- 11 prototype satellites (1978-86)
- 28 production satellites (1989-95)

TRANSIT = NNSS
- Operational (1964-94)
- Typically 4-6 usable satellites
- Impact on control surveys

GLONASS
- Russian GPS
- 12 prototype satellites (1982-84)

TWO - WAY SYSTEMS   (civilian)

GEOSTAR (U.S. COMMERCIAL)
- Electronic packages piggy-backed on communication satellites
- Low cost (U.S.$450 + subscription)
- Planned U.S. coverage by late 1980s 100 000 users by 1990

NAVSAT (ESA PROPOSAL)
- Two-way GPS
- Regional control centres
- Deployment not yet funded

GPS AND OTHER SYSTEMS

A useful comparison may be made between GPS and some of the other satellite positioning systems presently in use or proposed for the future. The systems in use at present, including GPS, Transit, and the Russian equivalents GLONASS and Tsicada, were initially designed as military systems. They are one-way systems; i.e., signals are transmitted from the satellites to the receivers. This is a desirable feature from the military point of view as the user does not give away his position by transmitting any signals. The satellites must also be able to function for extended periods without any signal contact from the control stations. These features make one-way systems complex and place a high demand on the satellites and receivers. Nevertheless, these systems have been highly successful, especially within the civilian user community which dominates the military users in number (with the possible exception of GLONASS about which little is known except that it uses signal formats, carrier frequencies, and satellite orbits similar to those of GPS).

Civilian systems need not impose radio silence on the user or require the satellites to operate autonomously during a crisis. Consequently two-way systems are possible. The complexity of the system can then be transferred from the satellites and the receivers to the control segment. Two of the proposed two-way systems are Geostar and NAVSAT. Geostar requires two-way communication between the user and the satellites. NAVSAT requires continuous two-way communication between the satellites and the control stations. These systems are described on the following pages of this chapter.

GEOSTAR

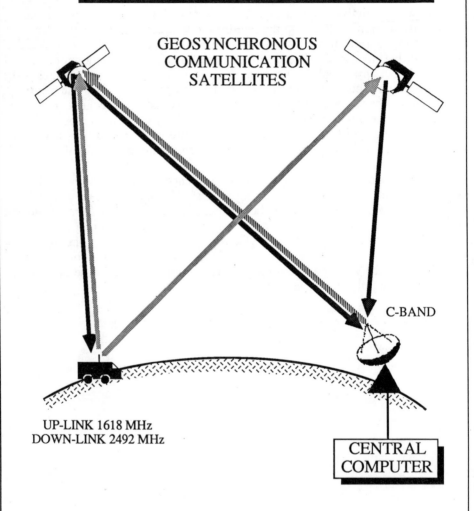

GEOSYNCHRONOUS
COMMUNICATION
SATELLITES

C-BAND

UP-LINK 1618 MHz
DOWN-LINK 2492 MHz

CENTRAL
COMPUTER

GEOSTAR

Geostar is one of several satellite-based positioning systems [Anon., 1986] that have been proposed by commercial interests. The concept of the system has evolved since 1983 when it was first proposed. The current design [O'Neill, 1984] calls for two geosynchronous satellites to relay two-way signals between a central computational facility, 'Geostar Central,' and user terminals. Spread-spectrum signals are transmitted to one satellite which retransmits the signals to the user terminals. The user terminals transmit identically-coded signals back through both satellites to the central facility using a time-division multiple-access scheme, adding a unique digital identification code for security and billing purposes. The two-way travel times of the signals via each of the two satellites are then determined for each of the user terminals. By combining the two ranges with height information obtained from a digital terrain map, the two-dimensional coordinates of a land- or sea-based user can be determined as often as required. Accuracy is improved by combining data from a fixed reference station within 200 km of a user terminal. The system also has a message capability. Messages can be sent from the central facility to users or vice versa. For aircraft in flight, height information can be supplied by the pilot or through automatic interrogation of an encoding altimeter. The two satellites would cover the continental U.S. and peripheral regions. Four additional satellites could provide essentially worldwide coverage (except at high latitudes). The system is estimated to have sufficient capacity to serve a user population of 50 million user terminals.

As all of the positioning computations are performed at the central facility, the user terminals can be kept very simple. A terminal consists of a transceiver to relay the radio signals and processing and message storage integrated circuits. Messages and position information are displayed on a liquid crystal panel and outgoing messages entered on a calculator-like keypad. Hand-held versions of the terminal will be powered by penlight batteries, weigh about half a kilogram, and could cost as little as $US 450 (1984 dollars) if produced in quantities of the order of 100 000.

Initial tests of the Geostar concept were carried out in the fall and winter of 1983/84 using 'pseudo-satellites' on mountain tops in the vicinity of Lake Tahoe, Nevada. Those tests, using pedestrians, automobiles, and aircraft, demonstrated a positioning accuracy of about one metre. The first true satellite test (of message capability from user terminals to Geostar Central) began in March 1986 with the launch of GTE Spacenet's GStar 2 communication satellite. The satellite carries a one-way Geostar transponder called LinkOne. Unfortunately, both the primary and backup LinkOne L-band receivers failed in May 1986 [Anon., 1986].

NAVSAT

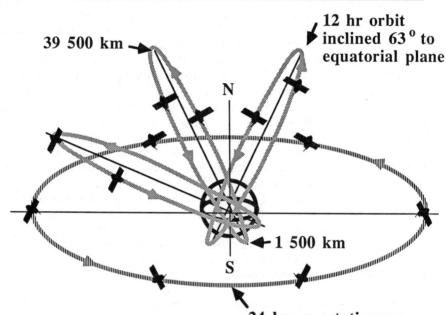

39 500 km

12 hr orbit
inclined 63° to
equatorial plane

N

1 500 km

S

24 hr geostationary
orbit; 36 500 km altitude

ORBITS

TYPE	i(°)	Ω(°)	ω(°)	# SATS	PHASES(°)
elliptic	63.4	0	270	2	180, 240
elliptic	63.4	120	270	2	168, 205.5
elliptic	63.4	240	270	2	154.5, 192
circular	0	0	0	6	0, 60, 120, 180, 240, 300

Diagram patterned after one by ESA

NAVSAT

NAVSAT is a multipurpose positioning system proposed by the European Space Agency [ESA, 1985]. It would offer a capability similar to GPS, but it would be a civilian system and would forego certain features required in military systems and hence operate with much simpler satellites and receivers. The system would consist of three segments: the satellites, the ground control facilities, and the users.

With a design principle similar to that adopted for Geostar, the space segment complexity has been transferred from the satellites to the ground. The satellites simply rebroadcast signals received from a network of up to six control stations. Each station continuously transmits signals, using C-band frequencies, to those satellites in view. When a satellite passes out of range, control is passed to a neighbouring station. The signals consist of a strong continuous wave (cw) carrier, pseudo-random noise (PRN) code with a chipping rate (see Chapter 4) of about 5 MHz, and a low bit rate message stream containing ephemeris and other data. The satellites rebroadcast these signals on the primary navigation frequency of 1.596 GHz and on a C-band frequency to be used primarily for satellite control. All satellites transmit on the same frequency and use the same PRN code. A time division multiple access format is used in order that the satellites not interfere with each other. Each satellite transmits in sequence a signal burst lasting 133 ms, every ~2 seconds. Frequency stability of the signals is obtained by use of synchronized atomic standards at the control stations. No atomic clocks are used in the spacecraft.

The configuration of the satellite constellation has been modified since NAVSAT was first proposed. The current design (see this figure and Chapter 5 for an explanation of orbit terminology) calls for a mixture of satellites in geostationary and highly elliptical orbits. Six satellites in geostationary orbit and six satellites in elliptical orbits would provide coverage in the northern hemisphere; an additional six satellites in elliptical orbits would extend the coverage worldwide. Orbit details are given in the figure. The satellites in geostationary orbit could be communications satellites carrying the additional NAVSAT transponders.

Three classes of users are envisaged: those requiring (moderate) positioning or navigation accuracy of ~100 m; those requiring a (high) accuracy of ~5-10 m; and those requiring geodetic accuracy. The moderate accuracy user would be served by a simple Doppler mode receiver accessing only the cw carriers. The high accuracy user would have a pseudo-range receiver accessing the PRN signals with Doppler aiding. Geodetic accuracy could be obtained by recording the carrier phase over an extended time interval in a similar fashion to that used with GPS.

Extensive design studies for NAVSAT have been prepared, however as of this date there are no firm deployment plans.

THE FUTURE OF SATELLITE POSITIONING

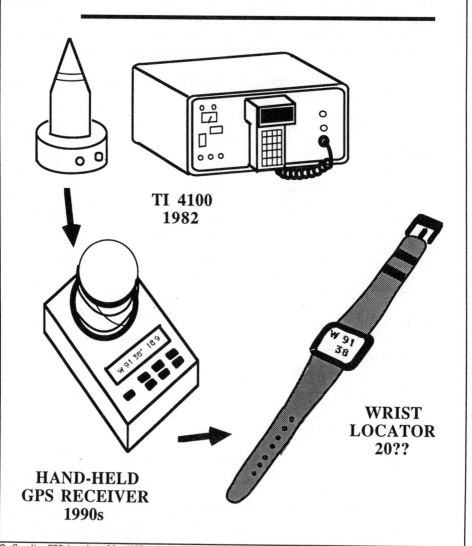

TI 4100
1982

HAND-HELD
GPS RECEIVER
1990s

WRIST
LOCATOR
20??

THE FUTURE OF SATELLITE POSITIONING

With the advent of the Global Positioning System, we are entering an era of accurate positioning, available on demand, twenty-four hours per day, every day of the year from any location in the world. Although there will possibly be some initial restrictions on the real-time accuracy available to civilian users, GPS will bring about a revolution in the practice of positioning, impacting not only surveyors, geodesists, and navigators but the general public at large. In the future, accurate positions will be a cheap, readily available commodity, much as time is today.

GPS will be accompanied and eventually supserseded by other satellite systems. Already GLONASS, the Soviet Union's equivalent to GPS, is in operation and the first tests with the civilian Geostar system have taken place. A number of other civilian systems are on the drawing boards.

The near-term trend in satellite positioning will be toward smaller, cheaper, and more easily-operated receivers. A hand-held GPS receiver not much larger than a standard deck of playing cards is under development by Rockwell Collins for the U.S. Department of Defense. The single-channel receiver with a pop-up antenna will make use of the latest gallium arsenide very high speed, very large scale integrated circuit technology. We foresee a natural evolution toward even smaller, more accurate receivers. Eventually, we may even have the 'wrist locator,' a cheap ($10 in current funds), accurate (1 mm) device that would be as ubiquitous as today's electronic wrist watches [Vaníček et al., 1983]. Such devices will influence our future daily lives in ways that are presently impossible to predict.

CHAPTER FOUR

GLOBAL POSITIONING SYSTEM
BASIC CONCEPTS

Guide to GPS Positioning
© Canadian GPS Associates, April 1986

GPS BASIC CONCEPTS

SATELLITES

- GPS satellite
- Prototype satellite constellation
- Final 21-satellite constellation
- Satellite ground tracks
- GPS ground stations

GPS SIGNAL STRUCTURE

MEASUREMENTS

- Propagation and ranging concepts
- Pseudo-range and carrier beat phase measurements

RECEIVER COMPONENTS AND FUNCTIONS

POSITIONS

- Static, kinematic, and relative positioning

ACCURACY

- Geometry and accuracy
- Dilution of precision (DOP)
- Constrained solutions

IMPACT

- U.S. Federal Radionavigation Plan
- How many GPS users will there be ?
- Main features of GPS
- Present and future GPS characteristics

GPS BASIC CONCEPTS

This chapter is the 'crossroad' of this *Guide to GPS Positioning*. In the first three chapters, we have concentrated on placing the Global Positioning System in context. From Chapter 5 onward, we will be dealing in some detail with various aspects of GPS. In this chapter, we describe the basic concepts upon which we will base these more detailed discussions. In going over these basic concepts, this chapter also provides a more or less complete and self-contained initial overview of GPS. The material in this longest chapter in the *Guide* can be grouped under seven topics:

• **Satellites.** The first nine figures describe the GPS satellite itself; the present (1986) constellation of seven prototype satellites; the final 21-satellite constellation, and how and when it is likely to be deployed; what sort of coverage each of these constellations provides; and the ground tracking stations required to manage the GPS constellation.

• **Signals.** The next figure quickly reviews the concepts behind the rather complicated GPS signal structure.

• **Measurements.** The next five figures review propagation and range-measuring concepts, and introduce the two types of GPS measurements — pseudo-ranges and carrier beat phase measurements.

• **Receivers.** The next two figures describe the components and functions of a typical GPS receiver.

• **Positions.** The next four figures present the concepts involved in static and kinematic positioning; relative positioning; multi-receiver positioning; and relative kinematic positioning.

• **Accuracy.** The next three figures introduce the relationship between the GPS satellite constellation geometry and positioning accuracy; the Dilution of Precision (DOP) concept; and the effect of constrained solutions.

• **Impact.** So far the material in this chapter has previewed the remainder of the *Guide*. In this final set of five figures, we discuss the policies and effects of the United States Government Federal Radionavigation Plan; the possible size of the GPS user community; the features of GPS that will form the basis for its impact on the positioning professions and on society at large; and a speculative look at the future of high-technology positioning capabilities.

GPS SATELLITE

4.01

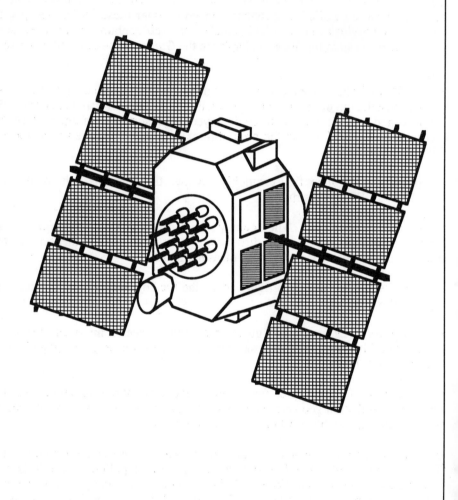

GPS SATELLITE

So far three generations of GPS satellites have been planned. These are known as the 'Block I,' 'Block II,' and 'Block III' satellites.

Eleven Block I satellites were constructed and launched between 1978 and 1985. These are the prototype satellites presently in use.

Construction of the 28 Block II satellites is nearing completion. Launch of 21 of these will signal the beginning of the GPS operational era.

Some Block II GPS satellites will weigh 845 kg (upon insertion into final orbit). Other Block II GPS satellites will be heavier, having a NUDET (NUclear DETection) module on board. Block II satellites are designed to fulfill their function for 7.5 years. This figure shows what these satellites look like in orbit.

Some of the basic functions of these satellites are:

(a) Receive and store information transmitted by the 'control segment,' i.e., by the operators of the system.
(b) Do limited data processing on board by means of its own microprocessor.
(c) Maintain very accurate time by means of several oscillators (two cesium, two rubidium) carried on board.
(d) Transmit information to the user by means of various signals.
(e) Manoeuvre by means of thrusters controlled by the system operators.

The activities of the satellites are powered by batteries charged by solar panels which when deployed have an area of 7.25 m^2.

The Block III GPS satellites are presently at the design stage. It is planned that they will be available for launch, to replace the Block II generation, beginning in the late 1990s.

GPS PROTOTYPE
SATELLITE STATUS

Launch Sequence Number	Orbit Pos'n	PRN code	IRON	NASA Catalog Number	International Identifier	Launch Date	Status
1	[C - 4]	4	5111	10684	1978-020A	78-02-22	not operating
2	[A - 4]	7	5112	10893	1978-047A	78-05-13	not operating
3	A - 3	6	5113	11054	1978-093A	78-10-07	okay
4	C - 3	8	5114	11141	1978-112A	78-12-11	okay
5	[C - 1]	5		11690	1980-011A	80-02-09	not operating
6	A - 2	9	5118	11783	1980-032A	80-04-26	okay
7						81-12-18	launch failed
8	C - 2	11	9794	14189	1983-072A	83-07-14	okay
9	C - 1	13	9521	15039	1984-059A	84-06-13	okay
10	A - 1	12	9783	15271	1984-097A	84-09-08	okay
11	C - 5	3	6374	16129	1985-093A	85-10-09	okay

Data as of April 28, 1986

GPS PROTOTYPE SATELLITE STATUS

At present GPS is in a testing stage. Only 10 prototype satellites have been successfully launched. Of these, only seven are presently functioning. Of these seven, three have various 'health' problems. There are several ways of identifying the individual satellites:

- the **NAVSTAR** number in the first column is the number in the sequence of GPS satellite launches;
- the second column shows the **position** of each satellite in space (see the following figure);
- the **PRN code** number denotes which of the available 37 seven-day segments of P-code pseudo-random-noise signal is presently used by each particular satellite;
- the **IRON** number is the Inter Range Operation Number. This is a random number assigned by the joint U.S./Canadian North American Air Defence Command (NORAD) to identify selected objects. At one time this was a sequential series of numbers, rather than the random numbers now assigned.
- the fifth column gives the number of the satellite in the **NASA** sequential file;
- the **international** identifier consists of the launch year, the sequence number of the launch in that year, and a letter. The letter A identifies the primary payload for that launch. Subsequent letters are used for other objects placed in orbit by the launch, such as booster rockets and other debris.

Three of the 10 satellites placed in orbit (NAVSTAR numbers 1,2, and 5) have failed. All satellites, and GPS satellites in particular, have redundant systems (spare components) built in, so that when certain components fail, the spares can be switched on in their place from the ground. The GPS prototype satellite component that has suffered the most failures is the clock. Each GPS prototype satellite has been launched with several clocks on board. Even so, a satellite will eventually run out of working clocks. The clock modules on board the first four satellites were not as reliable as those of later design on subsequent launches.

Those satellites with health problems are NAVSTAR numbers 3,4, and 8. The design lifetime of these prototype satellites is 5 years, determined by the mean time between failure of the electronic systems and their redundant backup spares; the aging of the power supply components, consisting of solar panels and rechargable batteries; and the supply of 'fuel' for the jets used to reposition the satellites in orbit. NAVSTAR numbers 3 and 4 have far exceeded this design lifetime. To extend the life of these two as long as possible, the GPS Joint Program Office has decided not to risk operating the electronics at low power levels (occurring when the satellite is in the earth's shadow, operating entirely on battery power). From late 1986, these satellites will be turned off during their eclipse periods. NAVSTAR number 8 began showing high frequency erratic oscillator behavior in November 1985, which was suspected to have come from a module located after the clock. This prevented some receivers from holding lock on this satellite's signal. The problem was corrected in mid-1986 by switching in a spare circuit.

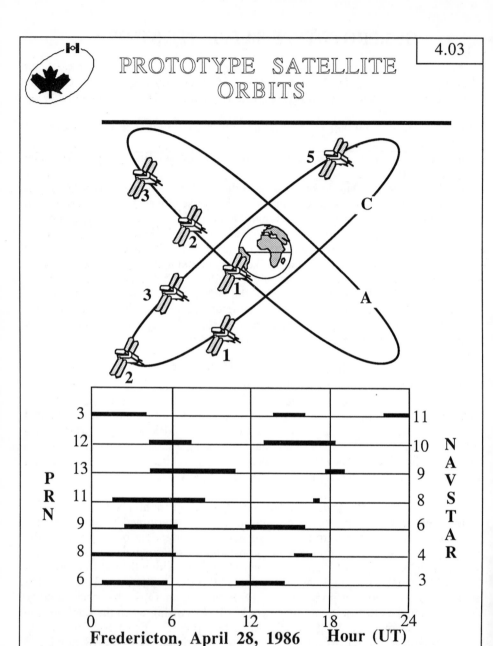

PROTOTYPE SATELLITE ORBITS

4.03

Fredericton, April 28, 1986   Hour (UT)

PROTOTYPE SATELLITE ORBITS

The seven functioning satellites are in two orbital planes (labelled A and C), and in positions within the planes labelled 1,2, and 3 for plane A, and 1,2,3, and 5 for plane C. Two adjacent positions are separated by an angle of 60° (reckoned in the orbital plane).

The prototype constellation has been selected in this way to give the best possible coverage, for the given number of satellites and their orbital characteristics, over two military test areas; the southwestern continental United States, and off the northeast coast of the United States in the North Atlantic. In fact this provides an uninterrupted period of about five hours per day during which GPS can be used over almost all of North America.

Presently (April 28, 1986) in Fredericton, New Brunswick, this five-hour period falls between 3 am and 9 am Universal Time. We see from the figure that the sequence of satellite risings is as follows:

- orbit position C-5 rises (NAVSTAR 11, PRN 3)
- orbit position C-3 rises (NAVSTAR 4, PRN 8)
- orbit position A-3 rises (NAVSTAR 3, PRN 6)
- orbit position C-2 rises (NAVSTAR 8, PRN 11)
- orbit position A-2 rises (NAVSTAR 6, PRN 9)
- orbit position A-1 rises (NAVSTAR 10, PRN 12)
- orbit position C-1 rises (NAVSTAR 9, PRN 13) .

Due to the orbit configuration, orbit position C-5 sets below the horizon about ten minutes before positions A-1 and C-1 rise. Thus the maximum number of visible satellites is six out of the seven now available. We see that this occurs during the period from the rise of A-1 and C-1, and the set of A-3.

This situation differs from one part of the world to another.

Because the GPS satellites circle the earth once every 12 hours, configurations repeat themselves every twelve hours (successively in opposite hemispheres). The orbital periods are 12 hours of sidereal time, and due to the difference between sidereal and solar time, the satellites appear about four minutes earlier each day. Thus each month the coverage period will advance by two hours, or roughly 30 minutes per week.

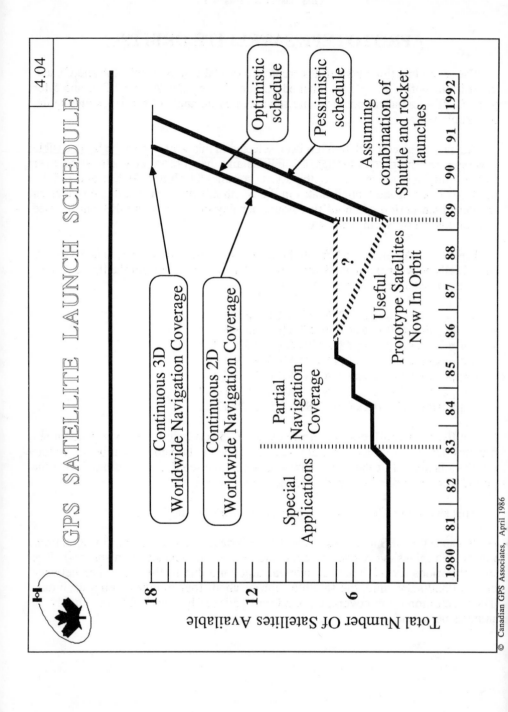

GPS SATELLITE LAUNCH SCHEDULE

4.04

Total Number Of Satellites Available

Optimistic schedule

Pessimistic schedule

Assuming combination of Shuttle and rocket launches

Continuous 3D Worldwide Navigation Coverage

Continuous 2D Worldwide Navigation Coverage

Partial Navigation Coverage

Special Applications

Useful Prototype Satellites Now In Orbit

?

18   12   6

1980 | 81 | 82 | 83 | 84 | 85 | 86 | 87 | 88 | 89 | 90 | 91 | 1992

GPS SATELLITE LAUNCH SCHEDULE

Prototype satellites have been launched by rockets, while operational satellites were supposed to have been launched by space shuttles. The full contingent of operational satellites was to have been in space by the end of 1988.

Due to the delays resulting from the space shuttle Challenger disaster, shuttle flights will not begin again before early 1988. The shuttle program was designed to replace supposedly more expensive rocket launching of satellites into orbit, not only for NASA but for the U.S. military as well. With the problems and delays in the shuttle program, a return to rocket launches appears likely. The USAF has contracted four design studies for conventional rocket launching GPS (and other) satellites. Rocket launches may start in late 1988.

Three scenarios are shown here. If shuttle-only launches are used, it may take as long as four years to place the full GPS constellation of 18 satellites in orbit. If a combination of shuttle and rocket launches is used, the most optimistic date for achievement of the full constellation is late 1989. The most likely guess, using both shuttle and rocket launches, is early 1991.

For a continuous three-dimensional navigation capability, at least 4 satellites have to be everywhere visible simultaneously at all times. Four satellites enable the user to eliminate unknown time offset between satellite and user oscillators. Similarly, for two-dimensional navigation capability, 3 simultaneously visible satellites are necessary. Dates when these capabilities may be reached are shown here.

GPS can be used in the navigation mode, three dimensional or two dimensional, even before these dates with the understanding that the coverage will not be continuous in time. This temporal discontinuity affects stationary applications less dramatically. It results only in the necessity of spending more time 'observing' the satellites thus making the position determinations more expensive.

GPS CONSTELLATION IN 1990

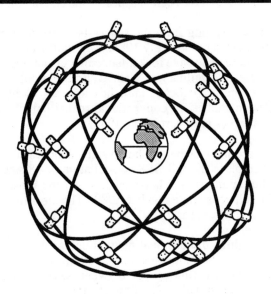

- **18 satellites, plus 3 active spares**
- **6 orbit planes**
- **12 hour period**
- **20,000 km height**
- **(almost) full coverage**
  (24 hours per day everywhere in the world)

GPS CONSTELLATION IN 1990

The final constellation is going to appear in the late 1980s or early 1990s. With this final constellation, at least four satellites will be visible simultaneously at any time from any point on the earth's surface. This constellation consists of 18 satellites arranged three in each of six orbit planes. In addition *active spares* are planned. These spares will be three additional satellites in orbit, making a total of 21. Up to three satellites may fail before it would be necessary to launch a replacement satellite. When all 21 satellites are working properly, the coverage provided by this constellation is better than it would be with only the minimum of 18 satellites.

The satellites are in circular orbits approximately 20 000 kilometres above the earth's surface. This is more than three times the earth's radius. At this height, the satellite revolves around the earth once every twelve hours. For an observer on the surface of the earth, any particular satellite will be above the horizon for about five of these twelve hours. At various times of day, and at various locations, the number of satellites above the horizon may vary between a minimum of four and a maximum of ten.

The coverage provided by this '18 + 3' constellation is not perfect — at certain localities, and at certain times of day, when only four satellites are available, the satellite geometry provides much worse positioning accuracy than usual. Such occurrences are brief (lasting less than 10 minutes usually). They are referred to as *outages*.

Constellations proposed earlier included:
- 24 satellites in three orbital planes of eight satellites each. This would have provided fewer outages than the current proposal, but was shelved when budget cuts reduced the number of satellites to 18;
- 18 satellites in three orbital planes of 6 satellites each. This resulted in more serious outages than the one currently adopted.

DEPLOYMENT OF 21-SATELLITE CONSTELLATION

WHERE ARE OTHER GPS SATELLITES WHEN SATELLITE NUMBER 1 CROSSES THE EQUATOR ?

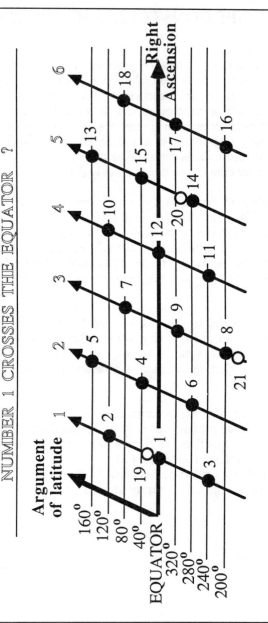

● 18 satellite constellation

○ active spare

 Canadian GPS Associates, April 1986

4.06

DEPLOYMENT OF 21-SATELLITE CONSTELLATION

All 6 orbital planes are inclined by 55° to the equatorial plane and rotated by 60° with respect to their neighbouring planes. Thus their separation in right ascension α is 60°.

The angular measure used for describing the position of a satellite in its orbit is called *argument of latitude.* It is reckoned in the orbital plane in the direction of satellite motion referred to the point of satellite ascension through the equatorial plane. The argument of latitude is the sum of the argument of perigee ω and true anomaly f and could more properly be called *argument of satellite.* (Note that the argument of latitude replaces both ω and f when the orbit is circular and the perigee is not defined.) The separation of satellites in argument of latitude within each orbital plane is 120°. Satellites in any plane are ahead (in argument of latitude) of corresponding satellites in the adjacent plane to the west by 40°.

The 3 active spares — numbers 19, 20, 21 — are in orbital planes labelled 1, 5, and 3, and have arguments of latitude of 30°, 310°, and 170°, respectively, at the instant when satellite number 1 ascends through the equatorial plane. Note that the satellite numbering used here corresponds to none of the numbering systems used for the prototype satellites. Also, the labelling of orbital planes is different from that used for the prototype satellites.

SATELLITE GROUND TRACKS

APRIL 28, 1986   03:00 to 05:00 UT

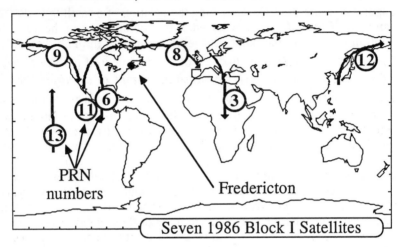

PRN
numbers

Fredericton

Seven 1986 Block I Satellites

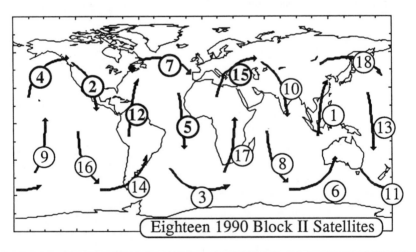

Eighteen 1990 Block II Satellites

SATELLITE GROUND TRACKS

These are plots of satellite tracks created by projecting satellite positions onto the earth along the earth's radii. The earth's globe is then mapped onto a cylinder tangent to the globe along the equator. If a point (ϕ, λ) on the earth's surface lies on the track, then the corresponding satellite would be in the zenith of that point at the instant shown by the time graduation of the track. Two plots are shown:

- The top plot is for the present seven prototype satellites, for two hours on April 28, 1986. Recalling Figure 4.03, this is a period during which all seven satellites are visible at Fredericton. Note that satellites as far away as over Japan, Alaska, Hawaii, and Greece are visible.
- The bottom plot is for the planned 18-satellite constellation (omitting the three active spares). It is assumed that these 18 satellites were in orbit on April 28, 1986, and the plot is for the same two-hour period as the top plot. The satellites identified by bold numerals would be visible from Fredericton during this two-hour period.

These plots show nicely the relation between the maximum latitude of the track, i.e., the maximum latitude at which the satellite appears in the zenith, and the inclination of the satellite's orbital plane. In fact, this maximum latitude equals to the inclination of the orbital plane with respect to the equatorial plane. This, of course, does not mean that the satellite is not visible above the maximum latitude, only that points above ϕ = i never experience the satellite in their zenith. Therefore, the top plot (of the prototype satellites) shows that they reach latitudes of 63° (the inclination of the prototype orbits), while the bottom plot shows maximum latitudes of 55° (the planned inclination for the Block II satellites).

Note that the 4 minutes per day regression of the satellites appears as an eastward shift of the tracks by approximately 1°.

These plots were prepared using program **MacSat**, available from the Geodetic Research Laboratory, Department of Surveying Engineering, University of New Brunswick.

SATELLITE POLAR PLOTS

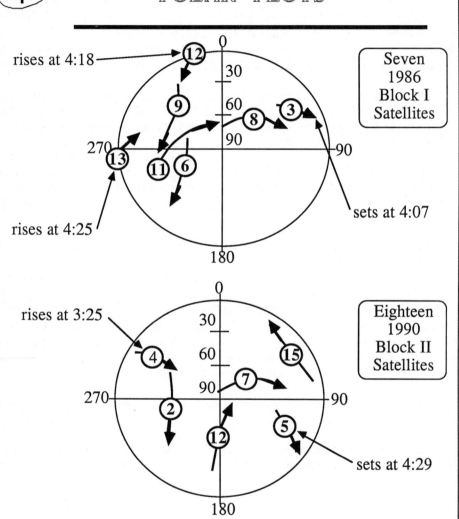

rises at 4:18

Seven
1986
Block I
Satellites

270

90

sets at 4:07

rises at 4:25

rises at 3:25

Eighteen
1990
Block II
Satellites

270

90

sets at 4:29

SATELLITE POLAR PLOTS

Polar plots (more correctly polar *coordinate* plots) of satellite orbits are often used to inspect visually the quality of a satellite configuration. These plots are produced by projecting satellite positions from the centre of the earth onto the celestial sphere and displaying the pertinent half of the celestial sphere as a circle. These plots are created by interpreting the azimuth and zenith distance (90° minus elevation) of the satellite at any instant of time as viewed by the observer as polar coordinates. By joining the positions computed for given time increments during a specified period of time, projected tracks are created. Individual points on those tracks are then labelled by the appropriate time. Here we have simplified the plot by taking only the start time (03:00 UT) and/or end time (05:00 UT) of each plotted track as a time mark. We note that the 4 minute daily regression would appear, on these plots, as a 4 minute shift of these time marks.

These plots correspond to the track plots of the previous figure. Both plots are for Fredericton, April 28, 1986, 03:00 to 05:00 UT. The top plot is for the present constellation. The bottom plot assumes that the final 18-satellite constellation was available for the same day and time.

These plots represent a handy tool to judge the satellite configuration at any given instant. For instance, the top plot shows that between the setting of PRN 3 at 4:07, and the rise of PRN 12 at 4:18 the configuration is poor; the remaining four satellites are bunched together (just past the middle of their two-hour tracks) towards the northwest, and all are at a relatively high elevation. However, once PRNs 12 and 13 have risen but remain at low elevations, and the other satellites have progressed further along their tracks, particularly PRNs 6 and 8 moving away from the bunching region, the configuration improves considerably.

A comparison between the two plots indicates the limits of the present constellation. The top plot shows that all seven of the prototype satellites are visible during the two hour period, and the bottom plot shows that only six of the 18-satellite constellation would be visible for the same period. However, the distribution of these six is far better, leading to a better configuration throughout the period, than is the case for the top plot. Also, satellite 4 rises before satellite 5 sets, so that there would always be at least five satellites visible. The conclusion is obvious — what counts is not only how many satellites you can see but also how they are distributed spatially around you.

These plots were prepared using program **MacGEPSAL**, available from the Geodetic Research Laboratory, Department of Surveying Engineering, University of New Brunswick.

GPS CONTROL STATIONS

Kwajalein
Diego Garcia
Ascencion
Colorado Springs
Hawaii

4.09

© Canadian GPS Associates, May 1987

GPS CONTROL STATIONS

The five control stations, spaced almost evenly around the world, perform three functions:

- All five stations are monitor stations, tracking all GPS signals for use in controlling the satellites and predicting their orbits. The tracking is done by means of two-frequency receivers equipped with cesium oscillators. Meteorological data are also collected to allow for the most accurate evaluation of tropospheric delays. Positions of these monitor stations are known to a very high accuracy.
- Three of the stations (Ascension, Diego Garcia, and Kwajalein) are capable of transmitting data up to the satellites, including new ephemerides, clock corrections, and other broadcast message data, and command telemetry.
- One station (Colorado Springs) is the Master Control Station.

Tracking data from the monitor stations are transmitted to the Master Control Station for processing. This processing involves the computation of satellite ephemerides and satellite clock corrections. The master station is also responsible for controlling orbital corrections when any satellite strays too far from the assigned position. The Master Control Station would also initiate the necessary manoeuvres to have a dead satellite replaced by a spare.

GPS SIGNAL STRUCTURE

FUNDAMENTAL FREQUENCY
- f_0 = 10.23 MHz

CARRIERS
- L1 = 154 f_0 = 1575.42 MHz
- L2 = 120 f_0 = 1227.60 MHz

C/A-CODE
- 1 ms long sequence of ±1 steps at f_0/10 (1 MHz)

P-CODE
- 267 day long sequence of ±1 steps at f_0 (10 MHz)

Y-CODE
- Similar to P-code, with secret generating equation

MESSAGE
- 1500 bit sequence of ±1 steps at 50 bps

PHASE MODULATION TECHNIQUE

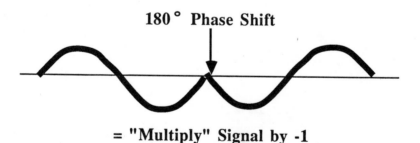

180° Phase Shift

= "Multiply" Signal by -1

GPS SIGNAL STRUCTURE

Every satellite transmits two frequencies for positioning: 1575.42 MHz, and 1227.60 MHz. The two carriers, called L1 and L2, are coherent and modulated by various signals.

A pseudo-random noise (PRN) code, known as the *C/A-code*, consists of a sequence of plus ones and minus ones, emitted at the frequency $f_0/10 = 1.023$ MHz, which repeats itself every millisecond. A second pseudo-random noise (PRN) code, known as the *P-code*, consists of another sequence of plus ones and minus ones, emitted at the frequency $f_0 = 10.23$ MHz, which repeats itself only after 267 days. The 267 days are chopped into 38, seven-day segments. Of these, one week segment is not used, five are reserved for use with ground stations, called pseudolites, leaving 32, seven-day segments, each assigned to a different satellite. The *Y-code*, a PRN code similar to the P-code, can be used instead of the P-code. However, the equation which generates the P-code is well known and unclassified, while the equation which generates the Y-code is classified. Therefore, if the Y-code is used, unauthorized users of GPS (generally anyone except military users of the United States and its allies) will no longer have access to the P- (or Y-) codes.

The L1 carrier is modulated by two codes (C/A-code and either P-code or Y-code), while L2 contains only the P-code or Y-code.

The codes are modulated onto the carriers in a conceptually simple way. If a code value is minus one, the carrier phase is shifted by 180°, and if it is plus one, there is no change in the carrier.

Both carriers carry the broadcast *satellite message*, a low frequency (50 Hz) stream of data designed to inform the user about the health and position of the satellite. These data can be decoded by the receiver and used for positioning in real time.

PROPAGATION OF ELECTROMAGNETIC WAVES

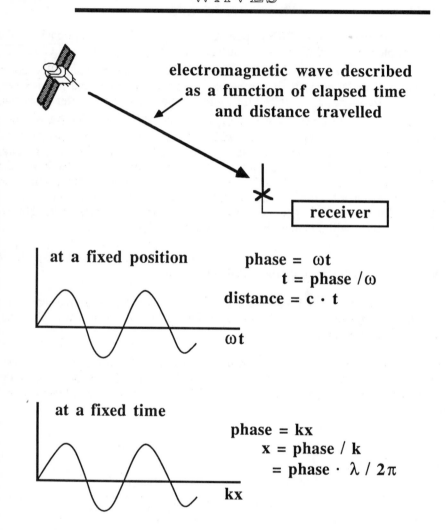

electromagnetic wave described
as a function of elapsed time
and distance travelled

receiver

at a fixed position

phase = ωt
t = phase $/\omega$
distance = c · t

ωt

at a fixed time

phase = kx
x = phase / k
= phase · λ / 2π

kx

PROPAGATION OF ELECTROMAGNETIC WAVES

The electromagnetic wave transmitted from the satellite to the receiver may be represented as

$$y = A \cos(\omega t - kx + \phi) \, ,$$

where A is the signal amplitude, ω is the radian frequency ($\omega = 2\pi f$), k is the propagation wavenumber related to the free space wavelength ($k = 2\pi/\lambda$), t is the elapsed time measured from the instant of transmission at the satellite, x is the distance travelled from the satellite to the receiver, and ϕ is the bias term. In any other propagation medium than in free space, the wavelength may be different from the free space wavelength. This is usually denoted by using the symbol β for the propagation wavenumber in other than free space, and reserving k for the free space propagation wavenumber.

The distance travelled by the wave between the satellite and the receiver may be determined by either of two methods. If both the frequency and the exact instant of transmission from the satellite are known, then a measurement of elapsed time (between signal transmission and reception) allows one to compute the distance by

distance = velocity of propagation $\times$ elapsed time .

This pseudo-range technique requires accurate time information.

The other method of distance determination is to measure the number of phase cycles over the transmission path. This can be done by mixing the incoming signal with the known signal frequency. Then, at any given instant, the propagation path distance is given from

$$\text{phase} = kx = 2\pi/\lambda \ x$$
$$x \quad = \text{phase} \times \lambda/2\pi \, .$$

This method requires that the frequency of the satellite signal be accurately known and that the phase of the signal can be accurately tracked.

TWO-WAY AND ONE-WAY RANGING

TWO-WAY RANGING (EDM)

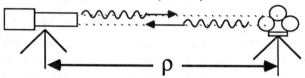

Measure $\Delta t = 2\rho / c$ = two way time of travel
Calculate $\rho = c \, \Delta t / 2$

One clock used to measure Δt

Single user system

ONE-WAY RANGING (GPS)

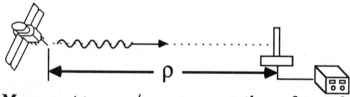

Measure $\Delta t = \rho / c$ = one way time of travel
Calculate $\rho = c \, \Delta t$

One clock (in satellite) generates signal
A second clock (in receiver) detects when it arrives
The two clocks must keep same time
(1 microsecond error = 300 m error in ρ)

Multi user system

TWO-WAY AND ONE-WAY RANGING

Ranging by means of an electromagnetic signal can be done in either of two modes: two-way ranging, or one-way ranging. Two-way ranging is conceptually the more simple. Timing of the range measurement is controlled only by one clock, situated in the transmitter-receiver. At the far end of the ranging line is a device that simply responds to the incoming signal. If this is a passive device (a target or reflector), it simply reflects the incoming signal back to the receiver. If this is an active device (transponder), it generates a return signal only upon reception of an incoming transmission from the transmitter-receiver, and in such a way that the timing relationship between the incoming and 'reflected' signals is constant and known. The measurement is the number of 'ticks' of the system clock between the transmission of the original signal and the reception of its return — the two-way time of travel. One of the disadvantages of two-way ranging is revealed if we consider the active or passive reflector to be a reference station. One transmitter-receiver tends to monopolize the use of one (or more) such reference stations. The number of simultaneous users is limited, most often to one.

One-way ranging, as used in GPS, is more complicated. Each terminal, transmitter and receiver, is controlled by a separate clock. The transmitter clock generates the signal. The receiver clock detects when the signal arrives. Both clocks must keep the same time. An error in the synchronization of the two clocks of 1 µs creates an error in range of 300 metres.

Since it is practically impossible to keep the two clocks perfectly synchronized physically, it is usually done mathematically. In general each clock will run at its own rate, keeping its own time. However, if the relationship between the two time bases defined by the clocks is known, then they can still be said to be synchronized. The problem, of course, is to find the relationship between the two time bases. GPS works only because we can assume that all GPS satellite clocks are synchronized (mathematically, not physically) among themselves. This is achieved by careful monitoring of differences in satellite clock timing by GPS ground station monitors, and including the resulting mathematical corrections in the satellite message broadcast to all users. Users can then assume that all the simultaneous GPS ranges measured by their receiver are related to the same (ficticious) clock at the satellite end of the range measurements. As we will see, synchronizing the receiver clock to this common fictitious satellite clock is then a 'piece of cake' (more or less).

PULSED AND CONTINUOUS WAVE RANGING

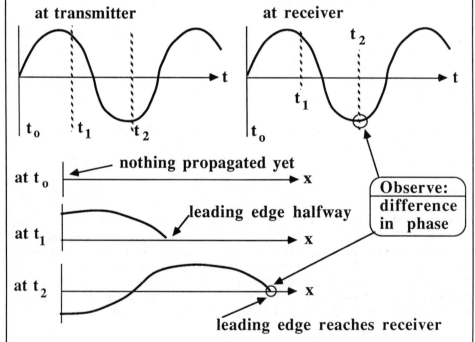

PULSED

T_x R_x

at t_0 ——————— x
at t_1 ——————— x
at t_2 ——————— x

Observe:
time of
arrival = t_2

CONTINUOUS WAVE

at transmitter   at receiver

t_0 t_1 t_2

t_2

t_1

t_0

at t_0 — nothing propagated yet ——→ x

at t_1 — leading edge halfway ——→ x

at t_2 ——————→ x

Observe:
difference
in phase

leading edge reaches receiver

PULSED AND CONTINUOUS WAVE RANGING

Range measurement systems use either pulsed signals or continuous wave (CW) signals. There are advantages and disadvantages to either method. Either method can be used with one-way or with two-way ranging. GPS is a one-way ranging system capable of both pulsed-type range measurements (pseudo-ranging using one of the codes), and continuous wave-type ranging (carrier beat phase measurements).

The top figure considers the concept of pulsed signal one-way ranging. 'Snapshots' of the signal pulse travelling from transmitter (GPS satellite) to receiver (user) are shown for three epochs. The one-way travel time is $t_2 - t_0$, where t_2 is measured by the receiver clock, and t_0 by the transmitter clock. Provided the two clocks are perfectly synchronized, the range can be determined *unambiguously* from

$$\rho = c\,(t_2 - t_0).$$

One of the disadvantages of the pulsed ranging is the sparse information content — pulses arrive only at discrete intervals rather than continuously. GPS pseudo-ranging shares this sparseness: code epochs occur at discrete intervals rather than continuously.

Representation of the continuous wave one-way ranging concept is more complicated. The transmitter is now an oscillator that continuously generates a wave whose phase varies both in time and in space. We now need two sets of 'snapshots':
(a) of the phase variation in time, viewed from a fixed point in space, and
(b) of the phase variation in space, viewed at a fixed epoch in time.
We assume the transmitter and receiver oscillators are perfectly synchronized in frequency and phase. In this case, plots of type (a) at both transmitter and receiver will be identical. To simplify the concept, consider plots of type (b) immediately after turning on the CW transmitter: i.e., 'snapshots' at three epochs as for the pulsed system. The range measurement made at t_2 is given by the difference between the phase of the incoming signal received from the transmitter, and the phase of the internal oscillator in the receiver. The total phase difference involved in the range measurement includes the number of full wavelengths, or cycles of phase, between the transmitter and receiver, in the snapshot at t_2. However, all we can directly measure is the fractional phase difference, between 0° and 360°, or within one cycle of the signal. We must determine the integer cycle count some way other than by directly measuring it. This *cycle ambiguity problem* is the most serious drawback to CW range measuring systems. The main advantage is the continuous information density — the CW wave is always available for measuring, not only at discrete epochs as for pulses.

PSEUDO-RANGE MEASUREMENTS

4.14

Code arriving from satellite

Replica of code generated in receiver

Time delay (pseudo-range measurement)

$-\Delta t \rightarrow$

© Canadian GPS Associates, May 1987

PSEUDO-RANGE MEASUREMENTS

A GPS receiver can make basically only two kinds of measurements: pseudo-range, and carrier beat phase.

Pseudo-range is the time shift required to line up a replica of the code generated in the receiver with the received code from the satellite multiplied by the speed of light. Ideally the time shift is the difference between the time of signal reception (measured in the receiver time frame) and the time of emission (measured in the satellite time frame). In fact, the two time frames will be different, which introduces a bias into the measurement. These biased time delay measurements are thus referred to as *pseudo*-ranges.

Pseudo-ranges are measured by a correlation detector that controls a delay lock loop which maintains the alignment (correlation peak) between the receiver-generated code replica and the actual incoming code. In simple terms, the code correlation concept involves generating a replica of the code sequence (the sequence of +1 and -1 values) within the receiver, and aligning this replica in time (correlate) with the incoming signal.

The pseudo-range measurement is then the delay which must be added to epochs of the receiver clock to keep the replica and incoming code aligned (correlated).

A rule of thumb for the precision of pseudo-range measurements (that is, the precision with which the correlation peak can be maintained) is 1% of the period between successive code epochs. For the P-code, successive epochs are 0.1 microsecond apart, implying a measurement precision of 1 nanosecond. When multiplied by the speed of light, this implies a range measurement precision of 30 centimetres. For the C/A-code, the numbers are ten times less precise, or a range measurement precision of 3 metres.

CARRIER BEAT PHASE
MEASUREMENT

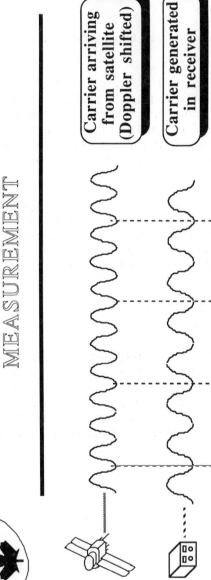

Carrier arriving from satellite (Doppler shifted)

Carrier generated in receiver

Beat signal

120°

360° • n + 120°

45°

360° • (n + 3) + 45°

Observed phase: 120°

Total phase: 360° • n + 120°

Integer cycle count n is

- not observed, but counted inside the receiver
- loss of lock leads to loss of n-count (called cycle slip)
- initial value for n-count must be determined (cycle ambiguity problem)

© Canadian GPS Associates, April 1986

CARRIER BEAT PHASE MEASUREMENTS

Carrier beat phase is the phase of the signal which remains when the incoming Doppler-shifted satellite carrier is differenced (beat) with the constant frequency generated in the receiver. This observable is obtained as a by-product of the correlation channel or from a squaring channel. A squaring channel multiplies the received signal by itself to obtain a second harmonic of the carrier, which does not contain the code modulation.

The squaring concept is simply shown by squaring the equation of the carrier wave to obtain

$$y^2 = A^2 \cos^2(\omega t + \phi) = A^2[1 + \cos(2\omega t + 2\phi)]/2 .$$

Since A(t) is the sequence of +1 and -1 values representing the code, $A(t)^2 = A^2$ is always equal to +1 and may be dropped. The resulting signal, y^2, is then pure carrier, but at twice the original frequency.

Because the wavelength of the carrier is much shorter than the wavelength of either of the codes, the precision of carrier beat phase measurements is much higher than the precision of code pseudo-ranges. For the GPS L1 carrier signal, the wavelength is about 20 cm. Using the rule of thumb that phase measurements can be made to about 1% of the wavelength, this implies a precision of 2 mm.

The two main disadvantages of carrier beat phase measurements both involve the cycle ambiguity problem.

• Obtaining the initial number of integer cycles of the carrier between the satellite and the receiver is very difficult, if not impossible. One way out is to take measurements which can be assumed to have the same (unknown) initial cycle ambiguity, and subtract one from another. More about this later.
• Maintaining an integer cycle count as the satellite-to-receiver range changes with time is something most good quality GPS receivers can do most of the time. However, for a variety of reasons, such as a noisy signal or a shaded antenna, any receiver will suffer cycle slips, or the loss of a coherent integer cycle count. In many cases painstaking postprocessing permits the detection and correction of cycle slips. However, the possibility of cycle slips restricts the use of carrier beat phase measurements for real-time applications.

GPS USER EQUIPMENT COMPONENTS

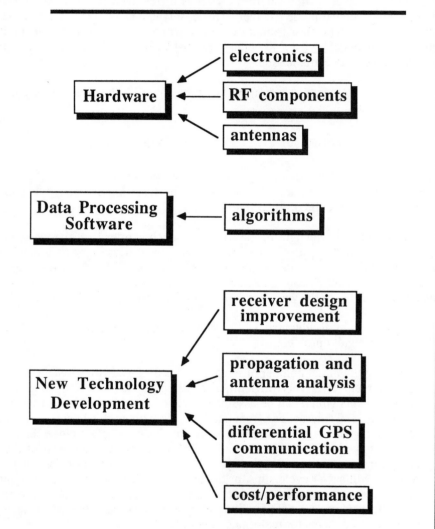

Hardware ← electronics
Hardware ← RF components
Hardware ← antennas

Data Processing Software ← algorithms

New Technology Development ← receiver design improvement
New Technology Development ← propagation and antenna analysis
New Technology Development ← differential GPS communication
New Technology Development ← cost/performance

GPS USER EQUIPMENT COMPONENTS

The GPS user equipment package may be thought to consist of three main segments:

- hardware
- software
- technology development.

The hardware segment includes the electronic circuitry, RF components and antennas, and any peripheral equipment required to operate the receiver. The main features in this segment must include ruggedness, portability, field reliability, and ease of operation.

The software segment includes the obvious programming and data processing needed to convert the GPS messages into useful positioning or navigation information. This programming must allow adequate user interaction in order to take full advantage of the many features of GPS. It must also be adapted to ready field use and should be designed to provide useful system status and progress messages to the operator. Also included in the software segment are the programs developed independent of the GPS receiver which can evaluate such factors as satellite availability and precision confidence levels.

Automatically included in the user equipment package is the technology which went into the various hardware and software components. This technology spans every area related to GPS, such as receiver design improvement, analysis and modelling of the various antenna and propagation effects and their incorporation into the data processing software, development of reliable communication link systems for short- to long-range differential GPS operation, and monitoring of the developing trends in equipment cost and performance.

GENERIC GPS RECEIVER

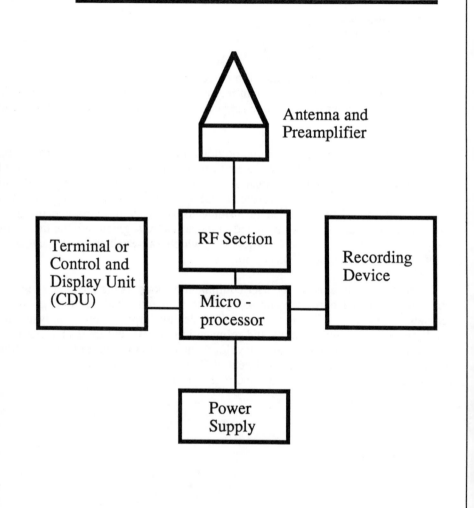

Antenna and
Preamplifier

RF Section

Terminal or
Control and
Display Unit
(CDU)

Recording
Device

Micro -
processor

Power
Supply

GENERIC GPS RECEIVER

The satellite receiver is the piece of hardware used to *track* the satellites, i.e., to receive the satellite signals described above. A basic GPS receiver configuration consists of

- antenna and preamplifier
- radio frequency (RF) section
- microprocessor
- terminal or control and display unit
- recording device
- power supply

Antenna and preamplifier: Antennas used for GPS receivers have broadbeam characteristics, thus they do not have to be pointed to the signal source like satellite TV dishes. The antennas are rather compact and may be tripod or vehicle mounted. The actual position determined is the phase centre of the antenna which then has to be properly related to the survey mark.

Radio frequency section: The RF section contains the signal processing electronics in a combination of digital and analog circuits. Different receiver types use somewhat different techniques to process the signal. The different approaches are

- code correlation
- code phase and frequency
- carrier signal squaring.

The RF section consists of channels using either of these three appproaches to track a received GPS signal. The number of channels varies between 1 and 7 for different receivers.

Control unit: The control unit enables the operator to interact with the microprocessor. Its size and type varies greatly for different receivers, ranging from a hand-held unit to a video monitor with full size keypad.

Recording device: Either tape recorders or floppy disks are utilized to record the observations and other useful information extracted from the received signal.

Power supply: Most receivers need low voltage DC power; only a few require AC power.

STATIC AND KINEMATIC POSITIONING

STATIC POSITIONING

• Receiver may observe for an extended period of time

• Receiver is stationary

• Least-squares solution for 3 station coordinates and a time offset time series

• If code receiver, solution with build-in microprocessor possible

• Post-processed solution

KINEMATIC POSITIONING

• Receiver observes on a moving vessel

• Solution for time series of vessel coordinates and time offset

• Possible combination with other position sensors

• If code receiver, solution with built-in microprocessor possible

• Post-processed solution

STATIC AND KINEMATIC POSITIONING

GPS can be used to position static objects or moving objects. Although the observations (ranges) are the same, the fact that the antenna is either stationary or moving introduces significant differences.

If the antenna is stationary, we can observe many repeated ranges to each of several satellites. This gives us redundant observations, overdetermined solutions (e.g., least squares), and consequently a higher accuracy of the determined position. When the antenna moves, we can only get instantaneous 'fixes' (from usually 4 ranges observed simultaneously or almost simultaneously) with no redundancy.

In the static case, we may get either a real-time result, where each new observation is processed so as to give an improvement to the previously determined position, or observations may be processed after the field campaign is over. We speak of a postprocessed solution.

In kinematic positioning, the real-time solution is normally sought. This solution consists of one position (fix) at a time. The resulting string of fixes (discretized track of the vessel) can be also postprocessed using one of a number of existing smoothing operations.

RELATIVE POSITIONING

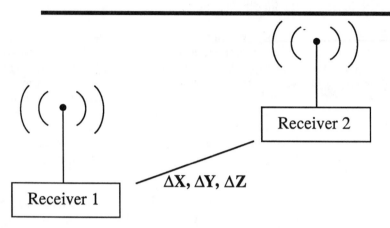

Receiver 2

$\Delta X, \Delta Y, \Delta Z$

Receiver 1

Two (or more) receivers observe GPS signals simultaneously

Some errors are common (or similar) in the measurements made by all receivers

When solving for relative positions $\Delta X, \Delta Y, \Delta Z$, these errors are eliminated or reduced

Relative positions are more accurately determinable than absolute positions

RELATIVE POSITIONING

When a higher accuracy is required, then relative positioning must be used. In this operational mode, two antennas are positioned with respect to each other and two receivers (at the ends of the observed baseline) are operated simultaneously. The higher accuracy achieved in this mode occurs because several errors burdening the observed ranges are either identical or at least similar at both ends of the baseline. These errors then get either eliminated or, at least, significantly reduced when relative positions are sought.

One particularly intriguing and promising mode of relative positioning, first suggested by Ben Remondi of the U.S. National Geodetic Survey, is relative semi-kinematic positioning. The idea is to use one stationary instrument and rove around with the other instrument. As long as no cycle slips occur in either receiver, accuracies of better than one cycle (20 cm) of the carrier beat phase signal can be continuously maintained in the relative positions between the stationary and roving receiver. This suggestion has two implications:
• kinematic applications may benefit from the much higher carrier measurement accuracies, rather than being limited to code measurement accuracies, and
• a much wider spectrum of GPS applications has been opened up. Setting out surveys, and aerotriangulation without ground control are two that are under investigation at present.

MULTI-RECEIVER
POSITIONING

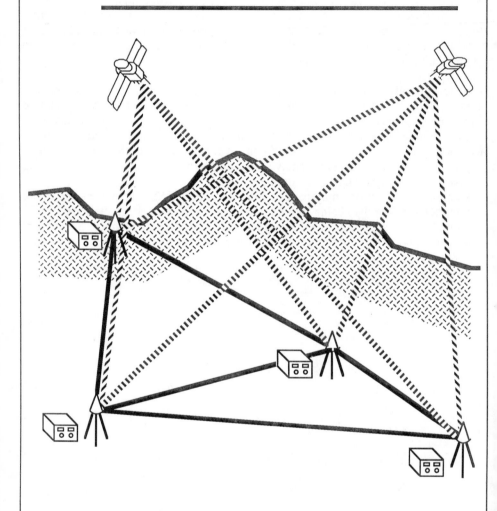

MULTI-RECEIVER POSITIONING

Accuracy of results can be significantly improved when several receivers are deployed in a network positioning mode. A network is a geometrically stronger configuration than a single baseline because of redundancy — the individual baselines connected into the network have to satisfy the conditions imposed by the geometry. This redundancy is used to control the effect of different errors, random as well as systematic, contained in the observations. We note that even with only two receivers available, it is preferable to connect desired baselines into a network, thus improving the accuracy of the positions.

When several receivers are deployed, one is faced with unique logistic problems concerning the pattern in which these are moved around and observing periods at individual stations. Under these circumstances, it is advisable to pay particular attention to the optimization of observing schedules to achieve the best accuracy with the most economical means.

RELATIVE KINEMATIC POSITIONING

4.21

RELATIVE KINEMATIC POSITIONING

If a very accurate kinematic position is needed, the point positioning mode described earlier may not be good enough. Then the concept of relative (differential) positioning can be used. The idea is to use one stationary antenna as a reference point. The stationary antenna's receiver then tracks at least the same satellites (preferably all visible satellites) as the moving receiver does. Accurate knowledge is assumed of the stationary receiver's position and clock behavior. The discrepancies between the measured ranges to each satellite, and the ranges computed from the 'known' stationary receiver position and clock (that is the range misclosures), and the resulting apparent changes in the position of the stationary receiver are due to temporal variations in the orbital information, atmospheric delays, and clock performance.

Either the position offsets or the range misclosures can be transmitted to the moving receiver through a real-time communication link. Studies have demonstrated that better results, and an easier implementation of the corrections, result when the range misclosures are used rather than position offsets. The moving receiver applies the range misclosures to correct the equivalent measurements it has made. This real-time correction improves both the accuracy and the reliability of kinematic positions. Real-time relative kinematic positioning accuracies of a few metres under most GPS error scenarios appear feasible.

The stationary receiver may be regarded as a pseudo-satellite (pseudolite) and made to transmit signals and messages coded the same way as those transmitted by the satellites. This has the added advantage of providing one more range meaurement signal (between pseudolite and user). On the other hand, pseudolite signals at the GPS frequency are limited to line of sight applications. The pseudolite concept is being considered for such applications as aircraft landing approaches.

GPS GEOMETRY AND ACCURACY

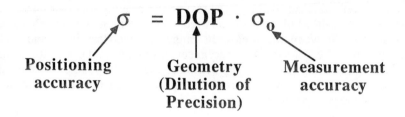

$$\sigma = DOP \cdot \sigma_0$$

| Positioning accuracy | Geometry (Dilution of Precision) | Measurement accuracy |

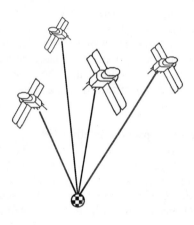

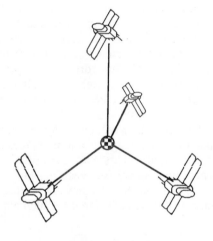

POOR GDOP
satellites bunched together

GOOD GDOP
(ideal case)
- one satellite overhead
- 3 on horizon,
  120° apart in azimuth

GPS GEOMETRY AND ACCURACY

The accuracy with which positions are determined using GPS depends on two factors: the satellite configuration geometry, and the measurement accuracy. The usual term for GPS measurement accuracy is the *user equivalent range error* (UERE), which represents the combined effect of ephemeris uncertainties, propagation errors, clock and timing errors, and receiver noise.

The effect of satellite configuration geometry is expressed by the *dilution of precision* (DOP) factor, which is the ratio of the positioning accuracy to the measurement accuracy, or

$$\sigma = DOP \cdot \sigma_0,$$

where σ_0 is the measurement accuracy (standard deviation), and

σ is the positioning accuracy (e.g., standard deviation in one coordinate).

DOP is a scalar representing the contribution of the configuration geometry to the positioning accuracy. There are many varieties of DOP, depending on what particular coordinate, or combinations of coordinates, we are considering the accuracies of. The more common DOPs are:

- VDOP $\cdot$ σ_0 is the standard deviation in height (Vertical)

- HDOP $\cdot$ σ_0 is the accuracy in 2D Horizontal position

- PDOP $\cdot$ σ_0 is the accuracy in 3D Position

- TDOP $\cdot$ σ_0 is the standard deviation in Time

- HTDOP $\cdot$ σ_0 is the accuracy in Horizontal position and Time

- GDOP $\cdot$ σ_0 is the accuracy in 3D position, and time (Geometrical)

Where does the DOP come from? Recall the confidence ellipsoid discussed in Chapter 1. The standard deviation in one coordinate (say height) is represented by the distance from the centre to the surface of the ellipsoid along the local vertical direction (the height axis). According to the above equation, it is also equal to VDOP $\cdot$ σ_0. For horizontal positioning, in confidence ellipsoid terms, we want to express the 'size' of the horizontal ellipse: one reasonable measure is square root of the sum of squares of the two axes of the horizontal ellipse. This is HDOP·σ_0. In general, any DOP is equivalent to the square root of the sum of the squares of the confidence region axes corresponding to the parameters being assessed.

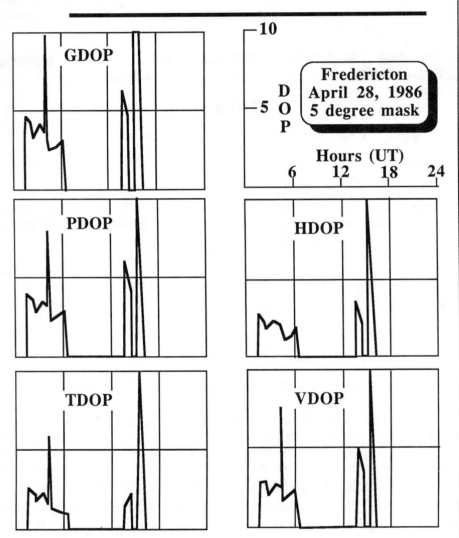

DILUTION OF PRECISION

DILUTION OF PRECISION

The dilution of precision, or DOP, is a measure of the geometrical 'strength' of the GPS satellite configuration. This will change with time, as the satellites travel along their orbits, and from place to place, since the satellite configuration is position-dependent.

This figure shows five different DOPs plotted for Fredericton for April 28, 1986. The present constellation of seven prototype GPS satellites was used, with a mask angle of 5°. These DOP plots correspond to the satellite configuration described in Figures 4.03, 4.07, and 4.08.

We want the DOP to be as small as possible. Assuming a measurement accuracy of 10 m, and a DOP value of 5, our positioning accuracy is 50 m. If the DOP value is close to unity, then our positioning accuracy is close to our 10 m measurement accuracy (a most blessed state!).

What can these DOP plots tell us? First we note that the GDOP plot has a spike at about 04:00. Recalling Figure 4.08, this occurs when PRN 3 sets at 4:07 and ends when PRNs 12 rises ten minutes or so later. What is the problem during this period? We note that PDOP, TDOP, and VDOP all contain the same spike, but HDOP does not. Because both TDOP (time) and VDOP (height) contain the spike, a common configuration weakness is suspected: when all satellites are too high in elevation, the solutions for time and for height become highly correlated, meaning that neither is well determined. Recalling the discussion of Figure 4.08, that appears to be the case here. Note that if our objective was horizontal positioning, we need not be concerned about this spike.

This figure was prepared with the help of program **MacGEPSAL**, available from the Geodetic Research Laboratory, Department of Surveying Engineering, University of New Brunswick.

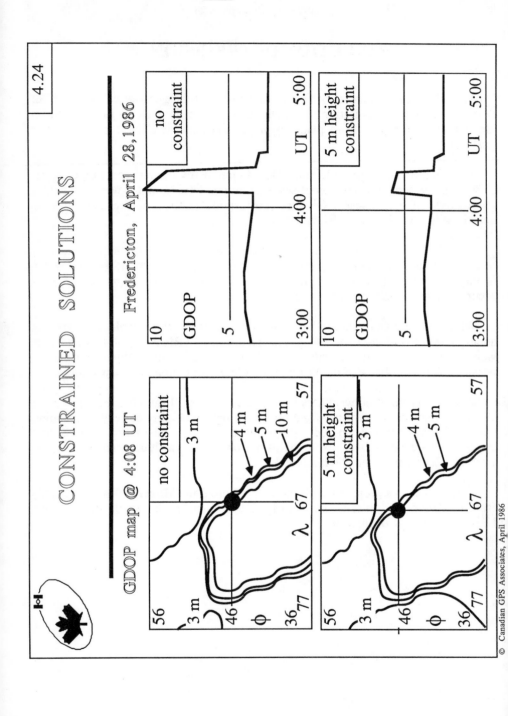

CONSTRAINED SOLUTIONS

4.24

GDOP map @ 4:08 UT   Fredericton, April 28,1986

CONSTRAINED SOLUTIONS

This figure has two purposes:
- it continues the discussion of the GDOP spike identified in Figure 4.23;
- it demonstrates the effect of a constrained solution on this spike.

The top right plot is a blow-up of the GDOP plot for Fredericton from Figure 4.23, during the period of the spike. The top left plot is a contour map of GDOP variations in space, for the instant the spike reaches its peak (at 4:08 UT). Note that to the north and east of Fredericton, the high GDOP value does not occur. Referring to Figure 4.08, we can see why. To the north, PRN 12 will already have risen. To the east, PRN 3 will not yet have set.

What is a *constrained solution?* Let us say we have a reasonably good idea of our height, for example, and that our primary interest is in horizontal positioning. Then we could hold our 'known' height fixed and solve only for latitude and longitude (and time offset). However, a better idea is not to hold height fixed absolutely, but to constrain it to not vary more than a specified amount (equal to the uncertainty in our knowledge of the height) from the 'known' value. The effect of constraining height (or any other parameter or parameters) is to improve the overall geometry — the constrained height acts rather like an added 'observation'.

The bottom two plots show what happens to our spike when we know our height with a standard deviation of 5 metres and use this fact by constraining the solution for height. The GDOP spike has been cut almost in half, from just over 10 to just over 5. This improvement appears to be over the whole of the GDOP map area on the left-hand plots.

This figure was prepared with the help of program **MacGEPSAL**, available from the Geodetic Research Laboratory, Department of Surveying Engineering, University of New Brunswick.

4.25

U.S. GOVERNMENT FEDERAL RADIONAVIGATION PLAN

SYSTEM	EST. NO. USERS (1986)	PHASE-OUT MILIARY USE BY†	NATIONAL DECISION	CIVIL USE UNTIL
Loran-C	100 000	1992	1987	at least 2000
Omega	20 000	1992*	1987	at least 2000
Transit	70 000	1994	-	1994
VOR/DME	320 000	1997	1987	at least 2000
TACAN	15 500	1997*	-	negligible use
ILS	180 000	to be replaced by MLS for all users		
Radiobeacons	675 000	1997	-	at least 2000

† assuming GPS operational by 1988

* some continued naval use after this date

© Canadian GPS Associates, April 1986

U.S. GOVERNMENT FEDERAL
RADIONAVIGATION PLAN

In the United States, as in most countries, responsibility for providing navigational services to the general public as well as the military is vested in the federal government. The U.S. Department of Transportation (DoT), primarily through the U.S. Coast Guard and the Federal Aviation Administration, is responsible for civil navigation, whereas the U.S. Department of Defense (DoD) operates navigation systems for military users. Civilian use of many of the U.S. systems is world-wide, including some of the military systems. The systems currently operated by either the DoT or the DoD include **Loran-C, OMEGA, Transit, VOR/DME, TACAN, ILS/MLS, radiobeacons**, and **GPS**.

The DoT and DoD have been mandated by the U.S. Congress to reduce the proliferation and overlap of federally-funded radionavigation systems. The *Federal Radionavigation Plan (FRP)* was initiated in part to implement this mandate. The FRP delineates policies and plans for the U.S. government-provided radionavigation services. The plan is issued biennally, or more frequently if necessary. The latest (3rd) edition was issued in December 1984. This edition of the FRP confirms the decisions by the DoD to phase out military use of some civilian navigation systems and to cease operation of selected military systems in favour of GPS. The FRP also describes DoT plans to possibly phase out existing civilian navigation systems in favour of GPS.

The FRP also delineates the accuracy civil users of the GPS C/A-code can expect after the system is declared operational. It also states that there will be no direct charges by the U.S. government for civil use of GPS services. According to the Federal Radionavigation Plan [U.S.DoT/DoD, 1984] it is U.S. government policy to:

Make the GPS Standard Positioning Service (SPS) continuously available worldwide for civil, commercial and other use at the highest level of accuracy consistent with U.S. national security interests [purposely reducing the inherent accuracy of C/A-code ranging, a procedure termed 'selective availability']. It is presently projected that a predictable and repeatable accuracy of 100 meters (3 drms [the radius of a circle that contains at least 95 percent of all possible fixes that can be obtained]) horizontally and 156 meters (2 sigma) vertically will be made available during the first year of full GPS operation. During the development phase of the GPS program, the satellites will be transmitting both the PPS and SPS signals in the clear in support of government sponsored tests. Civil users are cautioned that the system is developmental and signal availability and accuracy are subject to change without advance warning, at the discretion of the Department of Defense. Therefore, until the system is declared operational, any use of the system is at the user's own risk.

IMPACT OF GPS ON EXISTING POSITIONING TECHNIQUES

	immediate impact	near-term impact (<1990)	future impact (>1990)
ON LAND			
Transit	X		
ISS (horizontal)	X		
ISS (vertical)			X
EDM (engineering)		X	
EDM (cadastral)			X
Theodolite			X
Loran-C (nav)			X
ON THE SEA			
Transit	X		
Loran-C			X
Omega			X
Syledis, etc.		X	
IN THE AIR			
INS		X	
Omega			X
VOR			X
TACAN			X
ILS/MLS			X

IMPACT OF GPS ON
EXISTING POSITIONING TECHNIQUES

Despite the warning that GPS is still a developmental system, and presumably risky to use, it has already had an impact on some positioning applications. Since static positioning does not demand continuous coverage, this has been the first civilian market for GPS. Control surveys and offshore oil rig positioning surveys using the Transit system are being phased out in favour of GPS. This is mainly because the data collection time to obtain the best achievable accuracy for GPS is hours, and for Transit days.

The eventual impact on other positioning systems depends on two factors:
• the mandates of the US Federal Radionavigation Plan, and
• the eventual cost of GPS equipment and the market that generates.

Most military use of Loran-C and OMEGA will be phased out by 1992. This phase-out date assumes that GPS will be fully operational by 1988. Given the recent setback in space shuttle operations, this and other system phase-out dates may have to be revised. A decision on future civilian use of Loran-C and OMEGA will be made in 1987, based on consultations with national and international bodies concerned with navigation. In any case, operation of these systems for use by civilians is guaranteed until at least 2000. Military use of Transit is to be replaced by GPS by 1994. At that time, U.S. government operation of the Transit system will cease. Military use of VOR/DME (VHF Omni-directional Range/Distance Measuring Equipment) and TACAN (Tactical Air Navigation), which provide the basic guidance for en route air navigation in the U.S., will be phased out by 1997. A national decision on continued operation of VOR/DME for civil use will be made in 1987. Operation of VOR/DME will continue until at least 2000. The transition already underway to convert ILS (Instrument Landing System) facilities to MLS (Microwave Landing System), for precision aircraft approach navigation, will continue. Most miltary use of radiobeacons will be discontinued by 1997. A decision on continued operation of these widely-used facilities by the civil community will not be made for some time.

If and when GPS receiver costs drop below the costs of owning and operating equipment for competing positioning systems, then GPS will erode the user community for those systems. It is worth noting that the prudent navigator will always prefer to have at least two different systems to mutually check each other's performance. However, a system like GPS, under complete military control, will have to overcome initial skepticism before it will be unequivocally accepted where safety of navigation has paramount importance.

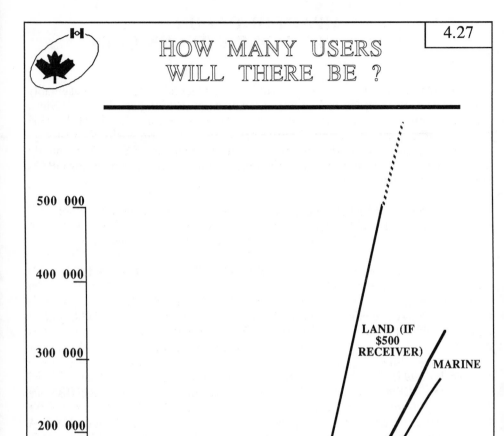

HOW MANY USERS WILL THERE BE ?

500 000

400 000

300 000

200 000

100 000

LAND (IF $500 RECEIVER)

MARINE

AIR (IF FAA/ICAO APPROVAL)

TRANSIT

MILITARY

GEODETIC

1975   1980   1985   1990   1995   2000

© Canadian GPS Associates, April 1986

HOW MANY USERS WILL THERE BE ?

This figure compares the actual user community for Transit with that projected for GPS.

Both Transit and GPS are military systems. However, the civilian user community for Transit and that projected for GPS dwarf the military user community for each. It is estimated that only about 1000 Transit receivers are in military use, and the initial plans for GPS are for 20 000 to 30 000 military receivers (although this could increase dramatically).

However, the number of civilian users of Transit is estimated now to be over 100 000, possibly increasing to 150 000 before the system is phased out in the mid-1990s. By far the largest group of users is small boat owners — fisherman and pleasure craft sailors. The rapid growth in the Transit receiver population came during the early 1980s, when a new generation of single frequency receivers was introduced, costing only a few thousand dollars. This was a market that no one suspected was there, until the cheap receivers proved its existence. Beside this group, the estimated 1000 receivers used for surveying and geodetic applications are very small in number.

This balance is expected to be repeated for GPS. The surveying and geodetic GPS user community may require 10 000 or more GPS receivers. However, the same marine market that snapped up Transit receivers will likely be willing to upgrade to GPS. This number pales beside the number of receivers required for general aviation, which may run to several hundred thousand. This, however, is dependent on approval from the International Civil Aviation Authority and from the Federal Aviation Authority in the U.S. These bodies initially showed strong resistance to GPS, but recently have softened their opposition to the system.

The largest market of all is likely to be the land navigation market. Provided very low-cost receivers become available, the use of GPS in fleets of trucks, taxis, railcars, and even in private automobiles would be in far larger numbers than in any other sector.

MAIN FEATURES OF GPS

HIGH ACCURACY

	Single Rx	Differential
P-code	20 m (5 m)	5 m (3 m)
C/A-code	50 m (50 m)	8 m (5 m)
Carrier (static)		1 ppm (0.01 ppm)
Carrier (kinematic)		10 cm (< 10 cm)

( ) = expected accuracy in 1990

LOW COST

Receiver costs (high now, low later)
Operating costs (no intervisibility requirement)

UNIFIED COORDINATE SYSTEM

Worldwide, all-weather, continuously available
GPS and local geodetic coordinates simply related
Forms the basis of land information systems

CONSEQUENCE

Widespread use of GPS
» by positioning professionals to replace or
    supplement existing techniques
» in society at large for many new applications

MAIN FEATURES OF GPS

From the user's point of view, GPS has three main attractions.

• **High accuracy**. There is a variety of ways in which GPS can be used, as described earlier in this chapter. The table on this figure compares the performance that can be expected today (1986), and once the full GPS constellation is in place (1990). Relative static accuracies, using carrier beat phase measurements, are typically 1 part per million today. On the other hand, single receiver C/A-code positioning accuracy is typically 50 m. However, for some applications (aviation, transoceanic navigation) this is high accuracy indeed in comparison with alternative methods.

• **Low cost**. No one would claim that GPS receivers are low cost today (1986). However, the real markets for GPS receivers await launching of the operational constellation. It is expected that at that time volume production will bring the cost of receivers down dramatically. However, receiver capital costs are not the only costs involved in positioning applications. The fact that GPS removes the need for intervisibility between stations decreases the number of stations that must be established and permits the selection of locations that are convenient logistically, rather than for intervisibility alone.

• **Unified coordinate system**. This is perhaps the feature of GPS which will have the broadest impact. If (because of the first two features mentioned) GPS becomes widely adopted for positioning, then it would form the basis for unifying data from heterogenous sources in position-related information systems.

The consequence of these features is that GPS will likely be used not only by positioning professionals, such as surveyors and mappers, but also by large segments of the general public for new position-related tasks which were not previously feasible. The advent of a new emphasis in our society, that of the 'position based society,' may well result.

PRESENT AND FUTURE GPS CHARACTERISTICS

	1986	1990	Ideal
COST	$20k - $300k	$5k - $20k	**$10**
WEIGHT / BULK	5kg - 300kg	hand held	**wrist locator**
POWER SUPPLY	AC external DC internal DC	internal DC	**watch battery**
OBSERVING TIME	10 min-hours (1 min)	15 min (1 min)	**milliseconds**
REAL TIME ?	No	Yes	**Yes**
ACCURACY	< 1 ppm (10 cm)	0.01 ppm (few cm)	**1 mm**
		?	**? ?**

PRESENT AND FUTURE GPS CHARACTERISTICS

The user and potential user of GPS is mainly concerned with basic practical questions, such as,
• how much will it cost ? and
• what performance will I get for that cost ?
Except as it affects cost or performance he cares little whether there are seven or 21 satellites in orbit or whether his equipment makes C/A-code or carrier beat phase measurements. This figure attempts to address these 'bottom line' concerns. The state-of-the-art today (1986) is represented in the first column. The figures in parentheses refer to relative kinematic characteristics. By the time GPS becomes fully operational in about 1990, the variety and number of users are expected to mushroom dramatically. The second column (labelled 1990) speculates on what the response of the equipment manufacturers to this market may be. It would be reasonable to place a confidence level of about 50% on the speculations in this column. Achievement of the characteristics identified as ideal, in the third column, is a real possibility over the next three or four decades. This may involve GPS or perhaps a successor system. A confidence level of about 20% on the speculations in this third column is appropriate.

Some of the trends behind these speculations are as follows:
• Several manufacturers have developed specialized GPS Very-Large-Scale-Integrated circuits (VLSI chips) which dramatically reduce the receiver parts count (and hence cost and power consumption). The ultimate goal of a standard GPS receiver-on-a-chip may well be achieved by 1990.
• A GPS receiver constructed for as little as $500 was predicted as early as 1978. While this low cost is a prerequisite for GPS success in the consumer market, positioning professionals will need and want a complete package, including warranty, servicing, data recording hardware, real-time and postprocessing software, and training. The receiver hardware cost will likely be a minor component in such a package.
• The U.S. Department of Defense has contracted the development of hand-held receivers for military use. Commercial exploitation of this development is sure to follow.
• It is becoming standard to provide carrier beat phase measurements in GPS receivers or to use them at least internally in the receiver.
• The initial military design specification that a GPS receiver need not be capable of tracking more than the required minimum of four satellites is being replaced with receivers capable of tracking up to the maximum possible number of visible satellites.
• Dual frequency receivers not dependent on access to the P-code are expected to become widely available over the next few years.
• Real-time communication links, and receivers capable of using them, are beginning to emerge, making possible real-time relative GPS positioning.

CHAPTER FIVE

ORBIT DESCRIPTION DETERMINATION AND DISSEMINATION

Guide to GPS Positioning
© Canadian GPS Associates, April 1986

REQUIREMENTS

- accurate information
- approximate information
- satellite selection

ORBIT DESCRIPTION — IDEAL WORLD

- coordinate systems
- forces acting on satellites
- Kepler's laws
- Keplerian orbital elements
- position and velocity

ORBIT DESCRIPTION — REAL WORLD

- non-central earth gravity
- third body, tides, solar radiation, drag

ORBIT DETERMINATION

- ephemeris prediction
- postcomputed ephemerides
- active control system concept

ORBIT DISSEMINATION

- broadcast ephemeris
- orbit description
- coordinate computation

ORBIT DESCRIPTION, DETERMINATION, AND DISSEMINATION

In this chapter we describe the role of orbital information in GPS positioning. Orbital information is required for four major tasks involved in the GPS positioning process: receiver position determination, planning, receiver aiding, and satellite selection. The first requirement demands accurate orbital information. The latter three requirements need only approximate information.

The nature of satellite orbits depends on Kepler's three laws, each of which is discussed. The application of the Keplerian orbit description to obtain satellite coordinates in the conventional terrestrial (CT) system is described. However, Kepler's laws do not take into account perturbing forces acting on satellites such as the effect of the earth's equatorial bulge, the attraction of the moon and sun, solar radiation pressure, and atmospheric drag. Each of these effects is described.

Orbital information comes in two flavours: predicted and postcomputed. The methods, sources, and accuracies of each type are discussed. In particular the orbital information broadcast by the GPS satellites is described in detail.

Recommended further reading:

Broughton, D.W., R.I. Esai and P.J. Farrow (1984).
Brouwer, D., and G.M. Clemence (1961).
Buffett, B.A. (1985).
Delikaraoglou, D. and R.R. Steeves (1985).
Henriksen, S.W. (Ed.) (1977).
Kaula, W.M. (1966).
Mertikas, S.P., D. Delikaraoglou and R. Santerre (1986).
Nakiboglu, S.M., B. Buffett, K.P. Schwarz, E.J. Krakiwsky, B. Wanless (1984).
O'Toole, J.W. (1976).
Remondi, B.W. (1985d).
Russell, S.S. and J.H. Schaibly (1978).
Steeves, R.R., D. Delikaraoglou and N. Beck (1986).
Swift, E.R. (1985).
van Dierendonk, A.J., S.S. Russell, E.R. Kopitzke and M. Birnbaum (1978).

POINT POSITIONING

Ephemeris

dr

dρ

True orbit

dR

dr = satellite position error
dρ = equivalent range error
dR = resulting station position error

RELATIVE POSITIONING

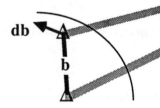

RULE OF THUMB

$$\frac{\|db\|}{b} = \frac{\|dr\|}{\rho}$$

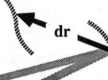

Ephemeris

dr

True orbit

ρ

db

b

dr = satellite position error
b = baseline
ρ = range to satellite
db = resulting baseline error

REQUIREMENTS FOR
ACCURATE ORBITAL INFORMATION

Accurate orbital data is essential for the reduction of the observations collected by the GPS receivers in order to obtain the user's position, which is usually the final product sought in GPS positioning. In the case of **point position** computations, there is clearly a stricter requirement for precise orbital information since any error in the ephemeris data will be directly transferred into an equivalent range error, and hence it will bias the final position results in a systematic way.

For **relative positioning**, the effects of any uncertainties in the ephemeris data on the final position results are somewhat alleviated because, for baselines which are short compared with the 20 000 km GPS satellite altitudes, satellite orbit errors tend to cancel out. The equation that defines the vector error **db** in the baseline vector **b**, as a function of the vector errors $\mathbf{dr_i}$ in the positions of the i satellites used to determine **b** is

$$\mathbf{db} \; \Sigma_i \, \mathbf{e_i} \, \rho_i \; = \mathbf{b} \, \Sigma_i \, \mathbf{dr_i} \; ,$$

with ρ_i denoting the range to the ith satellite, and $\mathbf{e_i}$ denoting the unit vector to the

i^{th} satellite. Clearly **db** depends not only on the magnitudes of ρ, **b**, and **dr** but also on their directions. As well, the baseline solution depends on measurements from several satellites over an extended time period, and the satellite position errors $\mathbf{dr_i}$ involved will, in general, be different. The effect of one particular satellite orbit error, say $\mathbf{dr_k}$, is given by

$$\mathbf{db} \; \mathbf{e_k} \, \rho_k \; = \mathbf{b} \; \mathbf{dr_k} \; ,$$

Taking the length of the vectors in this equation, we obtain the rule of thumb shown in the figure. This rule of thumb is an upper bound for the magnitude ||**db**|| of the baseline error as a function of the ephemeris error. Evidently, on baselines a few tens of kilometres long, the orbit error has a very small impact: accuracy of a few centimetres can be obtained with present techniques. On longer baselines, of the order of several hundreds of kilometres, the impact can be large enough to be a major obstacle at present for the general use of GPS for precise geodetic and geodynamic applications.

Relative accuracy db / b	Satellite position error dr (m)	Baseline length b (km)	Baseline error db (cm)
1 ppm	20	10	1
		100	10
		1000	100
0.1 ppm	2	10	0.1
		100	1
		1000	10

REQUIREMENTS FOR APPROXIMATE ORBITAL INFORMATION

5.02

Planning a Calgary-Fredericton baseline, April 28, 1986

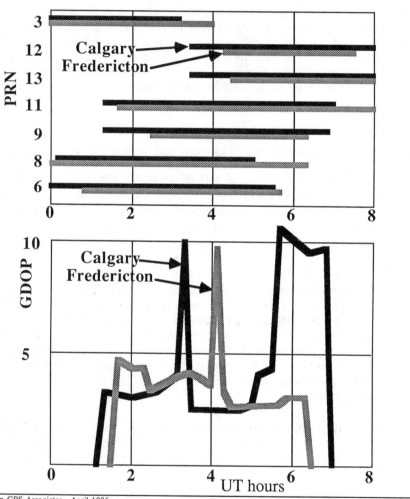

REQUIREMENTS FOR
APPROXIMATE ORBITAL INFORMATION

The actual computation of GPS positions requires accurate orbital information. Other tasks involved in the use of GPS also require knowledge of satellite positions, but at a much lower accuracy—perhaps only within a few hundred kilometres. Two of these tasks are:
• **Planning the use of GPS.** Knowing when (what part of the day) to use GPS receivers requires orbital information. During the present period of incomplete coverage, when the satellites are visible only during short 'windows' each day, this is particularly important.
• **Signal acquisition.** The first thing any GPS receiver must do is acquire the satellite signals to be used. If nothing whatever is known about the satellites to be tracked, then the receiver must perform a 'cold start' and do an 'all sky search.' This involves selecting each of the 32 possible C/A-codes, and searching over all possible Doppler shifted frequencies for each signal, attempting to lock on to any one of them. Provided that at least one satellite is visible, this search may take as long as 30 minutes. This time can be reduced considerably if the receiver knows which satellites are visible, which limits the search to only a few of the 32 possible codes. If the satellite positions are known as well, then estimates of the Doppler shift can be predicted, limiting the frequency band over which the search must be performed. In this way, the search can be reduced to a few minutes.

Once one GPS satellite signal has been acquired, the message from that satellite provides the receiver with the approximate location of all of the other GPS satellites ('almanac' data), so that their signals can be acquired very rapidly.

The approximate satellite positions computed for planning or receiver aiding are known as *satellite alerts*. For planning purposes, there are several useful graphical representations of the results:
• a linear plot against time of the elevation and azimuth (with respect to a specified location) for each satellite.
• a *polar plot*, in which elevations and azimuths as a function of time for each satellite, with respect to a specified location, are predicted and plotted.
• a *track plot*, in which the satellite subpoint (the point where the line joining the satellite to the geocentre pierces the earth's surface) is plotted on a map.
• a *visibility plot*, against time of day, of the number of satellites which are visible from a specified location, or of the period during which each satellite is visible from a specified location (shown here).
• a *Dilution of Precision (DOP) plot*, against time of day, showing the changing geometrical strength of the visible GPS satellite constellation (shown here). Area contours of DOPs at the specific time epoch are also used.

SATELLITE SELECTION

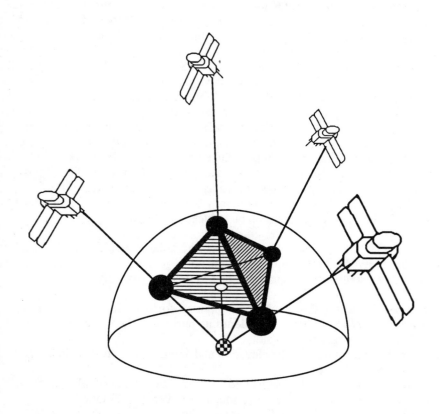

SATELLITE SELECTION

Using the present GPS constellation of seven satellites, it is possible that as many as six satellites will be above the observer's horizon (be visible) at once. With the full operational GPS constellation, as many as ten satellites may be visible at any one time. Most GPS receivers do not have the capability of tracking all visible satellites at once. In many cases, only four satellites can be tracked simultaneously.

The question then arises: How to select the 'best' satellites to be tracked? The usual criterion to be used is to choose those satellites which will result in the most accurately determined receiver positions. One measure of how accurately positions are likely to be determined is the relevant Dilution of Precision factor, or DOP. The satellite selection problem then reduces to finding those satellites which provide the lowest DOP.

The most straightforward use of GPS is for point positioning in four dimensions (latitude, longitude, height, and time). In this case the appropriate DOP is the Geometrical Dilution of Precision, or GDOP. For the case of a receiver capable of tracking four satellites simultaneously, it has been shown that GDOP is related to the volume V of the spatial tetrahedron formed by the unit vectors from the receiver to four satellites. GDOP is inversely proportional to this volume V, hence the satellite selection that maximizes V also minimizes GDOP. This has provided a simple algorithm that can be used for selection of the best available satellites to be tracked. This algorithm is simple enough to be programmed into software contained within the receiver itself.

However, for receivers capable of tracking more than four satellites simultaneously, but still less than the maximum number of visible satellites, this simple algorithm does not apply. Similarly if GDOP is not the most appropriate DOP for the GPS application (for example, for two-dimensional horizontal positioning, or for time transfer applications), then again this simple algorithm will not necessarily yield the best satellite selection. Finally for relative positioning and network surveying applications, the satellite selection problem is also more complicated. It has been found that the optimal satellite selection for point positioning will also be the optimal selection for relative positioning, when the baselines are short. However for long baselines (say 5000 km), this is no longer the case.

The optimal satellite selection changes with time, as satellites rise and set, and the spatial tetrahedra which they form change in shape. One strategy is to switch satellites whenever a new optimal selection occurs. However, there are other criteria which may be more important, such as maintaining continuity of tracking the same satellites for longer periods. In these cases, the satellite selection problem has not yet been solved.

MOTION OF SATELLITES AROUND AN IDEAL EARTH

THE IDEAL EARTH:
- Perfectly uniform spherical shape
- No atmosphere

NEWTON'S LAW OF UNIVERSAL GRAVITATION:

$$F = G \, (Mm)/r^2$$

M = mass of the earth
m = mass of the satellite
G = universal gravitational constant
r = distance of the satellite from the geocentre
F = force of the attraction

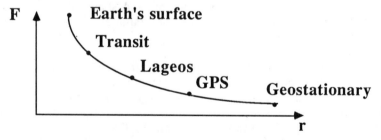

PRACTICAL LIMITATIONS:

- Gravity never becomes zero, although the earth's pull may become very small compared to that of other bodies of deep space

- Gravity has a direct effect on satellite launches

MOTION OF SATELLITES
AROUND AN IDEAL EARTH

In order to study a satellite's motion, it is convenient to start by examining the natural laws governing the motion around an 'ideal' earth, which has:

- a perfectly radial gravitational field; and
- no atmosphere.

After the satellite is launched, it begins its unrestrained revolution around the earth. This motion in a radial gravitational field is governed by Newton's gravitational law:

$$F = G M m / r^2$$

where F is the force of attraction, M is the mass of the earth, m is the mass of the satellite, r is the distance of the satellite from the geocentre, and G is the universal gravitational constant.

The practical implication of Newton's gravitational law is that gravity never becomes zero. No matter where a satellite is in space, there always is a force pulling it toward the earth, although the earth's pull may become very small compared to that of other bodies in deep space.

GETTING A SATELLITE
LAUNCHED AND INTO ORBIT

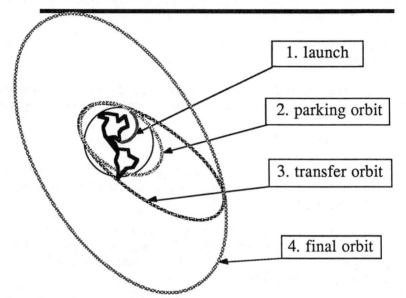

1. launch

2. parking orbit

3. transfer orbit

4. final orbit

- shuttle takes satellite up to parking orbit

- Payload Assist Module spins satellite up to 70 rpm and boosts satellite into elliptical transfer orbit

- after 4 or 5 revolutions, satellite thrusters start drift into final orbit

- drift corrections place satellite into final orbit

- satellite is then 'despun', oriented toward earth, acquires earth command signals, sun orientation, electronic turn on and checkout

GETTING A SATELLITE LAUNCHED
AND INTO ORBIT

Gravity has also a direct effect on satellite launches. A minimum launch speed of about 4 km/sec is required to put a GPS satellite in a circular orbit. Actual ground launches make truly circular orbits extremely difficult to obtain. All earth orbiting satellites, including GPS satellites, are strictly speaking in elliptical orbits.

It was originally planned to launch all the operational GPS satellites from the space shuttle by placing the satellites and their Delta-class Payload Assist Module (PAM-D II) into an initial low-altitude circular orbit. The PAM-D will then boost the space vehicle into a near-circular drift orbit. Through velocity increments, the satellite's thrusters will propel the spacecraft to its final operational orbit.

Because of the space shuttle Challenger disaster, a partial return to rocket launches will be made, to place GPS and other military satellites in orbit. As of October 1986, the shuttle schedule was still being negotiated, but the expected launch schedule, assuming rocket launch vehicles are ready by January 1989, was as follows:

GPS#	Booster	Date		GPS#	Booster	Date	
1	rocket	Feb 89		16-17	shuttle	Feb 91	**3D**
2	rocket	May 89		18	rocket	Feb 91	
3-4	shuttle	Jun 89		19	shuttle	Apr 91	
5	rocket	Aug 89		20	rocket	May 91	
6-7	shuttle	Sept 89		21	shuttle	Jun 91	
8	rocket	Nov 89 **2D**		22	rocket	Aug 91	
9	rocket	Feb 90		23	shuttle	Sept 91	
10	rocket	May 90		24	rocket	Nov 91	
11	shuttle	May 90		25	shuttle	May 92	
12	shuttle	May 90		26	shuttle	Nov 92	
13	rocket	Aug 90		27	shuttle	Feb 93	
14	shuttle	Oct 90		28	shutle	May 94	
15	rocket	Nov 90					

Achievement of worldwide 2D coverage by Nov 1989 assumes that four of the present prototype satellites are still functioning. Achievement of 3D coverage by February 1991 assumes that two of the present satellites are still functioning.

COORDINATE SYSTEMS

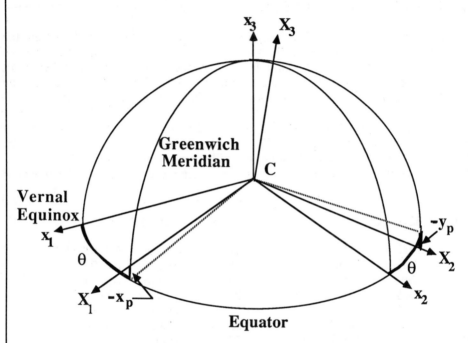

Satellite motion is described in RA-system (x_1, x_2, x_3)

Terrestrial positioning refers to CT-system (X_1, X_2, X_3)

The two are related by :

Greenwich apparent sidereal time (θ)

Polar motion components (x_p, y_p)

COORDINATE SYSTEMS

The dynamics of satellites is governed by Newton's law of motion which states that the acceleration of the centre of mass of a free body is proportional to the force applied to it. The proportionality constant here is the mass of the body. The position, velocity, acceleration, and force components should refer to a special coordinate system called inertial. An *inertial coordinate system*, loosely speaking, is one which is either stationary or in uniform motion (with no accleration) in space. Our first task in describing satellite motion, therefore, is to define an appropriate inertial coordinate system. We conveniently adopt the right ascension (RA) system, which fulfills our reference frame requirements for short time periods. The orientation of the RA-system relative to the fixed stars changes by about 1" per year, due to the forced periodic motion of the earth's rotation axis and the plane of the ecliptic. However, this motion, called *precession and nutation*, is known very well, and the orientation of the RA-system at different epochs may be traced back.

The RA-system is not a convenient reference frame for terrestrial positioning purposes. For the latter, we require a coordinate system which is 'fixed to the solid earth' so that a stationary point on earth will have time-invariant coordinates. The conventional terrestrial system (CT-system), which is also known as the average terrestrial system, is one such system. The first axis of the CT-system passes through the intersection of the Greenwich meridian and the equatorial plane. The third axis of the CT-system is defined by the Conventional International Origin (CIO), which is the average position of the earth's rotation pole for the years 1900 to 1905. The second axis is orthogonal to the first and third axes. The RA-system and CT-system are related as

$$R = R_2(-x_p) \, R_1(-y_p) \, R_3(\theta) \, r.$$

Here, θ is Greenwich apparent sideral time; x_p and y_p are the components of polar motion; R and r are the CT-system and RA-system coordinates, respectively; and R_i (i=1,2,3) are rotation matrices.

Until July 1985, the realization of the CT-system used to describe the GPS broadcast ephemeris was the World Geodetic System 1972 (WGS-72). From July 1985 to December 1986 the WGS-84 system is used for all ephemeris prediction computations, but the broadcast ephemeris information is then converted back to WGS-72. Since January 1987 the WGS-84 system has been used throughout.

FORCES ACTING ON SATELLITES

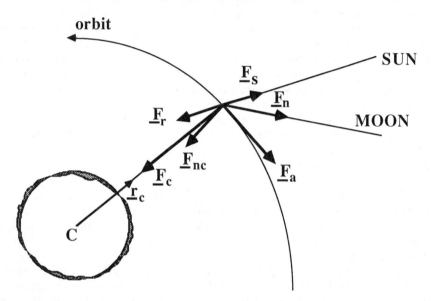

Important for GPS satellites	•$\underline{F}_c$	Geocentric gravitational attraction of the earth
	•$\underline{F}_{nc}$	Non-central gravitational attraction of the earth
	•$\underline{F}_n, \underline{F}_s$	Third body effects of the moon and the sun
	•$\underline{F}_r$	Solar radiation pressure
Other forces	•$\underline{F}_a$	Atmospheric drag force Tidal forces (not shown) Magnetic forces (not shown)

FORCES ACTING ON SATELLITES

In general, forces that contribute to satellite motion comprise:

(a) gravitational attraction of the earth,
(b) gravitational attractions of the sun, moon, and planets (called the third body effects),
(c) atmospheric drag force,
(d) solar radiation pressure, both direct and albedo effects,
(e) magnetic forces, and
(f) the variable part of the earth's gravitational field arising from tidal and other deformations of the solid earth and oceans.

Among the forces listed above, the most dominant is the gravitational attraction of the earth. The **earth's gravitational attraction** may be further separated into two parts:

(a) the main part, called the **central part**, is the radial gravitational attraction, and
(b) the **non-central part**, which is the rest.

The central part of the gravitational attraction is three orders of magnitude larger than the non-central part and all the other forces combined. Therefore, the main characteristics of satellite motion are determined by the central gravitational field, while the remaining forces introduce some small variations into the motion. These small variations and forces causing them are called the *perturbations* and *perturbing forces*, respectively.

KEPLER'S FIRST LAW

THE ORBIT IS AN ELLIPSE WITH ONE OF THE FOCI LOCATED AT THE EARTH'S CENTRE OF MASS

PRACTICAL IMPLICATIONS

Latitude of launch site equals minimum orbit inclination

To get lower inclinations requires "parking orbit" with second stage launch at equator crossing => heavy, complex and expensive satellites

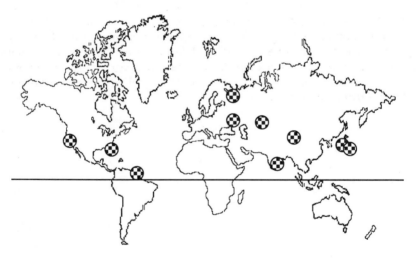

⊕ = ten launch sites now in use

KEPLER'S FIRST LAW

The idealized satellite motion caused solely by the earth's central gravitational field is called *Keplerian motion*, which may be deduced from Newton's laws of motion and gravitation. Note that Kepler's laws are valid for **any** central field, gravitational or otherwise. The main characteristics of Keplerian motion are:
(a) The motion relative to the RA-system occurs in a stationary plane which contains the centre of mass of the earth. The orbit is a conic with one of the foci located at the earth's centre of mass (the geocentre). This is the first of Kepler's laws.
(b) The closest and farthest points of the orbit to the earth's centre of mass, called *perigee* and *apogee*, respectively, are stationary in inertial space.
(c) The size and shape of the elliptical orbit are constant.

Kepler's first law has practical implications today in determining the orbits which are achievable by satellites launched from various launch sites. It is not possible to launch directly into an orbit with an angle of inclination less than the latitude of the launch site. In order to understand why, consider a launch directly to the east or west of the launch site. Since the satellite must enter an orbital plane which contains the geocentre (Kepler's first law), the orbital plane will intersect the earth's surface in a great circle. The furthest point from the equator on this great circle will be the launch site, and the angle between the great circle and the equator (the orbit inclination angle) will be equal to the launch site latitude. Launching slightly northwards or southwards, rather than directly east or west will mean that some point on the great circle will be further from the equator than the launch site, and therefore the inclination angle will be greater. Note that it is dangerous to launch satellites in directions which would initially carry them over populated areas (falling boosters, etc.), which further restricts the launch directions which can be used at each launch site. To obtain inclinations lower than the launch site latitude, the satellite must first be launched into a 'parking orbit,' and at a subsequent crossing of the equator, the satellite must undergo a 'second stage launch,' using an additional booster stage. Such second stage launches are more expensive than a direct launch into orbit. The most used launch site locations are:

	Site	Latitude	Longitude
European Space Agency	Kourou	5° N	52° W
United States	Canaveral	28° N	81° W
	Vandenberg	35° N	120° W
Soviet Union	Plesetsk	63° N	41° E
	Tyuratam	46° N	62° E
	Kapustin Yar	49° N	46° E
India	Sriharikota	14° N	80° E
China	Shuang-Ch'eng-Tzu	41° N	100° E
Japan	Tanegashima	30° N	131° E
	Kagoshima	31° N	131° E

KEPLER'S SECOND LAW

GEOCENTRIC POSITION VECTOR OF A SATELLITE SWEEPS EQUAL AREA IN EQUAL TIME

PRACTICAL IMPLICATION

Satellite speed is not constant: minimum at apogee; maximum at perigee

Design reconnaissance satellites with perigee over the target

Design communication satellites with apogee over target area

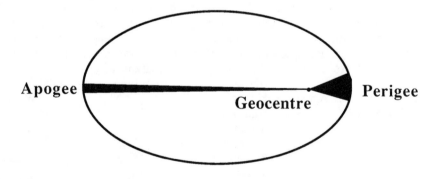

KEPLER'S SECOND LAW

The second and third characteristics of Keplerian motion follow from conservation laws. Kepler's second law defines the speed of a satellite in an elliptical orbit. It states that the satellite radius vector (i.e., the line joining the earth's centre to the satellite) sweeps out equal areas in equal time. This is so because the total energy of a satellite must remain constant. Like any moving object, a satellite possesses two kinds of energy — potential and kinetic. Potential energy is governed only by the gravitational field and is at its lowest when the satellite is closest to the attracting body (i.e., at the perigee), and highest at apogee. Kinetic energy is simply a function of the satellites velocity. For the sum of the potential and kinetic energies to remain constant, the kinetic energy (and thus velocity) must be the largest at perigee and lowest at apogee.

This law states that the speed of a satellite in an elliptical orbit is not constant. Practical use can be made of this law.

• It is desirable for *spy satellites* to travel low and fast over their target area — consequently, they are placed in highly elliptical orbits with perigee over the target area.

• It is desirable for *communication satellites* to have as wide a coverage area as possible, and for as long as possible. Most communications satellites are placed in geostationary orbits over the equator, in which they appear to be stationary in the sky. Unfortunately, this does not provide very good coverage at high latitudes. Therefore other communications satellites are placed into highly elliptical orbits with apogees over their coverage areas. They are not geostationary, but (from Kepler's second law) they travel very slowly near apogee, and hence can be used for most of their orbital period.

• The *lifetime* of a satellite before it decays into the atmosphere is determined by how quickly it is slowed down by atmospheric drag. This slowing effect is proportional to the satellite's speed, and is felt mostly at perigee, where the atmosphere is densest and the speed highest (Kepler's second law again). Hence the initial perigee height determines the lifetime of the satellite. Typical satellites and their lifetimes are:

Satellite	Perigee (km)	Apogee (km)	Lifetime	
Spy	118	430	15	days
Sputnik I	225	946	3	months
Explorer I	361	2550	12	years
TRANSIT	1000	1000	1000	years
Geostationary	36000	36000	10^6	years

KEPLER'S THIRD LAW

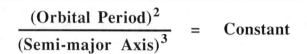

$$\frac{(\text{Orbital Period})^2}{(\text{Semi-major Axis})^3} = \text{Constant}$$

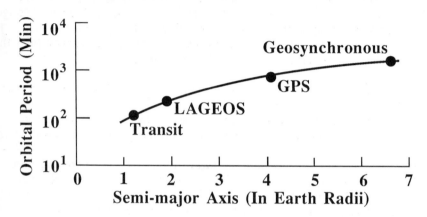

PRACTICAL IMPLICATION

Two satellites with the same semi-major axis length have equal orbital periods regardless of eccentricity

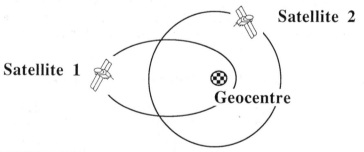

KEPLER'S THIRD LAW

Kepler's third law concerns the period, T, of the satellite (i.e., the time taken to complete one orbit revolution around the earth). It states that the ratio between the square of the orbital period and the cube of the semi-major axis, a, is the same for all satellites. The constant to which this ratio is equal is the reciprocal of μ = GM, that is, the product of the universal gravitational constant, G, and the mass of the earth, M. Thus

$$T^2 / a^3 = 4\pi^2/\mu \quad .$$

If the period is in seconds, and the semi-major axis in metres, then μ is approximately 3.986×10^{14} m^3 / sec^2. Often the period is expressed in terms of its reciprocal, the *mean motion* n = $2\pi/T$. Then we can write

$$n^2 a^3 = \mu \quad ,$$

or, since we usually know a and μ, and want to find n,

$$n = (\mu / a^3)^{1/2} \quad .$$

This is the usual form in which Kepler's third law is expressed.

It is a direct consequence of this law that the GPS satellites, which have an orbital radius equal to about four earth radii, have a longer orbital period (about 12 hours) than other commonly used geodetic satellites, like Transit or LAGEOS, which are in much lower orbits.

KEPLERIAN ORBITAL ELEMENTS

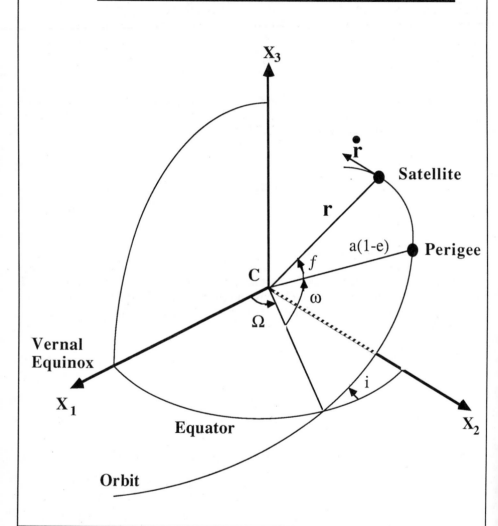

KEPLERIAN ORBITAL ELEMENTS

High flying satellites 'see' the earth's gravitational field as more or less central and, hence, more or less obey Kepler's laws (i.e., follow a Keplerian motion). Low flying satellites 'feel' the irregularities of the gravity field which perturb the orbits more or less depending on how low they are.

The stationarity of orbital plane, perigee, size, and shape of the orbit, together with constant period, lead to a realization that the Keplerian motion is fully describable in terms of six parameters, of which only one is a function of time.

The choice of these parameters is not unique. A particular set of parameters called the *Keplerian elements* is commonly used in satellite positioning. The definitions of these are as follows:

(a) Right ascension of the ascending node (Ω). The geocentric angle between the nodal directions and vernal equinox measured in the equatorial plane.
(b) Inclination (i). The angle between the equatorial and orbital planes.
(c) Argument of perigee (ω). The angle between the nodal and perigee directions measured in the orbital plane.
(d) Semi-major axis of the elliptical orbit (a).
(e) Eccentricity of the orbit (e).
(f) An element describing the position of the satellite on the orbital ellipse. One of the *anomalies* is normally used.

The Keplerian elements, Ω and i, define the orientation of the orbital plane in space; ω defines the location of the perigee on the orbit; and a and e define the size and shape of the orbit. The choice of Keplerian elements as the constants of motion is inappropriate in some cases. For example, for circular orbits we have e=0, and ω and f are undefined.

SATELLITE POSITION AND VELOCITY IN TIME

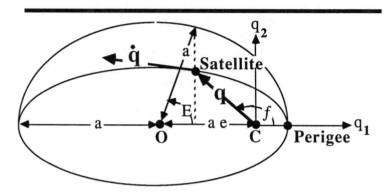

POSITION AND VELOCITY IN ORBITAL SYSTEM :

$$
\mathbf{q} = \frac{a(1-e^2)}{(1+e\cos f)} \begin{bmatrix} \cos f \\ \sin f \\ 0 \end{bmatrix} = \begin{bmatrix} a\cos E - a\,e \\ a\sqrt{1-e^2}\,\sin E \\ 0 \end{bmatrix}
$$

$$
\dot{\mathbf{q}} = \frac{n\,a}{(1-e\cos E)} \begin{bmatrix} -\sin E \\ \sqrt{1-e^2}\,\cos E \\ 0 \end{bmatrix}
$$

POSITION AND VELOCITY IN RA-SYSTEM :

$$\mathbf{position} = \mathbf{R}_{xq}\,\mathbf{q} \quad \text{and} \quad \mathbf{velocity} = \mathbf{R}_{xq}\,\dot{\mathbf{q}}$$

$$\text{where} \quad \mathbf{R}_{xq} = \mathbf{R}_3(-\Omega)\,\mathbf{R}_1(-i)\,\mathbf{R}_3(-\omega)$$

SATELLITE POSITION AND VELOCITY IN TIME

Given the Keplerian elements of a satellite, its position and velocity vectors can be determined at all times. For this we need to relate the satellite position in its orbit to time. This is done by using one of three anomalies:
- The *true anomaly* f is the geocentric angle between perigee and the satellite.
- The *eccentric anomaly* E, is the angle subtended at the centre of the orbit between perigee and the satellite's projection on a circle of radius a.
- The *mean anomaly* M is a fictitious number. However, it can be visualized geometrically by thinking of a fictitious circular orbit with the same focus and period as the actual orbit. Satellites in the actual and fictitious orbits cross the perigee-apogee line of the actual orbit in phase. We can think of the mean anomaly of the actual elliptical orbit as being the same thing as the true anomaly of this fictitious circular orbit, that is, M is zero at perigee and then increases uniformly at a rate of 360° per revolution, or

$$M = n (t - t_p),$$ where

t_p is the time of perigee crossing

$$n = (\mu / a^3)^{1/2}$$ is the *mean motion*, and

μ is the *gravitational constant*.

The mean and eccentric anomalies are related by *Kepler's equation*

$$M = E - e \sin E .$$

The true and eccentric anomalies are related by

$$\tan f = [(1 - e^2)^{1/2} \sin E] / [\cos E - e].$$

The true and eccentric anomalies can be expressed in terms of the mean anomaly in a series form as

$$f = M + 2e \sin M + 5/4 \, e^2 \sin 2M + e^2/12 \, (13 \sin 3M - 3\sin M) + ...$$

$$E = M + e \sin M + (e^2/2) \sin 2M + e^3/8 \, (3 \sin 3M - \sin M) + ... \, .$$

The *orbital period* T of the satellite in terms of n is, as we have already seen,

$$T = 2\pi / n = 2\pi(a^3 / \mu)^{1/2} .$$

Satellite position and velocity vectors in the RA-system can now be expressed in terms of Keplerian elements and time, as shown in the figure.

TOPOCENTRIC RANGE AND RANGE-RATE

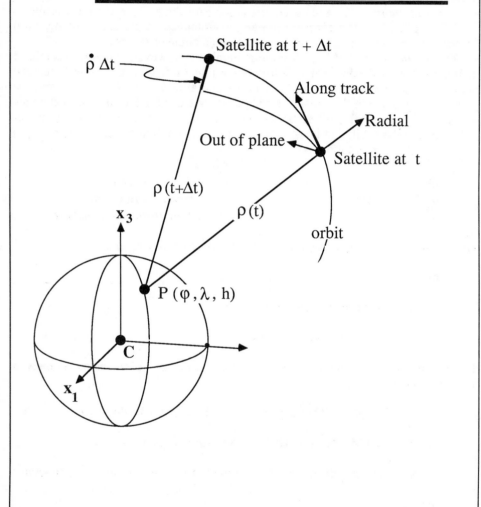

TOPOCENTRIC RANGE AND RANGE-RATE

In problems of orbit determination and terrestrial positioning, we rely on observations to satellites gathered at tracking stations. The observations must be expressed as functions of satellite and tracking station positions. This may be achieved by relating the satellite position and velocity in the RA-system to the tracking station coordinates in the CT-system.

Ignoring polar motion, CT-coordinates of a satellite are obtained from the RA-coordinates by rotating through Greenwich apparent sideral time θ

$$r = R_3 \ (\theta) \ R_{xq} \ q \ .$$

The topocentric range and range-rate of a satellite from a tracking station with geodetic latitude φ, longitude λ, and ellipsoidal height h are readily obtained as

$$\rho = \|r - R\|$$
$$\partial\rho/\partial t = (\partial \, r \, / \, \partial t)^T \, (r - R) \, / \, \rho,$$

where,

$$\partial \, r \, / \, \partial t = \partial R_3/\partial\theta \ R_{xq} \ q \ \partial\theta \, / \, \partial t + R_3(\theta) \ R_{xq} \ \partial q \, / \, \partial t \, ,$$

$$R = \begin{bmatrix} (N+ h) \cos \varphi \cos\lambda \\ (N + h) \cos\varphi \sin\lambda \\ [N + (1 - e_e^2) \, h \,] \sin\varphi \end{bmatrix} ,$$

$$\partial q \, / \, \partial t \ = \ n \, a \, /(1 - e \cos E) \ \begin{bmatrix} -\sin E \\ (1-e^2)^{1/2} \cos E \\ 0 \end{bmatrix}$$

$N = a_e /(1 - e_e^2 \sin^2\varphi)^{1/2}$ is the radius of curvature of the earth ellipsoid in the prime vertical direction; a_e and e_e are the semi-major axis and eccentricity of the earth ellipsoid; and $\partial\theta/\partial t = \omega_e \approx 0.729\ 211\ 514\ 7 \times 10^{-4}$ rad/sec is the earth's rotation rate.

Various satellite observations, like range, Doppler effect, and phase, may be expressed in terms of ρ and/or $\partial\rho/\partial t$.

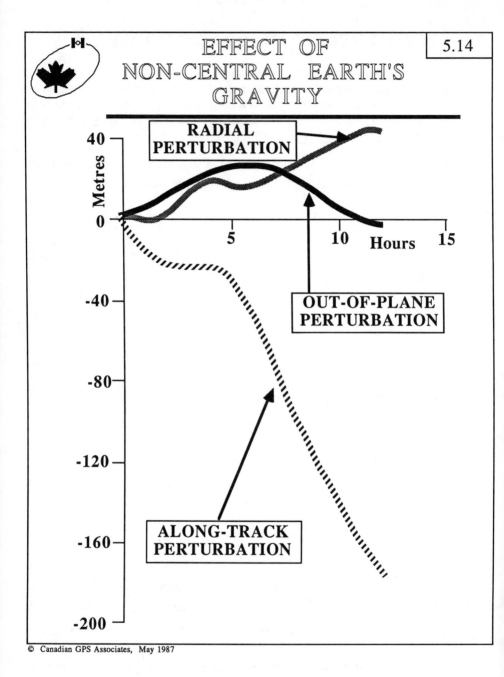

EFFECT OF
NON-CENTRAL EARTH'S
GRAVITY

5.14

RADIAL PERTURBATION

OUT-OF-PLANE PERTURBATION

ALONG-TRACK PERTURBATION

Metres

40

0

-40

-80

-120

-160

-200

5   10   15

Hours

EFFECT OF NON-CENTRAL EARTH'S GRAVITY

We have indicated, in the preceding section, that ignoring the perturbing forces yields a smooth yet reasonably accurate orbit called the Keplerian orbit. For GPS satellites, the departures of actual satellite position from the Keplerian orbital position do not exceed a few kilometres during a single pass. Yet orbital accuracy required for precise positioning may be three orders of magnitude smaller than this value. The influences of perturbing forces need be modelled to meet the orbital accuracy requirement.

• **Non-central part of the earth's gravitational attraction.** The density distribution within the earth departs considerably from radial symmetry. Consequently, the gravitational acceleration varies with latitude and longitude in addition to the geocentric distance. The non-central gravitational force is primarily due to the equatorial bulge of the earth. Also, the earth at the south pole is slightly more depressed than at the north pole resulting in a 'pear shape.' There are other lesser mass anomalies contributing to the non-central gravitational attraction. The attraction force attenuates rapidly with altitude. Therefore, only a few terms in the earth's gravitational potential are sufficient for modelling GPS orbits.

The equatorial bulge leads to 2 main perturbations of the ideal Keplerian orbit:
• Rotation of the orbital plane in space in a direction opposite to the satellite's east-west motion. This motion depends on inclination according to cos i. Thus an orbit with less than 90° inclination will precess to the west. For a truly polar obit (90° inclination), this effect is zero, and for an equatorial orbit (approaching 0° inclination), a maximum. This perturbation can be modelled by Ω-dot.
• Rotation of the major axis in the orbital plane. This perturbation depends on inclination according to $(1-5\cos^2 i)$, resulting in rotation in a direction which is forward for equatorial orbits, zero for an orbital inclination of 63.4°, and backward for polar orbits. This perturbation can be modelled by ω-dot.

The perturbations of GPS orbital arcs of four hours' duration, due to the non-central earth's gravitation effects are:

Orbital element	Effect of Equatorial bulge (m)	Effect of Higher order terms (m)
a	2600	20
e	1600	5
i	800	5
Ω	4800	3
$\omega + M$	1200	40

This figure shows the growth of the effect of the higher-order terms over 12 hours.

THIRD BODY EFFECTS AND TIDES

DIRECT EFFECT

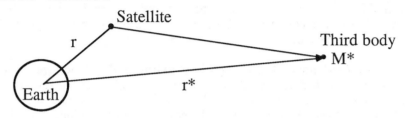

- THE DIRECT ATTRACTION OF THE MOON IS THE MOST SIGNIFICANT THIRD BODY EFFECT.

- ALTHOUGH THE SUN IS MORE MASSIVE, IT IS ALSO MUCH FARTHER AWAY AND, THEREFORE, ITS EFFECT IS LESS THAN THAT OF THE MOON.

- PLANETARY EFFECTS FOR GPS ARE NEGLIGIBLE.

INDIRECT EFFECT

- THIRD BODY DEFORMS EARTH (I.E., TIDES) WHICH IN TURN CHANGE THE EARTH'S GRAVITATIONAL FORCE AT THE SATELLITE.

- FOR GPS SATELLITES, THE INDIRECT EFFECT IS NEGLIGIBLE.

THIRD-BODY EFFECTS AND TIDES

• **Third-body effects.** The gravitational force per unit mass of a satellite due to the attraction of a third body of mass M* and geocentric position vector $\mathbf{r}^*$ is

$$F_{tb} = G\,M^*\,[(\mathbf{r}^* - \mathbf{r})\,/\,|\mathbf{r}^* - \mathbf{r}|^3 - \mathbf{r}^*\,/\,|\mathbf{r}^*|^3]\ \ .$$

Usually, the third-body effects of only the moon and the sun need be modelled for short to medium orbital arcs.

The perturbations of GPS orbital arcs of four hours' duration, due to the lunar third body effects are:

Orbital element	Lunar third body effect (m)
a	220
e	140
i	80
Ω	80
ω + M	500

Since the value of $M^*\,/\,|\mathbf{r}^*|^3$ for the sun is 0.46 that for the moon, the solar third body effect is about half that of the moon. For the planets, the masses M* are far smaller than for the sun, and distances $|\mathbf{r}^*|$ much greater than for the moon; the planetary values for $M^*\,/\,|\mathbf{r}^*|^3$ are so small that their third-body effects on GPS satellites are negligible.

• **Tides.** The gravitational attractions of the moon and the sun also have an indirect effect on satellite motion. The solid earth and the oceans undergo significant tidal deformations at primarily the semi-diurnal and diurnal frequencies. The tidal deformations cause a periodic re-arrangement of the earth's mass which in turn alters the earth's gravitational attraction. This potential change depends on the deformation characteristics of the earth, and it is closely related to the third-body potential. These effects are insignificant for GPS satellites over orbital periods.

SOLAR RADIATION

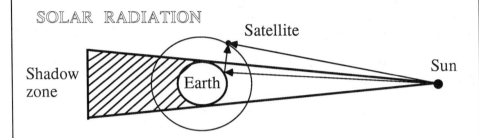

Satellite

Sun

Shadow zone

Earth

ACCELERATION DEPENDS ON

- SOLAR RADIATION AT SATELLITE (SHADOW EFFECT)
- SATELLITE MASS AND SURFACE AREA EXPOSED TO SUN
- WHETHER SATELLITE IS IN SHADOW OR NOT

TO GET ± 2 m GPS ORBITS, RADIATION MUST BE TAKEN INTO ACCOUNT

ATMOSPHERIC DRAG

ACCELERATION DEPENDS ON

- ATMOSPHERIC DENSITY
- SATELLITE CROSS SECTIONAL AREA AND MASS
- SATELLITE SPEED

EFFECT IS PRIMARILY ON APOGEE HEIGHT; PERIGEE IS CONSTANT. AT THE HEIGHT OF GPS SATELLITES, ATMOSPHERIC DENSITY IS SO LOW AS TO MAKE DRAG NEGLIGIBLE.

SOLAR RADIATION PRESSURE AND ATMOSPHERIC DRAG

• **Solar radiation pressure.** The light photons emitted by the sun create a repulsive pressure upon their impact on the satellite. The indirect solar radiation arriving at the satellite after being reflected from the earth's surface, called the *albedo effect*, is also considerable. The direct radiation pressure is zero when the satellite is in the earth's shadow. Hence, one must model the earth's shadow zone and direct radiation pressure by considering the motions of the earth and the satellite relative to the sun. The solar radiation force per unit mass on a satellite varies according to $v \, p \, A \, r \, / \, m$, where v is the eclipse factor (1 in sunlight, 0 in shadow), p is the solar radiation pressure, A is the cross-sectional area of the satellite on which the radiation falls, r is the reflectivity of the satellite, and m is the satellite mass.

Assuming an acceleration of the satellite due to solar radiation pressure of 10^{-7} m / s^2, the perturbations of GPS orbital arcs of four hours duration, due to the solar radiation pressure, are:

Orbital element	Solar radiation effect (m)
a	5
e	5
i	2
Ω	5
$\omega + M$	10

• **Atmospheric drag.** The atmospheric drag is a non-conservative force which arises from the friction between the satellite surface and the surrounding atmosphere. The consequence of frictional dissipation is that the satellite loses energy which results in secular (non-recoverable) changes in a and M. The atmospheric drag force per unit mass on a satellite varies according to $\rho \, v^2 \, A \, / \, m$ where ρ is the atmospheric density at the satellite, v is the satellite's velocity relative to the atmosphere, A is the satellite cross sectional area, and m is the satellite mass. The atmospheric density at GPS satellite altitudes, ~20 000 km, is so small that the drag effects are negligible.

EPHEMERIS PREDICTION

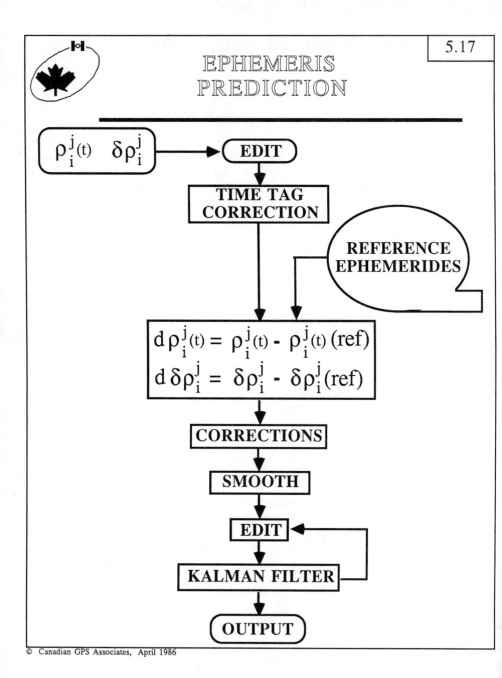

EPHEMERIS PREDICTION

The broadcast ephemeris information transmitted by the GPS satellites is computed and controlled by the GPS Master Control Segment. Ephemeris prediction is a two-step process:
(a) an off-line least-squares fit to produce a reference ephemeris, and
(b) an on-line first-order correction using a Kalman filter and additional measurements provides current estimates of the satellite states which, in turn, are used to predict future states.

The reference ephemeris is an initial estimate of the satellite trajectory, computed from about one week of data from the five GPS monitor sites (Colorado Springs, Diego Garcia, Ascension, Kwajalein, Hawaii). It is used to permit accurate linearization of the orbital model in the Kalman filter. Errors in the reference ephemeris of order 100 m would result in linearization errors well within the GPS ephemeris prediction specification of 1 m per day. Linear perturbations about this reference ephemeris are computed by the on-line Kalman filter. The reference ephemeris also is used to compute the time dependent state transition matrix (partial derivatives) required by the Kalman filter.

The on-line ephemeris prediction is driven by pseudo-range and integrated Doppler measurements (nominally at 6 sec intervals) from each satellite in view at each monitor station. After editing and time tag correction, these measurements are compared with equivalent quantities computed using the reference ephemeris and misclosures formed. These misclosures are corrected for various known biases, such as ionospheric delay, tropospheric refraction, relativistic effects, and satellite and monitor station antenna phase centre offsets. The range measurements are then smoothed to give a set of smoothed pseudo-range data every 15 minutes for each satellite-station pair. The integrated Doppler measurements are not smoothed but sampled every 15 minutes. These data are processed by a Kalman filter estimator to produce estimates of the satellite position and velocity states. The output of the Kalman filter is 6 orbital element perturbations, the satellite clock frequency offset and drift rate, 3 solar radiation pressure parameters per satellite, monitor station clock bias and frequency offset, tropospheric scaling bias for all monitor stations, and 3 earth rotation component residual states.

The orbital element perturbations are used to correct the reference ephemeris, and an extrapolated ephemeris is predicted for upload to the satellite. Similarly, the satellite clock states are propagated throughout the next prediction span, and a time polynomial representation is prepared for upload. Predicted ephemeris errors of about 1 m radially, 7 m along track, and 3 m cross track are expected, once GPS is fully operational. These predictions are reformatted into GPS message parameters and uploaded into the satellite memory at least once a day. The normal upload contains sufficient data for 26-hour orbits. Special 6-hour uploads are used to support testing requirements.

POSTCOMPUTED
EPHEMERIDES

PRECISE EPHEMERIS

● = GPS control stations
■ = DMA monitor stations

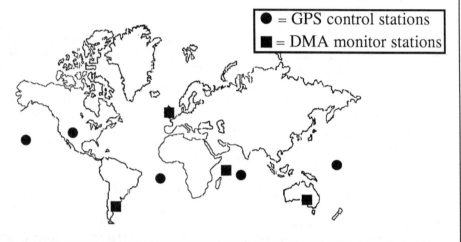

CIVIL NETWORKS IN NORTH AMERICA

● = UT network
■ = POLARIS network

POSTCOMPUTED EPHEMERIDES

The predicted broadcast ephemeris will not always satisfy the needs of all users. Some will use receivers which do not decode the broadcast message (for example, so called 'codeless' receivers). Some will want more accurately determined orbits than are provided by the broadcast ephemeris. The alternative to the broadcast ephemeris is a postcomputed ephemeris. Several sources for postcomputed ephemerides are presently available, or have been proposed.

• The so-called **precise ephemeris** is computed by the U.S. Naval Surface Weapons Center (NSWC). This orbital determination operation is similar to the operation used to determine the reference trajectories for the broadcast ephemeris computation. However, data from the five GPS monitor stations are augmented by data from sites in Australia, Seychelles, England, and Argentina. A more extensive and international network is planned for the future.

• The U.S. **National Geodetic Service** has announced that they will offer reformatted precise ephemeris data to civilian users, under two standard GPS orbit data product subscription services: one designed for large computers and magnetic tape distribution, and the other for small computers and telecommunications distribution. FORTRAN 77 routines to handle the data will also be provided. The proposed subscription costs would be $US 100 per week, or $US 2000 for six months.

• The U.S. Geological Survey has contracted with the **University of Texas** to produce postcomputed ephemerides, beginning in September 1986, based on data from three stations (Austin, Texas; Westford, Massachusetts; and Mojave, California). A Canadian station (Yellowknife) is to be added to the network in early 1987. A German station (Wettzell) may also be added. The initial operations are for six months, but may be continued for up to three years. TI 4100 receivers, controlled by IBM PC/XT computers and cesium clocks, are used at each station. Orbits are computed at the University of Texas. Alternative orbital predictions are planned by the Canadian Geodetic Survey.

• Three dual frequency Macrometer™ receivers have been in operation since mid-1985 at the **POLARIS** stations at Westford, Massachusetts; Fort Davis, Texas; and Richmond, Florida. Orbits based on this data are believed to be computed using the PEP program at MIT.

• **Litton** Aeroservices offer a commercial GPS orbit data product. The data source for this orbit has not been revealed by Litton.

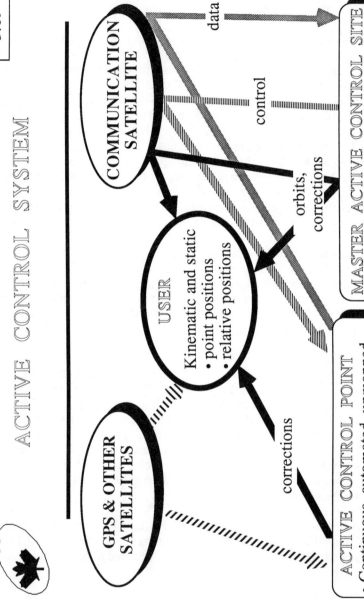

ACTIVE CONTROL SYSTEM

5.19

COMMUNICATION SATELLITE

GPS & OTHER SATELLITES

USER
Kinematic and static
• point positions
• relative positions

data

control

orbits, corrections

corrections

MASTER ACTIVE CONTROL SITE
• Data & system management & control
• Orbit improvement
• Better differential corrections

ACTIVE CONTROL POINT
• Continuous, automated, unmanned tracking and data collection
• Orbit data and differential corrections broadcast to users

ACTIVE CONTROL SYSTEM

The Active Control System (ACS), currently under study at the Canadian Geodetic Survey, is based on the concept of a sparse network of active control stations where continuous GPS tracking is carried out. This GPS network would be combined with a number of widely spaced, fixed VLBI antennas to ensure consistent scale and orientation of the terrestrial networks positioned with GPS. The two functions of the ACS would be regional GPS orbit improvement over Canada, and real-time data distribution for relative positioning within the framework defined by the ACS.

An initial capability for orbital improvement is envisaged for as early as 1987.

Real-time data distribution will depend on cost-effective mobile satellite communication services being available. This is expected early in the 1990s.

This conceptual diagram illustrates the various data and control communications which may be involved.

BROADCAST EPHEMERIS MESSAGE PARAMETERS

M_0	Mean anomaly
Δn	Mean motion difference
e	Eccentricity
$\sqrt{a}$	$\sqrt{}$ of semi-major axis
Ω_0	Right ascension parameter
i_0	Inclination at reference time t_{oe}
ω	Argument of perigee
$\dot{\Omega}$	Rate of right ascension
$\dot{i}$	Rate of inclination
C_{uc}, C_{us}	Corrections to argument of latitude
C_{rc}, C_{rs}	Corrections to orbital radius
C_{ic}, C_{is}	Corrections to inclination
t_{oe}	Ephemeris reference time

BROADCAST EPHEMERIS MESSAGE PARAMETERS

Broadcast ephemerides for the GPS satellites are readily available in the navigation message modulated on the GPS carrier signals. The parameters describing the orbital motion of the satellite are very similar to those of a Keplerian representation. Because the broadcast ephemeris is the result of an extrapolation of a postprocessed orbit into the future (which have first been precisely determined by numerical integration of the equations of motion), these parameters are Keplerian in appearance only, i.e., they only describe the satellite orbit for the period for which they are intended (about 1.5 hours from the reference epoch).

The six parameters ($\sqrt{a}$, e, i_o, ω, Ω_o, M_o) describe a smooth, elliptical orbit, with the satellite position being a function of time since t_o. However, the Ω_o parameter requires more discussion (see next figure).

The additional parameters (Δn, Ω-dot, i-dot, and the six sine and cosine coefficients) describe the deviations of the actual satellite motion from this smooth ellipse. These parameters primarily describe the perturbation effects of the non-sphericity of the earth while also absorbing the smaller perturbation due to the sun and moon gravitational attractions and solar radiation pressure.

Each broadcast ephemeris parameter set is intended for use only during the one hour period to which they refer. Extrapolation of the broadcast ephemeris well beyond this period leads to an exponential error growth which can affect significantly even differential positioning accuracies, especially for large station separations. The actual accuracy of the broadcast ephemeris information has not been adequately assessed to date. Reported results of several GPS campaigns have implied (from comparisons of GPS derived station coordinates at known locations) an accuracy at the level of 20 to 50 metres. However, such estimates are affected by the 'freshness' of the ephemeris and the area of application.

LONGITUDE OF ASCENDING NODE

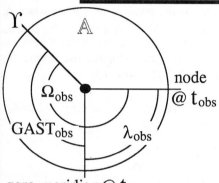

A

node @ t_{obs}

Ω_{obs}

$GAST_{obs}$

λ_{obs}

zero meridian @ t_{obs}

$$\lambda_{obs} = \Omega_{obs} - GAST_{obs}$$

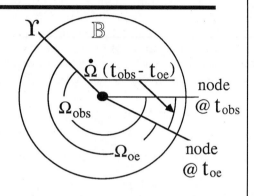

B

$\dot{\Omega}(t_{obs} - t_{oe})$

node @ t_{obs}

Ω_{obs}

Ω_{oe}

node @ t_{oe}

$$\Omega_{obs} = \Omega_{oe} + \dot{\Omega}(t_{obs} - t_{oe})$$

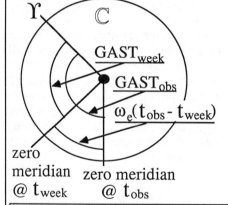

C

$GAST_{week}$

$GAST_{obs}$

$\omega_e(t_{obs} - t_{week})$

zero meridian @ t_{week}

zero meridian @ t_{obs}

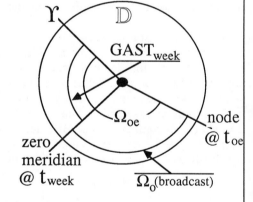

D

$GAST_{week}$

Ω_{oe}

zero meridian @ t_{week}

node @ t_{oe}

Ω_0(broadcast)

$$GAST_{obs} = GAST_{week} + \omega_e(t_{obs} - t_{week})$$

$$\Omega_0(\text{broadcast}) = \Omega_{oe} - GAST_{week}$$

$$\lambda_{obs} = \Omega_0(\text{broadcast}) + (\dot{\Omega} - \omega_e)(t_{obs} - t_{oe}) - \omega_e(t_{oe} - t_{week})$$

LONGITUDE OF ASCENDING NODE

In order to compute coordinates for a satellite in the CT-system, we need to know the longitude of the ascending node of the orbit plane, λ_{obs}, at the time of observation, t_{obs}. In A of the figure, we see that this is simply

$$\lambda_{obs} = \Omega_{obs} - GAST_{obs} \, ,$$

where Ω_{obs} is the angle between the vernal equinox and the ascending node (the right ascension of the ascending node) at t_{obs}, and $GAST_{obs}$ is the angle between the vernal equinox and the Greenwich meridian (Greenwich Apparent Sidereal Time) at t_{obs}. However the broadcast ephemeris does not supply values for Ω and GAST at t_{obs}. This complicates things slightly.

As shown in B of the figure, the value we use for Ω is for the ephemeris reference time t_{oe}. Since we are given the rate of change of right ascension Ω-dot, we can use

$$\Omega_{obs} = \Omega_{oe} + \Omega\text{-dot} * (t_{obs} - t_{oe}) \, .$$

Ω-dot (the orbit plane precession rate) is typically a few millidegrees per hour. New values for Ω-dot and t_{oe} are given hourly in the broadcast ephemeris.

As shown in C of the figure, the value we use for GAST is for the beginning of the week (Saturday/Sunday midnight in the GPS time system), t_{week}. Since a value for the earth's rotation rate, ω_e, is specified, we can use

$$GAST_{obs} = GAST_{week} + \omega_e * (t_{obs} - t_{week}) \, .$$

ω_e is approximately 15 degrees per hour (the earth's rotation rate). The times t_{obs} and t_{oe} are the elapsed time since t_{week}, so we can take it as having a zero value.

We must still obtain values for Ω_{oe} and $GAST_{week}$ (actually their difference). As indicated in D of the figure, the right ascension parameter in the broadcast ephemeris is $\Omega_0(\text{broadcast}) = \Omega_{oe} - GAST_{week}$, and **not**, as might be expected, equal to Ω_{oe} alone. It is therefore mislabelled as a right ascension.

Making all the above substitutions (and setting $t_{week} = 0$), we finally obtain

$$\lambda_{obs} = \Omega_0(\text{broadcast}) + (\Omega\text{-dot} - \omega_e) * (t_{obs} - t_{oe}) - \omega_e * t_{oe} \, .$$

GPS ORBIT DESCRIPTION

- **16 PARAMETERS**
- **NEW VALUES EACH HOUR**

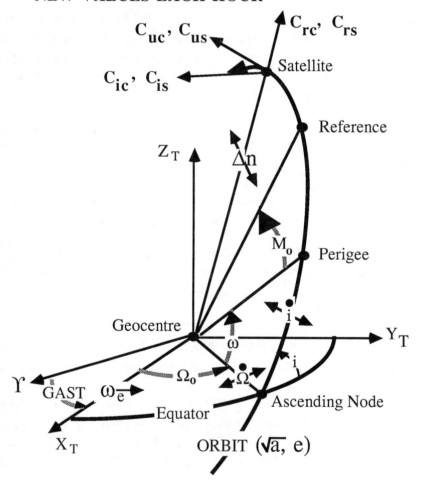

GPS ORBIT DESCRIPTION

There are four points of importance along the orbital ellipse. These are:

• The *ascending node*. This is the intersection of the orbital plane, and the equatorial plane, as the satellite passes from the southern hemisphere into the northern hemisphere.

• *Perigee*. This is point at which the satellite most closely approaches the earth. The angle between the ascending node and perigee, measured in the orbital plane.

• The *reference position*. This is position of the satellite at the reference time t_{oe} (the time for which M_o, i_o, and Ω_o are given).

• The *satellite position*. This is what we want to determine. It is separated from perigee by the true anomaly f, and from the ascending node by the argument of latitude $u = \omega + f$.

In order to transform the orbit parameters to CT-system coordinates, three rotations between four coordinate systems are used:

• The satellite position is defined in the plane of the satellite orbit in the (x''', y''', z''') coordinate system, with x''' toward the satellite, y''' in the orbital plane, and z''' normal to the orbital plane.

• A rotation of the (x''', y''', z''') system about the z'''-axis (3-axis) from the satellite to the node (through the argument of latitude u) produces the (x'', y'', z'') system, with x'' aligned to the ascending node, y'' in the orbital plane, and $z'' = z'''$.

• A rotation of the (x'', y'', z'') system about the x''-axis (1-axis) from the orbital plane to the equatorial plane (through the inclination angle i) produces the (x', y', z') system, with $x' = x''$, y' now in the equatorial plane, and z' aligned to the earth's rotation axis.

• A final rotation of the (x', y', z') system about the z'-axis (3-axis) from the ascending node to the Greenwich meridian (through the longitude of the ascending node at the observation epoch, λ_{obs}) leads to coordinates (x, y, z) of the satellite in the CT-system. These coordinates can be computed for any time during a given observation span.

SATELLITE COORDINATE COMPUTATION

CONSTANTS (these values must be used)

- gravitation constant $\qquad$ $\mu = 3.986008 \times 10^{14} \ m^3 / sec^2$
- mean earth rotation rate $\qquad$ $\omega_e = 7.292115147 \times 10^{-5} \ rad/sec$

$\qquad\qquad\qquad\qquad\qquad$ $\pi = 3.1415926535898$

TRUE ANOMALY f_k

- time since reference epoch $\qquad$ $t_k = t - t_{oe}$
- mean anomaly at t_k $\qquad$ $M_k = M_0 + (\sqrt{\mu} / \sqrt{a}^3 + \Delta n) \, t_k$
- solve Kepler's equation iteratively for eccentric anomaly E_k

$$M_k = E_k - e \sin E_k$$

- true anomaly f_k $\qquad$ $f_k = \tan^{-1} \left[\dfrac{\sqrt{1 - e^2} \, \sin E_k}{\cos E_k - e} \right]$

ARG OF LATITUDE u_k, RADIUS r_k, INCLINATION i_k

$$u_k = \omega + f_k + C_{uc} \cos 2 (\omega + f_k) + C_{us} \sin 2(\omega + f_k)$$

$$r_k = a (1 - e \cos E_k) + C_{rc} \cos 2 (\omega + f_k) + C_{rs} \sin 2(\omega + f_k)$$

$$i_k = i_0 + \overset{\bullet}{i} \, t_k + C_{ic} \cos 2 (\omega + f_k) + C_{is} \sin 2(\omega + f_k)$$

LONGITUDE OF ASCENDING NODE λ_k

$$\lambda_k = \Omega_0 + (\overset{\bullet}{\Omega} - \omega_e) \, t_k - \omega_e t_{oe}$$

CT-SYSTEM COORDINATES

$$\begin{bmatrix} X_k \\ Y_k \\ Z_k \end{bmatrix} = R_3(- \lambda_k) \, R_1(- i_k) \, R_3(- u_k) \begin{bmatrix} r_k \\ 0 \\ 0 \end{bmatrix}$$

SATELLITE COORDINATE COMPUTATION

We want the satellite position in the CT-system. We first compute the satellite position in the RA-system in the following steps:

- Find the true anomaly f_k, by
  - finding t_k, the time since reference time t_{oe},
  - computing M_k, the mean anomaly at t_k,
  - solving Kepler's equation (iteratively) for the eccentric anomaly E_k,
  - and finally computing the true anomaly f_k.

- Find the argument of latitude u_k, by adding
  - the argument of perigee ω,
  - the true anomaly f_k, and
  - the correction terms with coefficients C_{uc} and C_{us}.

- Compute the orbit radius r_k using
  - the expression for elliptical radial distance, and
  - correction terms with coefficients C_{rc} and C_{rs}.

- Compute the orbital plane inclination i_k, using
  - the inclination i_o, at reference time t_{oe}
  - the linear change in inclination since reference time, and
  - correction terms with coefficients C_{ic} and C_{is}.

- Compute the longitude of the ascending node λ_k, by adding
  - the right ascension parameter, Ω_0(broadcast),
  - the change in Greenwich Apparent Sidereal Time between the beginning of the week and the reference time t_{oe}, and
  - the change in longitude of the ascending node since the reference time t_{oe},

- Compute the CT-system coordinates by applying the three rotations (through u_k, i_k, and λ_k) described previously.

CHAPTER SIX

SIGNAL STRUCTURE

Guide to GPS Positioning
© Canadian GPS Associates, April 1986

SIGNAL STRUCTURE

BASIC CONCEPTS

- Why is the GPS signal so complicated?
- Definitions

SIGNAL COMPONENTS

- Code modulation technique
- Code generation
- Message format and content

SIGNAL GENERATION IN GPS SATELLITES

- What leaves the satellite antenna ?
- GPS signal tolerances
- Speculations on Selective Availability

PROPAGATION FROM SATELLITE TO RECEIVER

- Doppler effect on GPS signals

SIGNAL STRUCTURE

In this chapter we examine the structure of the signals sent out by the GPS satellites. Many of the strengths of GPS depend on various features of this signal structure. We start by considering why the structure is so complicated. In order to describe the signal, we need to understand some unfamiliar terms, so these are defined next.

The GPS signal consists of a carrier upon which three modulations are impressed: the C/A-code, the P-code, and the broadcast message. The method of modulating the carrier by binary biphase modulations is described. The two codes are pseudo-random noise codes. These are generated using a device called a tapped feedback switch register. The operation of this device, and how it leads to the C/A- and P-codes, is considered next. The message format and content conclude our discussion of the various GPS signal components.

The methods by which these signal components are combined to form the signal which actually leaves a GPS satellite are considered by tracing the signal through a simplified schematic of the satellite's inner workings. The specifications for the officially-stated tolerances on various aspects of the signal generation are reviewed.

The policy of the U.S. Department of Defense is to intentionally degrade the accuracy obtainable from GPS by civilian users, once the GPS system is fully deployed. This degradation, officially termed *Selective Availability* is reviewed, and some speculations are made on what parts of the signal generation might be involved.

Finally, one of the features of the signal as it is received on the ground, is its Doppler shift, due to the relative motion between satellite and receiver. We examine the features of the Doppler shift and its derivatives.

Complete details of the GPS signal structure are specified in the Interface Control Document [Rockwell, 1984]. A detailed review of the signal structure is given by Spilker [1978].

WHY IS THE GPS SIGNAL SO COMPLICATED?

MULTI-USER SYSTEM

- One-way measurements (listen only)

REAL-TIME POSITIONING

- Simultaneous measurements from many satellites
    - » how to identify signal from each satellite?
- Unambiguous range measurements
    - » signal modulation to get time delay
- Real-time satellite positions
    - » broadcast message containing ephemeris

HIGH ACCURACY (10 cm/s) VELOCITY

- Microwave carrier frequency (1.6 GHz)

HIGH ACCURACY (10 m) POSITIONS

- High frequency modulation (10 MHz)
- Dual frequency for ionospheric delay

FREQUENCY ALLOCATION RESTRICTIONS
ANTI-JAMMING REQUIREMENT

- Direct spread spectrum technique
    - » pseudo-random noise code

MIXTURE OF MILITARY AND CIVILIAN USERS

- Two codes (P and C/A)

WHY IS THE GPS SIGNAL SO COMPLICATED ?

In this figure we review the performance requirements for GPS that lead to the complicated nature of its signal structure.

• **Multi-user system.** The military requirement alone is for several tens of thousands of GPS users. Some predictions place the eventual civilian user community in the millions. For GPS satellites to process two-way communications from each user would make it a much more complicated system than the present strategy of broadcasting one-way only to passively listening users. Military security also dictates that users not announce their position by sending signals to the satellites. However, one way measurements require close attention to the problem of clock synchronization.

• **Real-time positioning.** In order to obtain instantaneous positions in real-time, measurements to several satellites must be made simultaneously. The problem of identifying which signal is coming from which satellite is solved by each satellite having a unique code. The range ambiguities associated with phase measurements cannot be resolved instantaneously, so the signal must be modulated in such a way that time delay measurements are possible: for example, using pseudo-random noise codes. Finally, the satellite positions must be known in real time, and the easiest way to disseminate this information is by including the ephemeris in the broadcast message.

• **High accuracy velocities (10 cm/s) and positions (10 m).** Continuous centimetre-per-second-level velocities require Doppler shift measurements on a centimetre-wavelength (microwave) carrier. Continuous metre-level positions require metre-wavelength modulations, such as the 10 MHz P-code. Metre-level positions also require compensation for ionospheric refraction, most easily accomplished by making dual-frequency corrections.

• **Pollution of the electromagnetic spectrum.** New systems like GPS do not easily gain permission to use parts of the electromagnetic spectrum. For military use deliberate electromagnetic pollution (jamming) is something to worry about. The modern communication-technology solution to both problems is to spread the signal over a wide bandwidth, in such a way that it can share the same part of the spectrum with many other users and, at the same time, be impervious to jamming. GPS uses such a spread-spectrum technique, implemented by the choice of modulating code, also used for the range measurements.

• **Mixture of military and civilian users.** GPS will have both the military Precise Positioning Service (PPS) using the P-code, and the civilian Standard Positioning Service (SPS) using the C/A-code.

DEFINITIONS

PSEUDO-RANDOM NOISE CODE

- A binary sequence (string of 0's and 1's)
- Has noise-like properties
- Maximum autocorrelation at zero lag

BINARY BIPHASE MODULATIONS

- Modulations on a constant frequency carrier
- Two phase states: normal and mirror image, modelled by $y = A(t) \cos(\omega t + \phi)$, where A(t) is a sequence of values which are either
  - +1 representing normal phase state (binary 0)
  - -1 representing mirror image state (binary 1)
- Phase shifts restricted to 0 and 180 degrees
- Transition from binary 0 to 1 or 1 to 0 results in 180 degree phase shift
- Sequence of all 1's or all 0's results in no phase shift

SPREAD SPECTRUM

- Characteristic of a signal which is spread over a frequency band much wider than the minimum bandwidth needed to transmit the information being sent.

DEFINITIONS

Three unfamiliar terms, necessary to understand GPS codes, are defined here.

• **Pseudo-random noise code.** A *code* is a system for representing information, together with rules for using the system. Many codes nowadays are binary codes (strings of 0's and 1's), because they are handled easily and naturally by computers. GPS codes are binary codes. In information theory, a quantity is *noise* if it is not wanted, or does not contain useful information. *Random noise* has some specific statistical properties; in particular, the *autocorrelation function* (plot of the scalar product of the noise sequence with a delayed copy of itself) is zero, except at zero delay. Random noise is assumed to arise from unpredictable causes, and therefore would be subject to the rules needed to specify a code. Pseudo-random noise, on the other hand, is predictable and may contain information (namely, a reading of the transmitter clock). The pseudo-random noise codes used in GPS are generated by a carefully specified algorithm, and precisely identical codes are generated independently in both the satellite and receiver in order to track the signal. The term *pseudo-random noise* is used to indicate that the code has some random noise-like properties, in particular the autocorrelation is small (but not zero) except at zero delay.

• **Binary biphase modulations.** This is the method used to **implement** the pseudo-random noise code in GPS signals. An unmodulated (pure) carrier signal carries no information and no code. Many kinds of modulations are possible: the frequency, amplitude, or phase of the carrier can be changed. Phase modulations are used for GPS. Since a binary code is used, there must be two states of the phase modulations. For GPS these two states are the **normal state**, representing a binary 0, and the **mirror image state**, representing a binary 1. The normal state can be modelled by multiplying the unmodulated carrier by +1 (no change). The mirror image state can be modelled by multiplying the unmodulated carrier by -1 (phase reversal to obtain the mirror image state). A code transition from 0 to 1 (normal to mirror image) or from 1 to 0 (mirror image to normal) each involves a phase reversal or 180° phase shift.

• **Spread spectrum.** An unmodulated carrier has a bandwidth approaching zero (its spectrum looks like a single spike). The modulations needed to communicate information result in a broader bandwidth. If the modulations result in a bandwidth much broader than the minimum required to transmit the infomation, then the signal has a spread spectrum. The reasons for using a spread spectrum signal are to combat interference and ensure communication security. For positioning, however, spread spectrum signals also permit more accurate range measurements. The signal spreading method used by GPS, called *direct sequence spreading*, [Dixon, 1976] uses a pseudo-random noise code and binary biphase modulations.

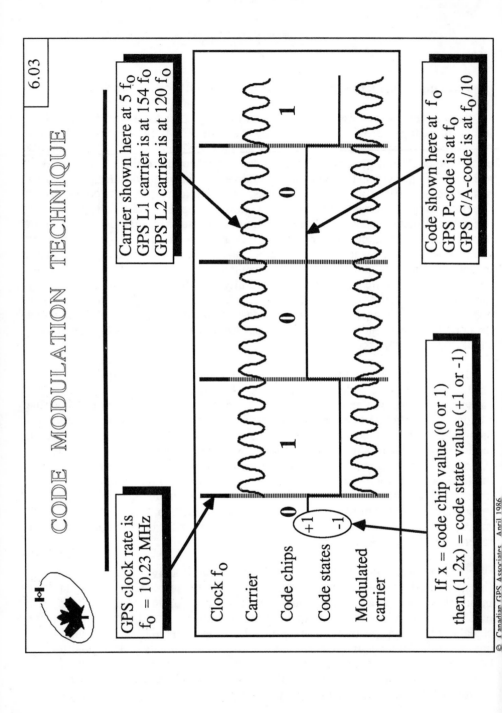

CODE MODULATION TECHNIQUE

6.03

GPS clock rate is
f_o = 10.23 MHz

Carrier shown here at 5 f_o
GPS L1 carrier is at 154 f_o
GPS L2 carrier is at 120 f_o

Code shown here at f_o
GPS P-code is at f_o
GPS C/A-code is at f_o/10

Clock f_o

Carrier

Code chips

Code states

Modulated carrier

If x = code chip value (0 or 1)
then (1-2x) = code state value (+1 or -1)

© Canadian GPS Associates, April 1986

CODE MODULATION TECHNIQUE

How code modulations are impressed onto the carrier is illustrated here.

• **Clock rate.** All components of the GPS signal are based upon the fundamental clock rate of 10.23 MHz. In fact, the satellite clock rate is deliberately set 4.45×10^{-10} below this nominal value (to 10 229 999.995 45 Hz) to compensate for the average relativistic effects: the sum of the general relativistic effect caused by the average difference in gravitational potential between the satellite and user, and the special relativistic effect due to the average relative velocity between satellite and user.

• **Carrier.** The actual GPS carriers are at $154 f_o$ (L1) and $120 f_o$ (L2). Here we illustrate the concept with a carrier at $5 f_o$. Every fifth cycle coincides with a tick of the fundamental clock frequency f_o.

• **Code chips.** The P-code is at f_o, and the C/A-code at $f_o / 10$. Here we illustrate the concept with code chips at f_o. The values are either 0 or 1, and are called *chips* rather than bits to indicate that they do not carry data.

• **Code states.** A code chip value of 0 corresponds to a code state of +1 (normal state). A code chip value of 1 corresponds to a code state of -1 (mirror image state).

• **Modulated carrier.** The carrier is modulated by multiplying it by the code states. Each transition from +1 to -1 or from -1 to +1 leads to a 180° phase shift of the carrier.

What happens when a GPS code is multiplied by a replica of itself? Since the code can be represented by a sequence of +1 and -1 values, when we multiply the two copies together, the states of the resulting signal will be the multiples of the individual states of each of the two copies.

When the code and its replica are *synchronized* (lined up in time), the corresponding states of each copy will also be synchronized: that is, +1 states will occur simultaneously in both copies, as will -1 states. Then the states of the resulting multiplied signal will be either $(+1)^2 = +1$ or $(-1)^2 = +1$. In other words, only the normal state remains, and the code modulation has been removed from the signal.

On the other hand, if the original code and its replica are **not** synchronized, then the modulation will not be removed from the resulting multiplied signal. Detecting the presence of modulations in this resulting signal permits adjustment of the time delay between the original code and its replica until the modulation is no longer present in the multiple and synchronization has been achieved.

These features of the GPS code are crucial to the design of GPS receivers.

CODE GENERATION

TAPPED FEEDBACK SHIFT REGISTER

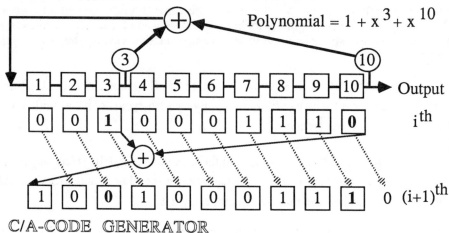

Polynomial $= 1 + x^3 + x^{10}$

| 1 | 2 | 3 | 4 | 5 | 6 | 7 | 8 | 9 | 10 | Output |

| 0 | 0 | **1** | 0 | 0 | 0 | 1 | 1 | 1 | **0** | i^{th} |

| 1 | 0 | **0** | 1 | 0 | 0 | 0 | 1 | 1 | **1** | 0 $(i+1)^{th}$ |

C/A-CODE GENERATOR

$$G1 = 1 + x^3 + x^{10}$$

$$G2 = 1 + x^2 + x^3 + x^6 + x^8 + x^9 + x^{10}$$

PRN	TAPS
1	2 ⊕ 6
2	3 ⊕ 7
3	4 ⊕ 8

Output

CODE GENERATION

The pseudo-random binary sequences of the C/A-code and the P-code are generated using devices called 'tapped feedback shift registers' [Golumb, 1967]. The operation of these devices is described and applied to the generation of GPS codes.

A *shift register* is a set of connected one-bit storage cells (here labelled 1 to 10). When a clock pulse is applied to the register the content of each cell is shifted one bit to the right. Hence the content of cell 10 is 'read out' as output. The special properties of such shift registers depends on how information is 'read in' to cell 1.

A *tapped feedback shift register* is a shift register for which the input (the value to be placed in the leftmost cell) is determined by the state of one or more of the other cells in the register. Here we show that the binary sum of the states of cells 3 and 10 are used to determine the input to cell 1. Hence, if cells 3 and 10 have different states (one is 1 and the other 0), a 1 will be read into cell 1 on the next clock pulse. If cells 3 and 10 have the same state (both either 1 or 0), then a 0 will be read into cell 1. A shorthand way of denoting this particular design is by the polynomial $1 + x^3 + x^{10}$. As illustrated, if we start with every cell containing a binary 1, 12 clock pulses later we will have the contents 0010001110. The next clock pulse will take the 1 in cell 3 and the 0 in cell 10, add them to get a binary 1, and place this in cell 1. Meanwhile, all other bits have shifted along one cell to the right, and the 0 in cell 10 becomes the next bit in the output sequence.

The C/A-code is generated by two 10-bit tapped feedback shift registers. One of these, G1, is the same as the $1 + x^3 + x^{10}$ register already described. The other shift register, G2, has a polynomial representation $1 + x^2 + x^3 + x^6 + x^8 + x^9 + x^{10}$. That is, cells 2,3,6,8,9, and 10 are tapped and binary added to get the new input value for cell 1. In this case, the output comes not from cell 10 but from a second set of taps. Various pairs of these second taps are binary added, and the result binary added to the output of G1. That becomes the C/A-code. The tapping shown here is for the C/A-code for the satellite with PRN 1. Various alternative pairs of taps are used to generate the complete set of 32 PRN C/A-codes. This family of codes is known as Gold codes [Gold, 1967], and has the property that any two have a very low cross correlation (are nearly orthogonal).

The P-code generation follows the same principles, except four 10-cell shift registers are used. Two registers are combined to produce the X1 code, which is 15 345 000 chips long and repeats every 1.5 seconds; and two registers are combined to produce the X2 code, which is 15 345 037 chips long. The X1 and X2 codes can be combined with 37 different delays on the X2 code to produce 37 different one-week segments of the P-code, five of which are associated with ground stations, and each of the remaining 32 with a different satellite.

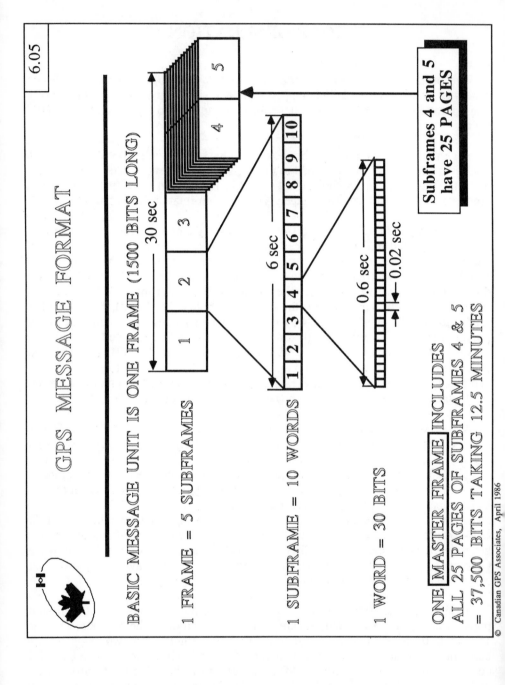

GPS MESSAGE FORMAT

6.05

BASIC MESSAGE UNIT IS ONE FRAME (1500 BITS LONG)

1 FRAME = 5 SUBFRAMES

1 SUBFRAME = 10 WORDS

1 WORD = 30 BITS

ONE MASTER FRAME INCLUDES
ALL 25 PAGES OF SUBFRAMES 4 & 5
= 37,500 BITS TAKING 12.5 MINUTES

Subframes 4 and 5 have 25 PAGES

© Canadian GPS Associates, April 1986

GPS MESSAGE FORMAT

The GPS message is formatted into 'frames' of 1500 bits. At the 50-bits-per-second message data transmission rate, this takes 30 seconds to transmit.

Each frame contains 5 subframes, and each subframe contains ten, 30-bit words. For subframes 1 to 3, the information does not in general change from frame to frame. However, for subframes 4 and 5, consecutive frames contain different 'pages.' There is a total of 25 such pages for each of subframes 4 and 5.

One Master frame contains all the information in all pages of subframes 4 and 5, and consists of 25 complete frames. One Master frame takes 12.5 minutes to transmit.

Each message bit lasts for 20 milliseconds. During this period. the complete C/A-code (1023 chips at 1.023 Mbps) will have repeated exactly 20 times. A divide-by-20 counter on the C/A-code output provides the timing for the message bits. During one message bit

- 20 460 C/A-code chips,
- 204 600 P-code chips, and
- 31 508 400 cycles of the L1 carrier will have occurred.

Each message subframe lasts for six seconds. During this period, the X1 component of the P-code will have repeated exactly four times.

GPS MESSAGE CONTENT

SUBRAME 1

- Flags (L2 code & data;
    week #;
    satellite accuracy and health)
- Age of data
- Satellite clock correction coefficients

SUBFRAMES 2 & 3

- Orbit parameters

SUBFRAME 4

- Almanac for satellites 25-32 (pages 2,3,4,5,7,8,9,10)
- Ionospheric model, and UTC data (page 18)
- Antispoof flag - 32 satellites (page 25)
- Satellite configuration - 32 satellites (page 25)
- Health of satellites 25-32 (page 25)

- Reserved (pages 1,6,11,12,16,19,20,21,22,23,24)
- Spares (pages 13,14,15)
- Special messages (page 17)

SUBFRAME 5

- Almanac for satellites 1-24 (pages 1-24)
- Health of satellites 1-24 (page 25)

GPS MESSAGE CONTENT

Each subframe has a particular kind of broadcast message assigned to it.

• **Subframe 1** contains satellite clock correction coefficients, various flags, and the age of the data.

• **Subframes 2 and 3** contain the broadcast ephemeris parameters.

• **Subframe 4**, so far, has sensible information on only 10 of its 25 pages. These pages contain an ionospheric model, UTC data, flags for each satellite indicating whether 'antispoofing' is on (the Y-code, or encrypted version of the P-code, replacing the P-code) and, if more than 24 satellites are in orbit, the almanac data and health for the satellites in excess of 24.

• **Subframe 5** contains the almanac data and health status for the first 24 satellites in orbit. The almanac data, a crude description of the satellite orbit, is used to determine where every satellite in the constellation is, and then to acquire signals from satellites which are above the observer's horizon but not yet being tracked. Hence, once one satellite is being tracked, acquisition of signals from all other satellites is relatively easy.

At the beginning of each 6-second subframe, are two special words called the telemetry word (TLM), and the hand-over word (HOW). The HOW word contains the so-called 'Z-count', and changes every 6 seconds. The TLM word changes when uploads or other satellite operations are underway.

The **Z-count** is the number of 1.5-second X1 code repetitions since the beginning of the week (Saturday/Sunday midnight in the GPS system time scale). The Z-count thus ranges from 0 at the start of the week to 403 200 just before the end of the week. If we know the Z-count, we know exactly where in the week-long P-code to attempt to acquire and track the P-code.

The HOW word contains a number which, when multiplied by 4, gives the Z-count of the **next** 6-second subframe. It also contains the subframe identification (1 to 5), and a warning flag indicating when the subframes are **not** exactly aligned with the X1 code (this is expected to be an extremely rare event).

The TLM word contains a fixed 8-bit synchronization pattern, and a 14-bit message which contains, when appropriate [van Dierendonck et al., 1978],
   • the status of uploading data to the satellite
   • diagnostic messages
   • messages such as the Z-count of roll momentum dump.

WHAT LEAVES THE SATELLITE ANTENNA ?

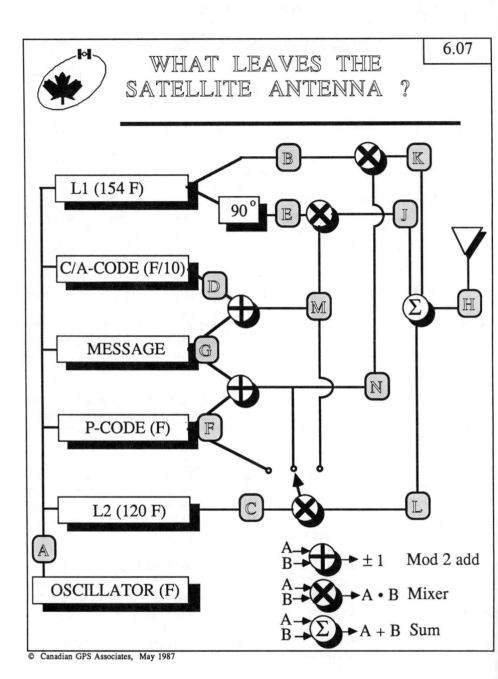

WHAT LEAVES THE SATELLITE ANTENNA ?

To answer this question, we must look carefully at how each of the several components of the GPS signals are generated inside the satellite, and then how they are combined to produce the signal which finally is broadcast by the satellite.

All components of the signals leaving the satellites are coherently generated from the same fundamental frequency, f_o = 10.23 MHz (point A on the figure).

Two carrier frequencies are used:
- L1 with f_1 = 154 f_o = 1575.42 MHz, and a wavelength of about 20 cm (point B),
- L2 with f_2 = 120 f_o = 1227.60 MHz, and a wavelength of about 25 cm (point C).

Three phase modulations are imposed on these carriers:
- The C/A-code C(t) has a chip rate of f_o /10 = 1.023 Mbps = f_1 / 1540, a wavelength of about 300 m, a length of 1023 bits, and a period of 1 ms (point D). A different C/A-code is assigned to each GPS satellite. Only a 90° phase shifted version (quadrature component) of the L1 carrier (point E) is modulated by the C/A-code.
- The P-code P(t) has a chip rate of f_o = 10.23 Mbps = f_1 / 154 = f_2 / 120, a wavelength of about 30 m, a length of 235 469 592 765 000 bits, and a period of 38 weeks (266 days), 9 hours, 45 minutes and approximately 55.5 seconds (point F). A different one-week segment of the P-code is assigned to each of up to 32 GPS satellites. Both the L1 and L2 carriers are modulated by the P-code.
- The data sequence D(t) has a bit rate of f_o / 204 600 = 50 bps = f_1 / 31 508 400 = f_2 / 24 552 000 (point G). One frame of D(t) has a length of 1500 bits, and hence a period of 30 seconds.

The complete signal leaving the satellite antenna (point H) can be represented by

$$A_cC(t)D(t) \sin(2\pi f_1 t+\phi_c)+A_p P(t)D(t) \cos(2\pi f_1 t+\phi_{p1}) + A_p P(t)D(t) \cos(2\pi f_2 t+\phi_{p2})$$

where
- the first component is the C/A-code signal (point J),
- the second component is the L1 P-code signal (point K), and
- the third component is the L2 P-code signal (point L).

The code and data phase modulation sequences can be modelled as sequences of ±1 amplitude states. The data-and-code combinations C(t) D(t) (point M) and P(t) D(t) (point N) are modulo 2 additions (e.g., C(t) D(t) = +1 if C(t) = D(t), and C(t) D(t) = -1 if C(t) ≠ D(t)). It is important to stress again that these modulations can be stripped from the carrier by multiplying them by a replica of themselves (or even by squaring them) — in other words, a double phase reversal recovers the original signal.

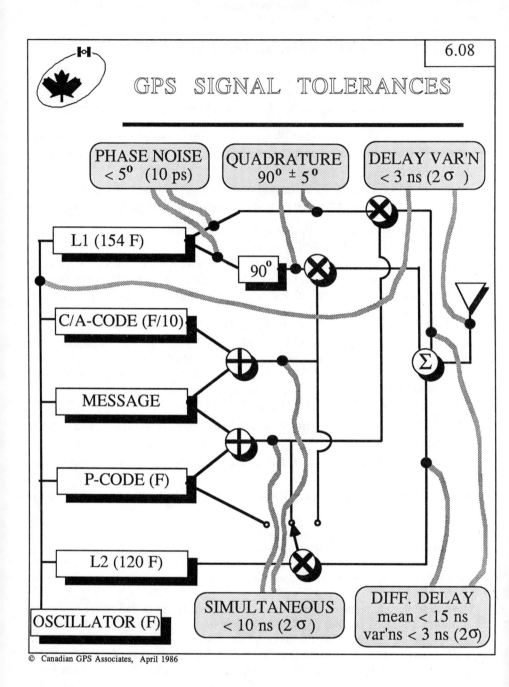

GPS SIGNAL TOLERANCES

PHASE NOISE
< 5° (10 ps)

QUADRATURE
90° ± 5°

DELAY VAR'N
< 3 ns (2σ)

L1 (154 F)

90°

C/A-CODE (F/10)

MESSAGE

P-CODE (F)

L2 (120 F)

Σ

OSCILLATOR (F)

SIMULTANEOUS
< 10 ns (2σ)

DIFF. DELAY
mean < 15 ns
var'ns < 3 ns (2σ)

GPS SIGNAL TOLERANCES

The source document used here is the GPS Interface Control Document [Rockwell, 1984]. This figure summarizes the appropriate information from Section 3 of that document. In particular,

- the **phase noise** specification (Section 3.3.1.3) is worded:
  The phase noise spectral density of the unmodulated carrier shall be such that a phase locked loop of 10 Hz one-sided noise bandwidth shall be able to track the carrier to an accuracy of 0.1 radians r.m.s.

- the **quadrature** specification (Section 3.3.1.5) is worded:
  The two L1 carrier components modulated by the two separate bit trains shall be in phase quadrature within ± 100 milliradians.

- the **equipment group delay** specification (Section 3.3.1.7) is worded:
  The delay between the L-band radiated output of a specific SV (measured at the antenna phase center) and the output of that SV's on-board frequency source consists of a bias term and an uncertainty. The bias term is of no concern to the user since it is included in clock correction parameters relayed in the NAV data, and is therefore accounted for by the user computations of system time. The uncertainty (variation) of this delay as well as the difference between the L1 and L2 delays are:

  ◊ *the effective uncertainty of the group delay shall not exceed 3 ns (2σ)*

  ◊ *the group delay differential between the radiated L1 and L2 signals consists of random plus bias (mean differential) components. For a given navigation payload redundancy configuration, the absolute value of the mean differential delay shall not exceed 15 ns. The random variations about the mean shall not exceed 3 ns (2σ).*

- the **signal coherence** specification (Section 3.3.1.8) is worded:
  All transmitted signals for a particular SV shall be coherently derived from the same on-board frequency standard; all digital signals shall be clocked in coincidence with the PRN transitions for the P-signal and occur at the P-signal transition speed. On the L1 channel the data transitions of the two modulating signals shall be such that the average time difference between the transitions does not exceed 10 ns (2σ).

SPECULATIONS ON
SELECTIVE AVAILABILITY

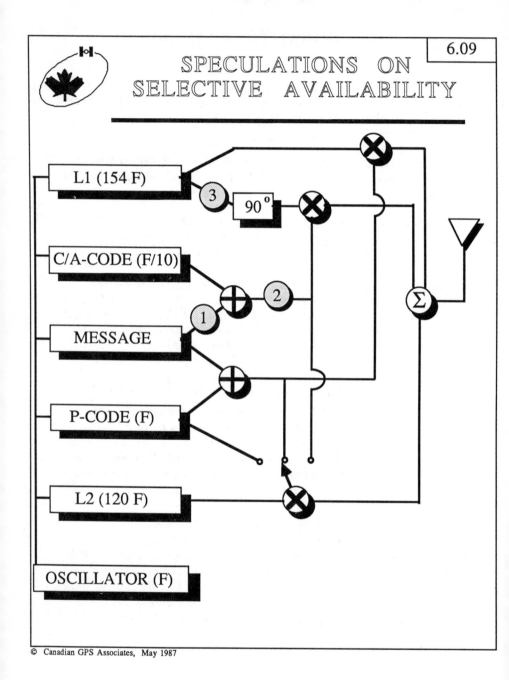

SPECULATIONS ON SELECTIVE AVAILABILITY

What do we know about Selective Availability (SA)?
• The GPS Standard Positioning Service (SPS) predictable and repeatable accuracy will be 100 metres (2 drms) horizontally and 156 metres (2 σ) vertically.
• The best relative accuracy for SPS will be 28.4 metres (2 drms) horizontally and 44.5 metres (2 σ) vertically [U.S. DoD/DoT, 1984].
• For SA test data designed to implement an SA level of 500 m rather than the revised 100 m , the distribution of range errors had a dispersion of 975 ns (2σ), and the distribution of range rate errors had a dispersion of 0.86 ns/s (2σ) [Kalafus et al., 1983; RTCM, 1985]. This test data consisted of 90-second samples of data from four satellites, taken every hour for one week (672 samples). While it may be appropriate to divide the range dispersion by 5, since accurate real-time velocity may in fact be of more concern to U.S. military security than accurate real-time position, it may not be appropriate to assume the range rate dispersion will be reduced from its value for this test data.

Two options for what we can assume about how SA will be implemented are:
• We can assume SA will affect both C/A-code receivers and P-code receivers. In this case, the SA must follow some algorithm that P-code receivers can overcome by using some special device or information.
• We can assume that SA will affect only C/A-code receivers, and thus be implemented by adding some kind of 'dither' to one or more parts of the C/A-code on L1

$$A_c \, C(t) \, D(t) \, \sin (2\pi f_1 t + \phi_c) \ .$$

This figure shows where three kinds of dither might be inserted:
• 1 - The message data $D^*(t)$ transmitted together with the C/A-code is changed (dithered) relative to the 'true' message data $D(t)$ transmitted together with the P-code. However, the message data is changed only once per hour. Hence any implementation of SA this way would have to be represented by 'constant' errors in some of the message parameters over that hour.
• 2 - The clocking of the combined data and code on the SPS signal $C(t^*) \, D(t^*)$ is dithered in time relative to the 'true' clocking for the $C(t) \, D(t)$ combined data and code. However, the P-code and C/A-code transitions are supposed to be simultaneous within 10 ns. This would place a limit on SA well below 100 m .
• 3 - The phase noise ϕ_c^* on the SPS carrier is increased. However, the phase noise (and quadrature) of the P-code and C/A-code carriers is supposed to be less than 5 degrees of phase. This is an infinitesimal size compared to the phase noise which would be required to implement 100 m SA.

Conclusion? Anything we say about SA at present is speculation.

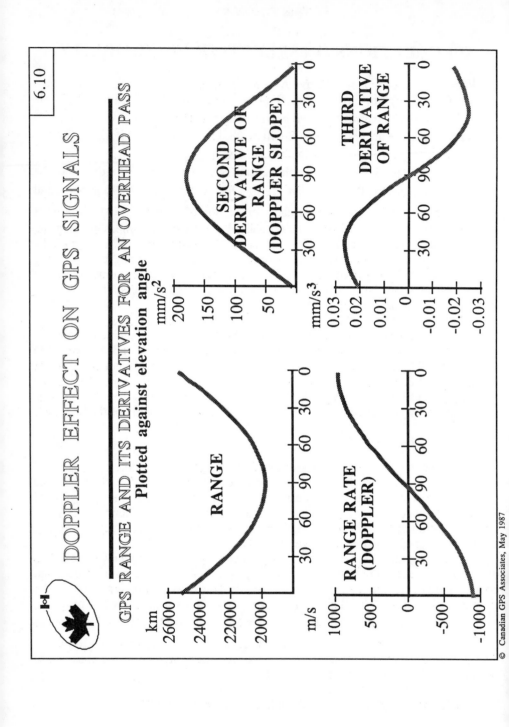

DOPPLER EFFECT ON GPS SIGNALS

GPS RANGE AND ITS DERIVATIVES FOR AN OVERHEAD PASS
Plotted against elevation angle

RANGE

RANGE RATE
(DOPPLER)

SECOND
DERIVATIVE OF
RANGE
(DOPPLER SLOPE)

THIRD
DERIVATIVE
OF RANGE

6.10

DOPPLER EFFECT ON GPS SIGNALS

In this figure. we show the GPS range plotted against elevation angle for a typical overhead pass. We also show the curves of the first three derivatives of this range, also plotted against elevation angle. The typical overhead pass shown here would take about five hours between rise and set. These curves represent only the changing geometry due to satellite motion. Clock drift, propagation effects, and receiver motion contribute to similar curves based on actual data [Clynch and Coco, 1986]. The characteristics of these curves are as follows.

• **Range.** The maximum range to a satellite occurs just as it rises or sets, and is, for GPS satellites, about 25 000 km. The minimum range accurs at closest approach, and is about 20 000 km.

• **Range rate.** If we multiply the range rate by -f/c we obtain the Doppler frequency shift curve. The maximum Doppler shift on the GPS L1 signal is about 5 kHz, half that for the Transit system.

• **Second derivative of range.** This is also the negative of the Doppler curve slope. The maximum value is 175 mm / s^2, or less than 1 Hz/s.

• **Third derivative of range.** The maximum value is 0.025 mm/s^3, or less than 2×10^{-4} Hz/s^2.

The main point here is the demonstration that the change in GPS range is exceptionally smooth. The basic reason for this is the extreme distance (3 to 4 earth radii) to the GPS satellites. Clock and propagation effects do not normally destroy this smoothness, with some exceptions, such as sudden ionospheric disturbances. Highly dynamic receiver motion can destroy this smoothness: here we consider only a stationary receiver. This smoothness is important for several reasons.

• **Receiver tracking bandwidth.** The precision of GPS measurements improves the narrower the receiver tracking bandwidth can be made. However, it must be wide enough to follow variations in the signal. The second and third derivatives indicate that bandwidth characteristics of less than 1 Hz/s and 2×10^{-4} Hz/s^2 are still capable of tracking the signal.

• **Fast switching carrier phase cycle count.** Fast switching GPS receivers are now available (for example, the WM101) which maintain continuous carrier phase cycle counts by predicting the range to better than 10 cm (half an L1 wavelength), based only on data from previous dwell periods on that satellite which are several seconds old. This is possible only because of the smoothness shown in these plots.

• **Preprocessing.** For high precision GPS applications, the smooth signal permits careful preprocessing to detect cycle slips, and to form 'normal point' data averages. For example, Clynch and Coco [1986] show that quadratic, cubic, or quartic algebraic polynomials very accurately represent the shape of the GPS range and range rate curves. Such polynomials can be fitted to actual tracked data, without any reference to orbital information.

CHAPTER SEVEN

ANTENNAS AND RECEIVERS

ANTENNAS

- Basic concepts
- Types
- Characteristics
- Trends

RECEIVERS

- Basic concepts
- Code and code-free channels
- Continuous, sequencing, and multiplexing receivers
- Single vs. dual frequency receivers
- Frequency standards and clocks
- Available receiver types
- Receiver cost trends

ANTENNAS AND RECEIVERS

In this chapter, we will look at the operation of GPS receivers and their antennas. The basic concepts of how antennas work is followed by a discussion of antenna types and their characteristics. The anticipated trends in antenna development for future GPS equipment is then outlined.

A basic understanding of how GPS receivers work is necessary in order to gauge the accuracies of the different types of observations and to assess the capabilities of the different receivers on the market. We describe code-tracking and code-free receiver channels and how a receiver made up of these channels handles signals arriving at the antenna from a number of satellites simultaneously.

An important component both in a receiver and in a GPS satellite is the oscillator, or frequency standard, from which the various frequencies for signal generation or reception are derived. We briefly describe the operation of crystal and atomic oscillators, their stabilities, and how their outputs are used to mechanize a clock.

We conclude this chapter with a classification of some of the receivers currently available and look at the trend in their cost.

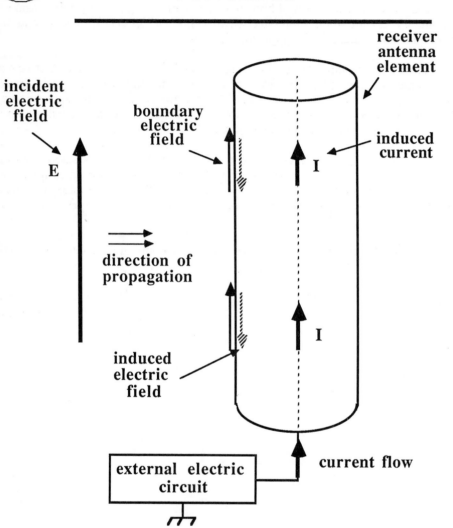

receiver antenna element

incident electric field

E

boundary electric field

induced current

I

direction of propagation

induced electric field

I

external electric circuit

current flow

BASIC ANTENNA CONCEPTS

A simple receiving antenna is a device used to convert the energy in a time-varying electromagnetic wave into electric current. This electric current is normally connected to some external electronic circuit, such as a radio receiver.

The incident electromagnetic wave is characterized by its *amplitude* (how strong the signal is), its *frequency* (time dependence), its *phase* (referenced to how far the wave has travelled from its source), and its *polarization* (orientation in space). When the wave is incident on the surface of an electrical conductor, a current is induced to flow in the conductor which then sets up its own electromagnetic field. The *boundary condition* (a statement of physical laws which describes the interaction between electromagnetic energy and electrically conducting materials) requires that the total tangential electric field (incident field plus induced field) on the surface of an ideal electrical conductor must be zero. The induced field is caused by the induced current, hence there is a direct relationship between the incident electric field and the induced current. If the receiving antenna is connected to a circuit, this induced current will flow through it. Since the current is directly responsive to the incident electromagnetic field, any information contained in the field will also be present in the induced current, hence coded (modulated) information can be extracted from the current in the receiver.

The relationship between the induced current and the incident field is a complex function of frequency, amplitude, and phase distribution of the incident wave, as well as the shape, size, and orientation of the antenna element.

GPS ANTENNA TYPES

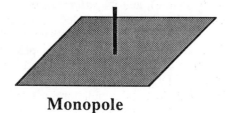

Monopole   Quadrifilar helix

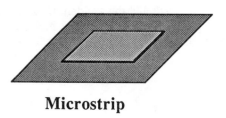

Microstrip

Spiral helices

GPS ANTENNA TYPES

Several different types of antennas are presently available in GPS systems. These may be generally categorized as:

(a)   monopole or dipole configurations
(b)   quadrifilar helices or volutes
(c)   microstrip
(d)   tapered or spiral helices.

All GPS system antennas are required to be circularly polarized. In most cases, the receiver preamplifier is built as an integral part of the antenna baseplate in an attempt to minimize signal loss and noise introduction.

The monopole/dipole configurations usually require a groundplane for proper operation. They are single frequency antennas and have the advantage of small element size and simplicity of construction. The groundplane size can be used as a design parameter to reduce multipath interference.

The quadrifilar or volute antennas are single frequency devices which are more complicated in construction than the dipoles, are difficult to adjust (at time of manufacture) for proper element phasing and polarization, and are not azimuthally symmetric. They do, however, have good gain and pattern coverage characteristics. They do not require a groundplane, although one may be used for rear lobe control. Some designs incorporate a small pad of electrically lossy material for a baseplate so as to reduce the rear lobe radiation.

Microstrip antennas are the most rugged and simple in construction. They may be either single or dual frequency antennas with a very low profile which makes them ideal for airborne applications. The main disadvantage of this class of antennas is the relatively low gain, although this can be largely offset by low noise preamplifiers.

Spiral helices offer the advantage of dual frequency operation at both L1 and L2. The antenna has good gain and pattern coverage characteristics, although its high profile puts it at some disadvantage with respect to its phase characteristics. Like the volute design, the tapered helices exhibit some azimuthal asymmetry which is partially offset by careful ground orientation.

REDUCED LOW-ANGLE RESPONSE TO AVOID MULTIPATH

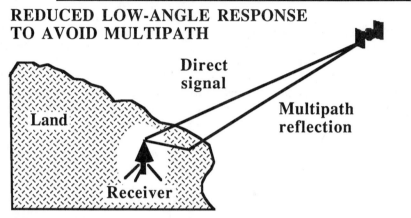

Direct signal

Multipath reflection

Land

Receiver

MODIFIED LOW-ANGLE RESPONSE FOR DYNAMIC APPLICATIONS

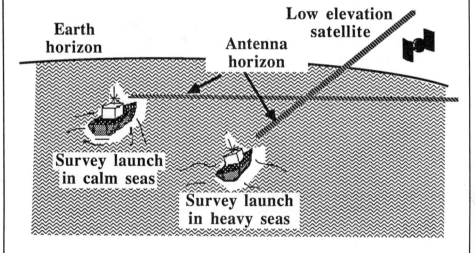

Low elevation satellite

Earth horizon

Antenna horizon

Survey launch in calm seas

Survey launch in heavy seas

ANTENNA GAIN PATTERN REQUIREMENTS

The GPS antenna gain characteristics must match the application requirements. Generally, we require full upper hemispherical coverage with no zenith null. The necessary low elevation angle coverage is determined by the application. For example, a static ground site may require a pattern null at low elevation in order to discriminate against ground reflection multipath. In another application, such as a hydrographic survey launch, we may require some low-angle response in order for a low satellite not to fall below the antenna horizon. This may require careful beam shaping in order to effectively trade off multipath interference and loss-of-track. The antenna design variables for beam shaping include the antenna type and groundplane size and shaping.

LET'S DEFINE PHASE CENTRE

TANGENT SPHERE METHOD

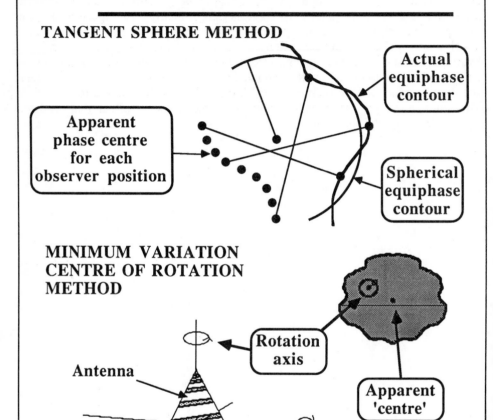

Actual equiphase contour

Apparent phase centre for each observer position

Spherical equiphase contour

MINIMUM VARIATION CENTRE OF ROTATION METHOD

Rotation axis

Antenna

Apparent 'centre'

LET'S DEFINE PHASE CENTRE

In addition to the antenna gain requirements, there are important antenna phase response requirements which directly determine the phase centre of the antenna. The *phase centre* of a transmitting antenna structure is defined as the apparent source of radiation. If the source is an ideal point source, the equiphase contours form spherical shells centred at the point source. The centre can be readily determined from an examination of the phase contour by the so-called tangent sphere technique, that is, locating the centre of curvature of the phase contour. All finite-size radiating sources generate non-spherical equiphase contours, the 'dimples' and undulations in the contour being responsible for the antenna beam shaping characteristics. In this case, each arc segment of the equiphase contour has its apparent centre of curvature. The phase centre of the antenna is thus not constant but is dependent upon the observation angle, i.e., it is angle dependent. Obviously the phase centre movement will be most pronounced in the vinicity of 'dimples' or cusps in the equiphase contour or pattern nulls.

An approximate experimental technique for locating the phase centre involves recording the pattern phase as the antenna is rotated about an axis. A search is made to locate an axis for which the phase variations are minimized in some sense. This technique actually produces a 'weighted average' position for the centre of phase variation and is accurate only if the equiphase contour is nearly spherical over the angular region of interest.

TRENDS IN GPS ANTENNA DEVELOPMENT

ACCURATE MEASUREMENT OF CURRENT ANTENNAS

INCREASED ANTENNA FLEXIBILITY

RECEIVER SOFTWARE TO INCLUDE PHASE CENTRE

NEW ANTENNA DESIGNS FOR PHASE CENTRE STABILITY

IMPROVED ANTENNA MANUFACTURING TECHNIQUES

TRENDS IN GPS ANTENNA DEVELOPMENT

We may anticipate that next generation GPS equipment will begin to incorporate recent advances in antenna technology in order to more fully exploit the accuracy of GPS. These trends in GPS antenna development include:

- **Accurate measurement of presently used antennas.** Some of the present antenna designs are particularly unsuited to GPS application, while others have proven well suited. It is important that these antennas be accurately and correctly calibrated in order to assure suitable performance.

- **Increased antenna flexibility.** Some antenna designs, while well suited to some applications, are poorly suited to others. It would be advantageous to have a variety of interchangeable antennas in order to meet specific application requirements.

- **Receiver software to include phase centre.** It would prove relatively easy to include antenna phase centre calibration data within the receiver data processing software, however, extensive data files, if necessary, would require considerable electronic memory.

- **New antenna design.** Antennas are required which are designed with GPS standard phase stability specifications in mind. Such antenna design must also incorporate amplitude pattern control for minimization of multipath interference.

- **Improved manufacturing.** Mechanical tolerances required for millimetre level phase centre stability are more stringent than those in effect for communication antenna fabrication. For this reason, manufacturing techniques must be used which can assure precision and unit-to-unit repeatability.

COMMUNICATION CHANNEL CONCEPTS

7.06

Output

Signal channels

1   2   3   • • •   n

Receiver

Front-end

Transmission medium (waveform channel)

Satellite transmitters (waveform channel)

1   2   • • •   s

© Canadian GPS Associates, April 1986

COMMUNICATION CHANNEL CONCEPTS

The omni-directional antenna of a GPS receiver simultaneously intercepts signals from all satellites above the antenna's horizon. If s satellites are above the horizon, then s components of electrical current will be generated in a single-frequency antenna or 2s components in a dual-frequency antenna. The receiver must be able to isolate the signals from each particular satellite in order to measure the code pseudo-range or carrier phase. The isolation is achieved through the use of a number of separate signal *channels* in the receiver, each dedicated to a particular satellite and frequency at a particular time. These channels may be implemented either in hardware or software or a combination of the two. The signals from different satellites may be discriminated by the unique C/A-code or portion of the P-code they transmit or by the Doppler shift of the received codes or carrier.

The term *channel* may also be applied to the transmission medium (the space between the satellite and the antenna) or the complete circuit comprising the satellite transmitter, transmission medium, and the path through the receiver that a particular signal follows.

From the point of view of the broadcast message, GPS is a *spread-spectrum* communications system [Ziemer and Peterson, 1985; Jordan, 1985]. A spread-spectrum system is one that takes a signal of small bandwidth γW, where $\gamma \ll 1$, and converts it (spreads it) into a signal of large bandwidth, W, by modulating the information waveform with a wideband waveform, such as pseudo-random noise. For GPS, the message bandwidth (null-to-null in power spectrum) is 100 Hz, and the P-code bandwidth, W, is about 20 MHz, hence, γ is 5×10^{-6} or, for the C/A-code, W is about 2 MHz and γ is 5×10^{-5}. The wideband signal is transmitted through the channel, received, and then compressed back (despread) into the original small bandwidth signal by demodulating the signal with the identical wideband waveform. Spread spectrum systems have the advantage of being secure since the receiver must have access to the wideband waveform used at the transmitter. They also possess some immunity from jamming and, of course, are capable of high resolution ranging.

The signals transmitted by the satellites are detected and decoded by the hardware and software channels in a GPS receiver. These channels can be mechanised in different forms depending on the measurement type being sought and whether a message-decoding capability is required.

RECEIVER RF COMPONENTS

 Lowpass filter
- removes unwanted high frequencies

 Bandpass filter
- passes a selected band of frequencies

 Frequency multiplier
- used to obtain a higher frequency harmonically related to oscillator frequency

 **Mixer**
- multiplies two signals together to generate additional signals with frequencies equal to the sum and difference of the original frequencies

RECEIVER RF COMPONENTS

In order that a reader with a limited background in the workings of radio receivers may understand how the different types of GPS receiver channels work, we will briefly describe the operation of some common radio frequency (RF) components.

Signal processing in a microwave radio receiver is generally more easily handled if the band of signals arriving at the antenna are translated to a common lower frequency band. This translation is achieved by combining the incoming signals centred on a frequency of f_c with a pure harmonic signal of frequency f_o from an oscillator in a device known as a *mixer*. The mixer functions as a mathematical multiplier of the two input signals. The output of an ideal mixer is a superposition of two bands of signals: one centred on a frequency of $f_c + f_o$ and one centred on $f_c - f_o$, called the up-conversion and down-conversion components, respectively. A *bandpass filter* is used to select the down-conversion component. All frequencies outside of the band centred on $f_c - f_o$ are rejected. The central frequency, $f_c - f_o$, is known as an *intermediate frequency* (IF) or *beat frequency*. A GPS receiver in general will have a series of IF stages. In order to pass the P-code pseudo-random noise modulation, the bandwidth of a filter near the front end of a GPS receiver must be about 20 MHz. Once the code modulation has been removed by despreading, and as long as the Doppler shift of the received signals has been annulled by phase tracking the received carrier, the width of a filter in a GPS receiver can be of the order of the bandwidth of the message (about 100 Hz). Initial signal acquisition may require a bandwidth of several kiloHertz.

If the signal of interest is a slowly varying direct current (DC) signal or is composed of a band of frequencies centred on DC, then a *lowpass filter* may be used to remove all higher frequencies, such as those of extraneous noise received by the antenna or generated within the receiver.

Frequency oscillators generate signals at a precise single frequency or, for a voltage-controlled oscillator, over a narrow range of frequencies. To obtain other frequencies that are harmonically-related to the oscillator frequency, a *frequency multiplier* (or divider) is used. The output of a frequency multiplier is a signal with a frequency which is an integer multiple of the input frequency. Similarly, a frequency divider yields the input frequency divided by an integer. By combining multipliers and dividers, a range of frequencies may be synthesized from a single input frequency.

CORRELATION CHANNEL

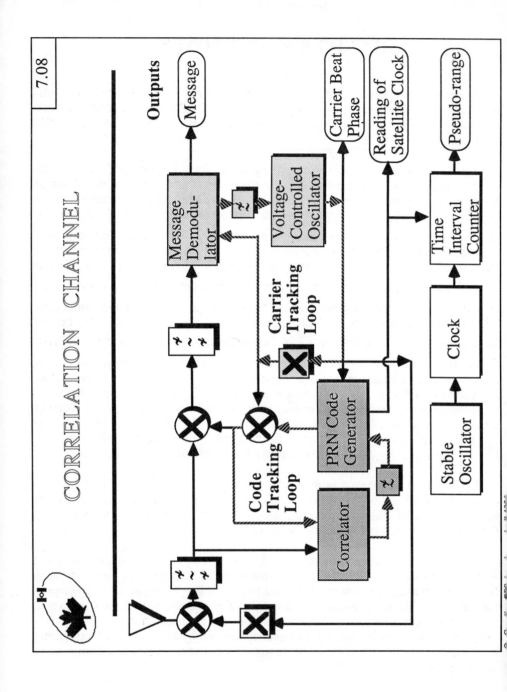

Outputs

Message

Carrier Beat Phase

Reading of Satellite Clock

Pseudo-range

Message Demodu-lator

Voltage-Controlled Oscillator

Carrier Tracking Loop

PRN Code Generator

Code Tracking Loop

Correlator

Stable Oscillator

Clock

Time Interval Counter

CORRELATION CHANNEL

Most of the receivers that have been developed are code-correlating receivers which are composed of one or more *correlation channels*. It is the only type of receiver that can decode the message. This block diagram of a correlation channel is intended to portray the concepts involved, and the detailed design of the channel will vary from receiver to receiver. Links to the receiver's microprocessor are not shown.

A correlation receiver consists of two major blocks: a *code tracking loop* and a *carrier tracking loop*. The purpose of the code tracking loop is to provide a measurement of the pseudo-range either from the P- or C/A-code and at the same time to 'despread' the signal so that the message may be subsequently retrieved. In the loop, a code generator replicates the code that is imposed on the signal at the satellite. The start of the code is offset in time to account for the propagation delay between the satellite and the receiver. The correct delay is achieved by cross-correlating the received signal with the receiver-generated code. If the two codes are not aligned, a correction signal is applied to the clock controlling the receiver code generator until a match is obtained. Once the receiver code is aligned with the incoming code, it stays locked to it. This type of tracking loop is called a *delay lock loop*. There are various ways of implementing a delay lock loop such as the 'full-time' and the 'tau-dither' early-late tracking loops [Ziemer and Peterson, 1985]. When the tracking loop is locked, a reading of the delayed code clock is essentially a reading of the satellite clock. The offset of the code clock from the receiver clock, which is assumed to be keeping GPS time, is the pseudo-range. Once the code tracking loop is locked, the PRN code can be removed from the satellite signal simply by mixing it with the locally generated one and bandpass filtering the resultant signal.

The despread signal then passes to the carrier tracking loop which demodulates the satellite message by aligning the phase of the channel's local oscillator frequency with the phase of the intermediate or beat frequency. This action is achieved by controlling the frequency of a voltage-controlled oscillator. If the phase of the oscillator signal is not correct, this is detected in the demodulator and a correction signal is then applied to the oscillator. Once the oscillator is locked to the satellite signal it will continue to follow the variations in the phase of the carrier as the range to the satellite changes. The carrier beat phase observable is obtained in principle simply by counting the elapsed cycles and by measuring the fractional phase of the locked local oscillator signal. Most implementations of carrier tracking use the Costas loop method [Ziemer and Peterson, 1985]. Some use the squaring method. All carrier tracking loops suffer from a 180° phase ambiguity which must be resolved using the message structure. Temporarily-incorrect choices of phase can lead to so-called 'half cycle slips'.

The message bits are decoded using bit synchronization and a data detection filter.

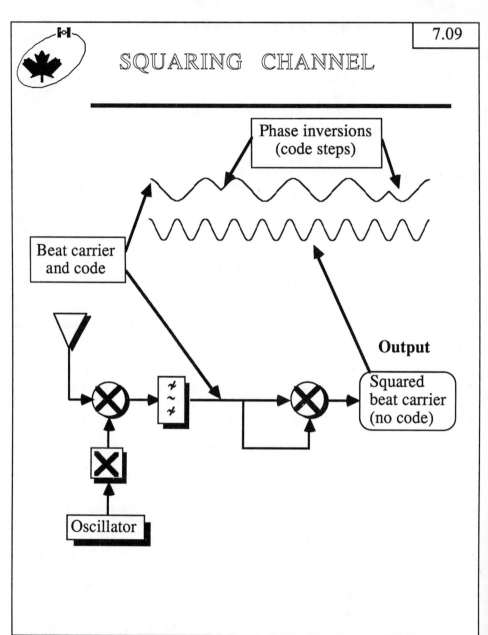

SQUARING CHANNEL

Phase inversions
(code steps)

Beat carrier
and code

Output

Squared
beat carrier
(no code)

Oscillator

SQUARING CHANNEL

When the Global Positioning System was being designed, it was not widely realised that the satellite signals could be used without explicit knowledge of either the P- or C/A-codes. Prof. Charles Counselman, at the Massachusetts Institute of Technology, and Peter MacDoran, then at the Jet Propulsion Laboratory, independently developed code-free receiver designs. Both designs evolved into commercial products. In this section, we discuss the squaring channel used in Counselman's Macrometer receiver; in the next section, we discuss the code phase channel used in MacDoran's ISTAC receiver.

A squaring channel provides only the carrier phase observable. Neither pseudo-range measurements nor the satellite message is available. In principle, the operation of a squaring channel is very simple. In common with other GPS receivers, the incoming signal is first translated to an IF signal. The carrier, or rather the beat frequency carrier, is obtained simply by squaring this signal. Any phase inversions in the IF signal due to the codes or message are thereby removed. This happens because a phase inversion can be considered as a change in the amplitude of the IF signal from +1 to -1 or from -1 to +1 and the instantaneous amplitude is therefore either plus or minus one. Squaring the signal results in a signal with a constant amplitude of unity, although with a frequency equal to twice the original. However, the phase of this signal is easily related to the phase of the original carrier. Of course, in the squaring process both the codes and the message are lost.

In practice, a channel in a squaring receiver would be more complex than that described here. Of particular concern, perhaps even more so than in a code-correlating receiver, are the noise levels on the signals, since squaring the signals also squares the noise. This results in a signal-to-noise ratio loss which must be made as small as possible.

Squaring can also be used in the carrier tracking loop of a code-correlating receiver to recover the beat carrier which is subsequently used to demodulate the message.

CODE PHASE CHANNEL

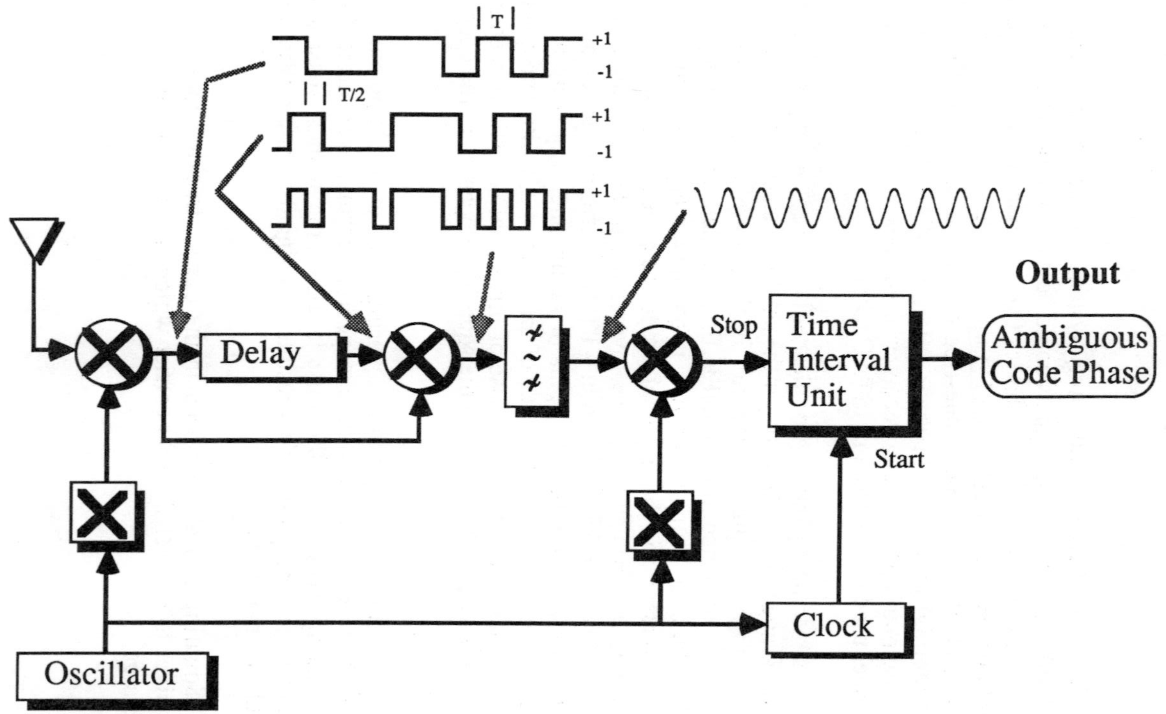

7.10

Output
Ambiguous Code Phase

Time Interval Unit
Start
Stop

Clock

Delay

Oscillator

© Canadian GPS Associates, April 1986

CODE PHASE CHANNEL

A second type of channel that can be used to mechanise a code-free receiver is a code phase channel. This type of channel is used in the JPL SERIES and in the ISTAC receivers. Like the squaring channel, the code phase channel does not require explicit knowledge of the code, only its chipping rate. Whereas the squaring channel provides access to the carrier (actually the squared beat frequency), the code phase channel, as its name suggests, provides a measurement of the ambiguous phase of either the C/A-code or the P-code.

The code phase channel uses the autocorrelation or cross-spectrum technique used to provide symbol or bit synchronization in digital communications systems [Ziemer and Peterson, 1985]. The received GPS signal (either the L1 or L2 channel) after being mixed to a lower, more manageable frequency, is multiplied by a delayed version of itself. The delay is equal to one-half the chipping period; 487 nsec for the C/A-code, 49 nsec for the P-code. When the resulting cross-spectrum signal is bandpass filtered, the code modulation rate (1.023 or 10.23 MHz) is recovered. The positive-going zero crossings of this sine wave (or a coherently related lower frequency) are used to stop a time interval counter started by a 1 pulse per second signal from the receiver clock. The measured time interval is the range between the satellite and the receiver's antenna; modulo 978 nsec (293 m) if using the C/A-code, or 97.8 nsec (29.3 m) if using the P-code with an unknown possible bias between the satellite and receiver clocks.

The ambiguity of the time delay measurements must be resolved before they can be utilized to determine the precise coordinates of the receiver's antenna. One technique that has been adopted to resolve the ambiguity uses the unambiguous Doppler shift of the received code frequency [Buennagel et al., 1984]. The frequency of the code can be measured using, say, a Fast Fourier Transform technique, from which the position of the receiver car be established to about 100 m. The C/A-code ambiguity can then be resolved. The P-code ambiguity can subsequently be resolved by interpolating within the C/A-code modulation.

CODE CORRELATION VS. SQUARING

CODE CORRELATION

SQUARING

ADVANTAGES

CODE CORRELATION

* Access to broadcast message
* Both code and phase measurements possible
* S/N advantage
* Single frequency C/A-code receiver least expensive

SQUARING

* Code-free
* Less sensitive to multipath
* Access to encrypted L2 signal

DISADVANTAGES

* Need P-code for ionospheric correction

* Receiver clocks must be externally synchronized
* No access to broadcast message; needs external almanac
* Cycle slips at twice the carrier frequency

CODE CORRELATION VS. SQUARING

There are advantages and disadvantages to both code correlation and squaring receivers. For the purposes of this discussion we will lump receivers measuring code phase together with the squaring receivers as they share a number of common features. Specific differences will be pointed out where necessary.

Only code correlation receivers have access to the satellite message. As we have seen, either the P- or the C/A-code is required to despread the arriving signal without destroying the message. A direct consequence of this fact is that squaring receivers need an external satellite almanac in order to operate and need externally-provided orbital data for signal processing. This makes accurate real-time positioning with squaring receivers difficult. Either a communication link must be established to provide the required data in real-time or if only low accuracy positions are required, say for navigation purposes, an extrapolated orbit provided. For such kinematic positioning, cycle ambiguities must be resolved in real or near-real time. In a code phase receiver, this is accomplished using the measured Doppler shifts. In a pure squaring receiver, the ambiguities can only be resolved by starting from a known point and collecting sufficient data before moving off. However, if the receiver subsequently loses lock of the satellite signals, the ambiguity cannot, in general, be recovered.

Squaring receivers must be synchronized with each other and UTC (or GPS time) before observations begin. Code-correlation receivers can synchronize themselves with GPS time at a point with unknown coordinates after acquiring four satellite signals.

Code-correlation receivers may enjoy a signal-to-noise advantage because of the inherent insensitivity of spread-spectrum signals to noise in a decoding receiver.

Code-correlation receivers are capable of both pseudo-range and carrier phase measurements, however, not all such receivers provide the carrier phase data at an accessible output. With the exception of the TI 4100, all current non-military code correlation receivers work exclusively with the C/A-code which is only available on the L1 frequency. Without the use of the P-code (or its successor, the Y-code) dual-frequency ionospheric delay correction of either the pseudo-range or carrier phase data is impossible. The ionospheric delay must then be either modelled, which cannot be done very successfully, or ignored. Squaring receivers can access both the L1 and L2 frequencies without knowledge of the codes and are therefore capable of very accurate relative positions on long baselines. With the announced intention of the DoD to deny access to the Y-code to most civilians, geodetic accuracy from GPS in the future may only be possible with squaring receivers or hybrid receivers with C/A-code correlation channels on L1 and squaring channels on L2.

Cycle slips in pure squaring receivers may sometimes be harder to repair as they are always at twice the carrier frequency. By the same token, such receivers should be less sensitive to multipath.

The single-frequency C/A-code receivers are presently the cheapest GPS receivers on the market

CONTINUOUS VS. SWITCHING RECEIVERS

CONTINUOUS

- Four or more dedicated hardware channels
- Each channel tracks a single satellite signal
- Inter-channel biases must be calibrated
- May enjoy a signal-to-noise advantage
- Redundancy capability

SWITCHING

- One or more hardware switching channels
- Each channel samples more than one signal
- Software more complex
- Potentially more difficult to keep track of phase
- In principle, cheaper than continuous receiver

HYBRID

- Mixture of continuous and switching channels

CONTINUOUS VS. SWITCHING RECEIVERS

A GPS receiver may be described as continuous or switching depending on the type of channel(s) it has.

A *continuous-tracking receiver* has four or more dedicated hardware channels. Each channel tracks a single satellite and maintains continuous code and/or phase lock on the signal. Each channel is controlled and sampled by the receiver's microprocessor with input/output operations being performed fast enough so that tracking is not disturbed. Continuous-tracking receivers may enjoy a signal-to-noise advantage over switching receivers in that the satellite signal is continuously available and may be more frequently sampled. A further advantage is a potential redundancy capability. Should one of the hardware channels fail, it may still be possible to obtain sufficient data to determine a position. One disadvantage of a multichannel receiver is that the differences in signal path delay in the channels, the so-called inter-channel biases, must be well calibrated.

A *switching receiver* has one or more hardware channels. Each channel samples more than one satellite signal. Code and/or carrier tracking for the individual signals is performed in software (or, more usually, firmware) by the microprocessor. As a result, greater demands are placed on the microprocessor in a switching receiver and its programming is necessarily more complex; hardware complexity is exchanged for software complexity. The term pseudo-channel is sometimes used to identify software tracking channels. Depending on the application and the environment, a switching receiver may be more susceptible to cycle slips than a continuous-tracking receiver. If the cost of hardware components is a significant factor in determining the selling price of a receiver, then in principle, the cost of a switching receiver should be cheaper than a continuous receiver.

It is possible to combine continuous and switching channels in the same receiver. Such a receiver is termed a *hybrid*.

MULTIPLEXING AND SEQUENCING CHANNELS

MULTIPLEXING CHANNEL

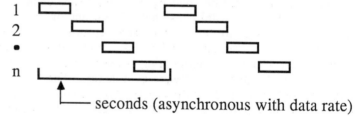

signals 1 2 • n

└── 1 bit period (20 milliseconds)

FAST SEQUENCING CHANNEL

signals 1 2 • n

└── seconds (asynchronous with data rate)

SLOW SEQUENCING CHANNEL

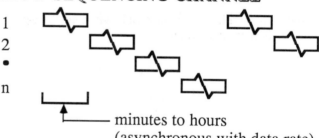

signals 1 2 • n

└── minutes to hours
(asynchronous with data rate)

MULTIPLEXING AND SEQUENCING CHANNELS

A switching receiver is composed of one or more channels each of which is capable of tracking a number of satellite signals by sampling the signals in sequence. There are three basic kinds of switching receivers. They are distinguished by the time required to sequence through the signals assigned to a particular channel.

A *multiplexing channel* is one for which the sequencing time to sample all satellites assigned to the channel is equal to 20 milliseconds, the period of one bit in the satellite message. The sampling can be arranged so that no message bit boundary is spanned by any tracking interval. In this way, the messages from all satellites phase tracked by the channel can be read simultaneously. A multiplexing channel can be used to obtain both L1 and L2 data by alternating between the frequencies every 20 ms. The TI 4100 has a single multiplexing hardware channel that is used to sample both L1 and L2 signals from up to four satellites.

If a channel switches between signals at a rate which is asynchronous with the message bit rate, the channel is referred to as a *sequencing channel*. A *fast* sequencing channel is one which takes the order of seconds to sequence through the signals. A *slow* sequencing channel takes minutes to hours. A single sequencing channel would lose bits in a particular satellite message during those intervals spent sampling the signals from other satellites. Consequently, sequencing receivers may have an extra hardware channel just for data reading. Alternatively, sufficient orbital data must be accumulated before the receiver starts the tracking cycle for real-time positioning. A disadvantage of a sequencing channel used to track both L1 and L2 signals is that since the measurements on the two frequencies are not simultaneous, the ionospheric correction may be degraded.

SINGLE VS. DUAL FREQUENCY

SINGLE FREQUENCY (L1 ONLY)

DUAL FREQUENCY (L1 and L2)

ADVANTAGES

SINGLE FREQUENCY (L1 ONLY)

* Cheaper

DUAL FREQUENCY (L1 and L2)

* Almost all of ionospheric effect removed by combining L1 and L2 observations

DISADVANTAGES

SINGLE FREQUENCY

* Results corrupted by ionospheric delay

* Results may be acceptable on short baselines

DUAL FREQUENCY

* More expensive

* Code correlating receivers must use P-code—may be denied

© Canadian GPS Associates, April 1986

SINGLE VS. DUAL FREQUENCY

Single frequency receivers access only the L1 frequency; *dual frequency* receivers access both L1 and L2. Most civilian receivers are single frequency receivers. Both code correlating and squaring single frequency receivers have been developed; the code correlating receivers generally use the C/A-code only. Single frequency receivers are much cheaper than dual frequency receivers, requiring fewer RF components and having a lighter demand on the controlling microprocessor.

Most military receivers have dual frequency capability. At the present time, only one civilian code correlating receiver is commercially available (the TI 4100). The Macrometer II is a dual frequency code-free receiver. Due to the DoD's policy of selective availability, dual frequency capability in civilian code correlating receivers may not be possible once the Y-code is introduced.

The disadvantage of single frequency receivers is that resulting positions are corrupted by ionospheric delay. However, since the delay will be correlated over short baselines, *relative* positions may be sufficiently accurate even for geodetic purposes.

FREQUENCY STANDARDS AND CLOCKS

QUARTZ CRYSTAL
- frequency generated by vibrating crystal with applied electric field (piezoelectric effect)
- inexpensive, compact, and robust

RUBIDIUM VAPOUR CELL
- based on 6.834 682 605 GHz resonance frequency of a hyperfine energy transition of rubidium 87 atoms
- least expensive of the atomic clocks, ~$5,000

CESIUM BEAM TUBE
- based on 9.192 631 770 GHz resonance frequency of a hyperfine energy transition of cesium 133 atoms
- resonance frequency used for the definition of the SI (atomic) second
- most accurate (frequency most precisely set) of the atomic clocks

HYDROGEN MASER
- based on 1.420 405 757 68 GHz resonance frequency of a hyperfine energy transition of atomic hydrogen
- most stable of the atomic clocks

FREQUENCY STANDARDS AND CLOCKS

The high accuracy positioning capability of GPS is due in part to the use of high precision atomic oscillators to control the generation of the carrier frequencies and codes within the spacecraft. Such high precision oscillators are often termed **frequency standards**. Precision oscillators are also required in GPS receivers. The oscillator frequency is multiplied and divided as necessary to provide the required local oscillator frequencies, and the cycles of the oscillator frequency are counted to mechanise a clock.

There are four types of precision oscillators commercially available. The most common is the oven-controlled quartz crystal. The source of oscillation is a quartz disc which is stimulated by an electric field. The other three types are atomic oscillators: the rubidium vapour cell, the cesium beam tube, and the hydrogen maser. Each is based on the transition of energy levels within the particular atom. The transition produces a microwave signal with a very precise and highly stable frequency which is used to control the frequency of a quartz oscillator by means of a feedback mechanism.

Each Block II GPS satellite contains four atomic frequency standards: two rubidiums and two cesiums. Any one of these oscillators can be commanded by the GPS control system to be the spacecraft primary oscillator.

STABILITY OF FREQUENCY STANDARDS

7.16

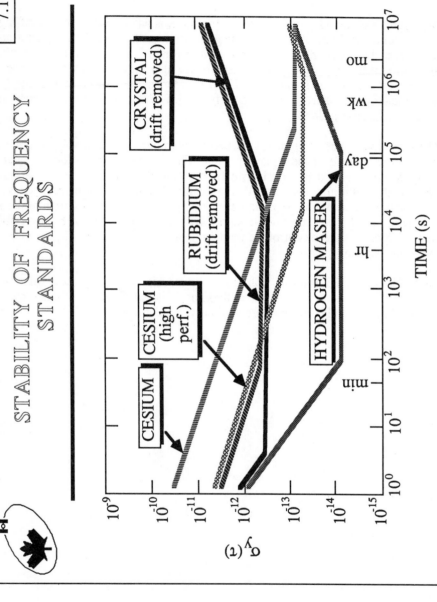

STABILITY OF FREQUENCY STANDARDS

An important parameter of an oscillator is its stability. To see how the stability of a frequency standard is characterized, consider an oscillator with instantaneous output voltage

$$v(t) = [v_o + \epsilon(t)] \sin[2\pi v_o t + \phi(t)]$$

where v_o is the amplitude with small fluctuations $\epsilon(t)$ with $|\epsilon(t)/v_o| \ll 1$, and where v_o is the frequency with phase fluctuations (noise) $\phi(t)$ with $|(d\phi / dt) / 2\pi v_o| \ll 1$. The instantaneous phase is given by

$$\Phi(t) = 2\pi v_o t + \phi(t)$$

and the corresponding instantaneous frequency by

$$v(t) = (1/2\pi)d\Phi/dt = v_o + (1/2\pi)(d\phi / dt) .$$

The stability of an oscillator can be characterized either in the frequency domain or the time domain.

Frequency domain stability is usually expressed by the one-sided spectral density of frequency fluctuations, $S_y(f)$, or the one-sided spectral density of phase fluctuations, $S_\phi(f)$, where f is the Fourier frequency offset from v_o. The two quantities are related by

$$S_y(f) = (f^2/v_o^2)S_\phi(f) .$$

These spectral densities are invariant when, with ideal equipment, the frequency $v(t)$ is multiplied or divided.

A more intuitive measure of frequency stability may be the time-domain two-sample (Allan) variance of the fractional frequency variations. If we define the fractional average frequency over an interval τ at time t as

$$y(t) = [\phi(t + \tau) - \phi(t)]/2\pi v_o \tau$$

then the Allan variance is given by

$$\sigma_y^2(\tau) = \langle(y(t + \tau) - y(t))^2\rangle/2$$

where the angular brackets denote an infinite time average.

The Allan variances of typical quartz crystal, rubidium vapour cell, cesium beam tube, and hydrogen maser oscillators are shown in this figure [Hellwig, 1979]. The typical drifts of 1 part in 10^{10} and 1 part in 10^{12} per day for the quartz crystal and rubidium oscillators respectively, have been removed.

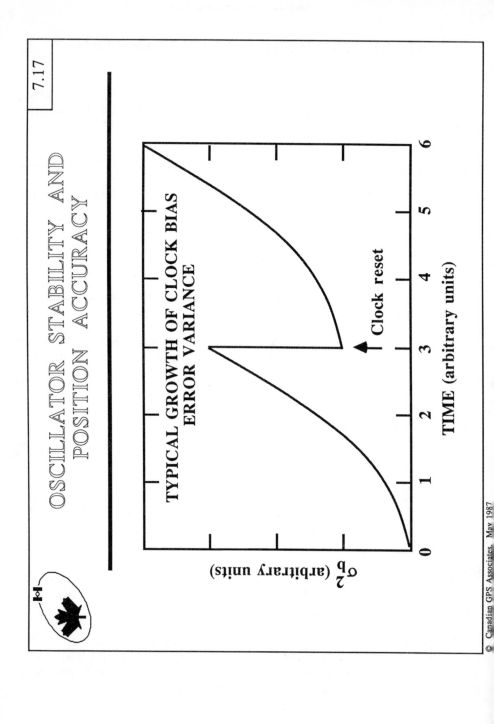

OSCILLATOR STABILITY AND
POSITION ACCURACY

7.17

TYPICAL GROWTH OF CLOCK BIAS
ERROR VARIANCE

Clock reset

TIME (arbitrary units)

σ_b^2 (arbitrary units)

OSCILLATOR STABILITY AND POSITION ACCURACY

Most GPS receivers employ high precision, oven-controlled, quartz crystal oscillators. These oscillators are small, light-weight, consume little power and are relatively inexpensive. They have sufficient short-term stability to add negligible noise to code tracking loops and have a long-term drift that can be measured and corrected using the GPS signals themselves.

For applications in which phase measurements are used to achieve baseline accuracies better than 1 ppm, there may be justification in using an atomic frequency standard to provide the receiver local oscillator signals. Some receivers are equipped with a jack for supplying such an external reference frequency. The ISTAC 2002 receiver has an internal rubidium oscillator as standard equipment.

Most code tracking receivers have the ability to update or reset their internal clocks to GPS time by solving for the clock bias from the pseudo-range measurements. Some receivers may be synchronized by an externally provided clock pulse. Codeless receivers must be synchronized in this fashion.

The clock bias error variance at time t is related to oscillator stability and the clock bias error variance at the time t_o of the last clock update by

$$\sigma_b^2(t) = \sigma_{bo}^2 + (t - t_o)^2 \, \sigma_y^2 (t - t_o) .$$

The value of σ_{bo} depends on the means used to update the receiver clock. If the update was accomplished through acquiring 4 GPS satellites, then

$$\sigma_{bo} = \text{TDOP} \cdot \sigma_p ,$$

where σ_p^2 is the pseudo-range residual error variance. If the update was accomplished by tracking a single satellite from an exactly known location, then

$$\sigma_{bo} = \sigma_p .$$

Good oscillator stability is particularly important in kinematic applications if the receiver clock is not updated at each solution epoch. Such will be the case during outages in the 18-satellite constellation.

A precision oscillator will enable navigation during a brief outage with minimal degradation in position accuracy. An atomic frequency standard, such as a rubidium oscillator, may be advantageous in these situations. A precision oscillator will also extend the useful period of navigation for the prototype GPS constellation.

GPS RECEIVER TYPES

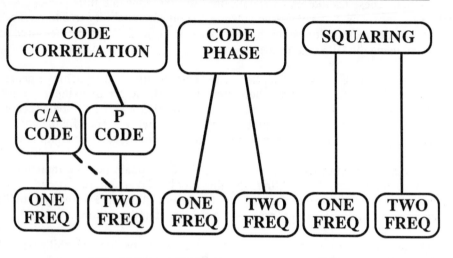

CODE CORRELATION		CODE PHASE		SQUARING	
C/A CODE	P CODE				
ONE FREQ	TWO FREQ	ONE FREQ	TWO FREQ	ONE FREQ	TWO FREQ

Trimble   TI-4100   ISTAC   Macrometer
4000A   Model 2002   V-1000   II
4000S

Magnavox
T-Set
WM-101

   EDO
SatTrak

Norstar
1000

GPS RECEIVER TYPES

Any GPS receiver may be classified as to the type of tracking channels it has (code correlation, squaring, or code phase) and whether it uses the L1 signal only or both L1 and L2. In addition, code correlation receivers may be further classified according to whether or not they use the P-code. We have so-classified some of the civilian GPS receivers commercially available or under development. Further details on these and other receivers may be found in Appendix A.

Most GPS receivers designed for civilian use are single frequency, C/A-code correlating receivers. Of the code correlation receivers presently available, only the TI 4100 has dual frequency capability. In addition, it is the only receiver that uses the P-code. If the P-code is not available, the TI 4100 can be operated with the C/A-code alone. Some manufacturers plan to add second frequency capability to their C/A-code receivers by adding L2 squaring channels.

The only code phase receiver currently available on the market is the ISTAC-SERIES GPS Positioner Model 2002. It operates on the L1 signals only, however, there are plans to extend its capability to two frequencies.

Single and dual-frequency versions of the Macrometer squaring channel receivers are available. The pioneering single channel version is known as the Macrometer V-1000; the dual-frequency model is known as the Macrometer II.

The selection of a specific receiver type or model should be predicated on its intended use. The physical environment, accuracy and reliability required, and the dynamics of the moving platform (if used) are parameters of major importance in the selection process.

GPS RECEIVER COSTS

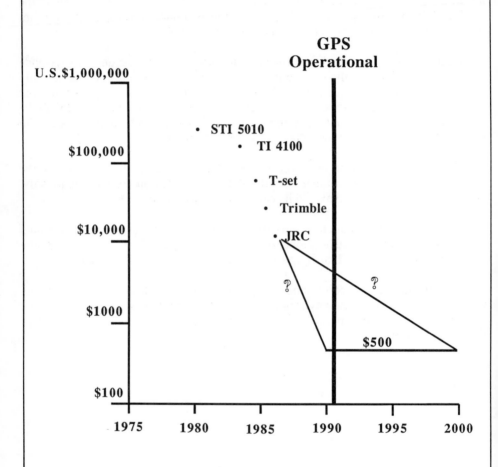

GPS RECEIVER COSTS

Of primary concern to anyone wanting to acquire the capabilities of GPS positioning is the cost of the equipment. As with all high-technology products, the cost of GPS receivers is driven by development cost, competition, and demand. The first commercial receiver on the market was the Stanford Telecommunications STI 5010, introduced around 1980. This receiver sold for several hundred thousand U.S. dollars. Only a few were manufactured. In the six years since 1980, many companies have entered the GPS market. At the present time, no less than 25 different receivers are commercially available. Many others are in the development stage.

This market competition and the perceived demand has resulted in a significant drop in the price of a basic GPS receiver. A number of receivers are now available at $(U.S.)30,000 or less. The downward trend in receiver cost will continue, especially after GPS is declared fully operational. However, it is difficult to predict the rate of the price drop and the ultimate level. In August 1985, one American manufacturer offered a basic receiver for $(U.S.)4,000 for orders in excess of 1,000 units [Merrifield, 1985]. As with most high-technology products, there will be significant competition from manufacturers in the Far East. Eventually, basic receivers should be available for about $(U.S.)500 [Yiu et al., 1982]. Dual-frequency receivers for geodetic work, primarily because of lower demand, will be somewhat higher in price.

CHAPTER EIGHT

OBSERVATION EQUATIONS

Guide to GPS Positioning
© Canadian GPS Associates, April 1986

OBSERVATION EQUATIONS

OBSERVATION TYPES

- Pseudo-range observations
- Carrier beat phase observations
- Continuous carrier phase

LINEAR COMBINATIONS OF OBSERVATIONS

- Between-epoch single differences
- Between-receiver single differences
- Between-satellite single differences
- Receiver-time double differences
- Receiver-satellite double differences
- Receiver-satellite-time triple differences

CORRELATIONS BETWEEN OBSERVATIONS

OBSERVATION EQUATIONS

In this chapter we first describe the two main GPS observation equations:
- the equation modelling code pseudo-ranges, and
- the equation modelling carrier beat phase measurements.

We will see that GPS observations can always be thought of as some kind of biased range. Both kinds of observation equations contain linear bias terms modelling the effects of receiver clock offsets, satellite clock offsets, ionospheric and tropospheric delays. The carrier beat phase observation equation contains an additional linear bias term — the initial cycle ambiguity term.

We then describe various linear combinations (single, double, and triple differences) of these observation equations. These linear combinations are often used in processing GPS data. This is because various linear combinations reduce or eliminate the effects of some of the linear biases in the observation equations: those due to receiver and satellite clock offsets, and initial cycle ambiguities. Differenced observations also tend to reduce the effects of orbital errors, and the effects of ionospheric and tropospheric delays. However, this reduction is more effective the closer the separation of the simultaneously observing receivers.

In developing the observation equations, where necessary we shall use subscripts to indicate the receiver station and superscripts to indicate the transmitting satellite. These indices will be dropped when there is no risk of confusing the meaning of each quantity.

PSEUDO-RANGE OBSERVATIONS

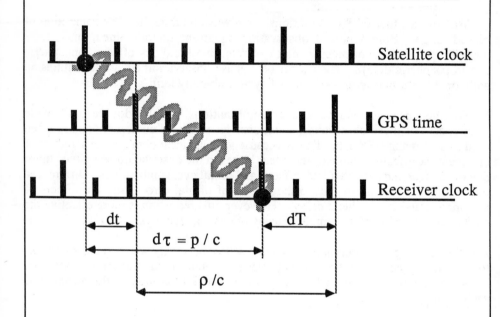

$$p = \rho + c \cdot (dt - dT) + d_{ion} + d_{trop}$$

✦ PSEUDO-RANGE OBSERVATIONS Jan 27

The basic *pseudo-range observable*, $d\tau$, is the difference between the time of transmission (in the satellite time scale t) and the time of arrival (in the receiver time scale T) of a particular signal transmitted by the satellite. In addition to the satellite and receiver time scales, there is a more or less ideal time scale called *GPS time* τ. For the pseudo-range, we can write:

$$d\tau = T(\tau_b) - t(\tau_a) \ .$$

Adding and subtracting the elapsed GPS time $\tau_b - \tau_a$ we have

$$d\tau = (\tau_b - \tau_a) + [\tau_a - t(\tau_a)] - [\tau_b - T(\tau_b)] \ .$$

Ideally, the first term is the travel time of the signal which, when multiplied by c = 299 792 458 m/sec—the speed of light in a vacuum—is equal to the true range ρ to the satellite, ignoring atmospheric effects. The second term represents the offset dt of the satellite clock from GPS time. The third term represents the offset dT of the receiver clock from GPS time. When ionospheric and tropospheric delays are taken into account, the complete pseudo-range equation takes the form

$$p = c \cdot d\tau = \rho + c \cdot (dt - dT) + d_{ion} + d_{trop} \ .$$

We are primarily interested in receiver coordinates. Where are they in this equation? In fact, they are hidden in the true range ρ. If the satellite coordinates are perfectly known, then $\rho = \|\mathbf{r} - \mathbf{R}\|$. However, $\mathbf{r}$ is generally **not** known perfectly, so we add a term, $d\rho$, to account for the effect of ephemeris errors and get $\rho = \|\mathbf{r} - \mathbf{R}\| + d\rho$. Then the observation equation becomes

$$p = \|\mathbf{r} - \mathbf{R}\| + d\rho + c \cdot (dt - dT) + d_{ion} + d_{trop}$$

which is in the form $l = f(\mathbf{R}, \mathbf{r}, \mathbf{b})$, where $\mathbf{b}$ is a vector of terms we may wish to consider as biases (any or all of $d\rho$, $c \cdot (dt - dT)$, d_{ion}, and d_{trop}). Ways of dealing with these bias terms are explained in Chapter 9.

Finally, we must consider effects due to measurement noise and unmodelled influences, both of which we assume to be random. These are included in the model by adding a residual term to the right-hand side of the observation equation.

CARRIER BEAT PHASE OBSERVATIONS

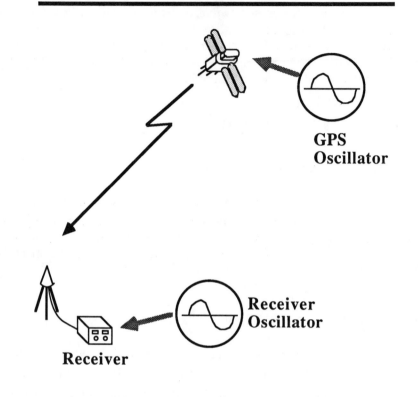

GPS Oscillator

Receiver Oscillator

Receiver

$$\phi = - (f/c) \cdot \rho - f \cdot (dt - dT) - (f/c) \cdot (-d_{ion} + d_{trop})$$

⚹CARRIER BEAT PHASE OBSERVATIONS   Jan 27
im por tant

Some receivers, for example the Macrometer™ V-1000 or the Texas Instruments TI-4100, are able to measure the difference between the carrier signal generated by its internal oscillator and the carrier signal coming in from the satellite. This difference is the *carrier beat phase observable*, the phase of the signal which remains when the incoming Doppler-shifted satellite carrier signal is beat with the nominally-constant reference frequency generated in the receiver:

$$\phi = \phi_i^k = \phi^k(t) - \phi_i(T) \ ,$$

where ϕ^k is the phase of the signal transmitted by the kth satellite at time t, and ϕ_i is the phase at the ith receiver at reception time T (both expressed in cycles).

The carrier beat phase model can be reformulated using two relations
• The phase/frequency relationship which is valid for highly stable oscillators over a short time interval is

$$\phi(t + \delta t) = \phi(t) + f \cdot \delta t \ . \ \Rightarrow \text{fundamental}$$

Letting $\delta t = T - t$ we can set

$$\phi_i(T) = \phi^k(t) + f \cdot (T - t) \ ,$$

and obtain

$$\phi = \phi^k(t) - \phi_i(T) = - f \cdot (T - t) \ .$$

• The fundamental approximation relating the transmit and receipt times is
    clock corrections

$$t + dt + (\rho - d_{ion} + d_{trop}) \ / \ c = T + dT \ .$$
Then

$$T - t = dt - dT + (\rho - d_{ion} + d_{trop}) \ / \ c \ ,$$

and the new carrier beat phase model is

$$\not{} \quad \phi = - (f/c) \cdot \rho - f \cdot (dt - dT) - (f/c) \cdot (-d_{ion} + d_{trop}) \ .$$

CONTINUOUS CARRIER PHASE

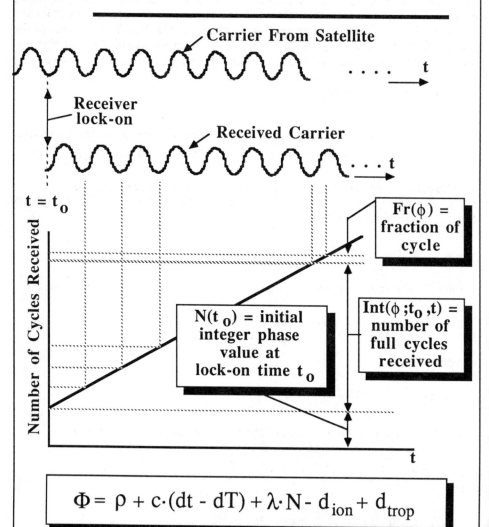

Carrier From Satellite

t

Receiver lock-on

Received Carrier

... t

$t = t_0$

Number of Cycles Received

$Fr(\phi) =$ fraction of cycle

$N(t_0) =$ initial integer phase value at lock-on time t_0

$Int(\phi; t_0, t) =$ number of full cycles received

t

$$\Phi = \rho + c \cdot (dt - dT) + \lambda \cdot N - d_{ion} + d_{trop}$$

*CONTINUOUS CARRIER PHASE J_{an} 27

In practice, the carrier beat phase measurement at some epoch t is based on a phase alignment of the receiver clock with the incoming carrier signal without the knowledge of which cycle would represent perfect cycle synchronization. Hence, the total phase ϕ_{total} consists of a measured fractional phase part $Fr(\phi)$, an integer count $Int(\phi)$ of phase cycles from the initial epoch t_0 to epoch t (which is continuously monitored by the receiver since the first measurement), and an unknown integer number N of cycles at the initial epoch t_0.

$$\phi_{total} = Fr(\phi) + Int(\phi; t_0, t) + N(t_0) .$$

The unknown cycle count N is usually referred to as the *cycle ambiguity* . This is analogous to the direction unknown in horizontal direction measurements, and thus could also be called the *cycle unknown*. As long as the receiver maintains continuous phase lock during an observing session (that is, as long as the $Int(\phi; t_0, t)$ count is maintained), there is only one ambiguity per satellite/receiver pair. However, if there are breaks in phase lock, several ambiguities or cycle slips per satellite may result. Ways of dealing with this problem will be discussed in Chapter 9.

What is then observed by the receiver? It is $\phi_{measured} = Fr(\phi) + Int(\phi; t_0, t)$.

Hence $\phi_{total} = \phi_{measured} + N(t_0)$. The equation for the instantaneous carrier beat phase observable for one satellite, one receiver, and one instant of time may be written as

$$\phi_{total} = - (f/c) \cdot \rho - f \cdot (dt - dT) - (f/c) \cdot (-d_{ion} + d_{trop}) + N ,$$

where the phase difference between the satellite and receiver oscillators are now implied by the term $f \cdot (dt - dT)$ for the satellite and receiver clock errors.

Multiplying by the wavelength $\lambda = c/f$, and defining

$$\Phi = - \lambda \cdot \phi_{measured} , \qquad \text{linear Measure of phase difference.}$$

one can obtain the corresponding carrier phase equation (in length units)

$$\Phi = \rho + c \cdot (dt - dT) + \lambda \cdot N - d_{ion} + d_{trop} , \qquad \text{*} \quad \text{adds extra unknown for each sat.}$$

which is directly comparable ~~with the pseudo-range equation,~~ except for the ambiguity term (and the sign of the ionospheric term). This clearly indicates that except for the initial ambiguity, N, Φ can be thought of as a range, and its observation equation is almost the same as that of the biased range. The biases for this kind of measurement are the same as for pseudoranges, except that the ambiguity term has been added.

LINEAR COMBINATIONS OF OBSERVATIONS

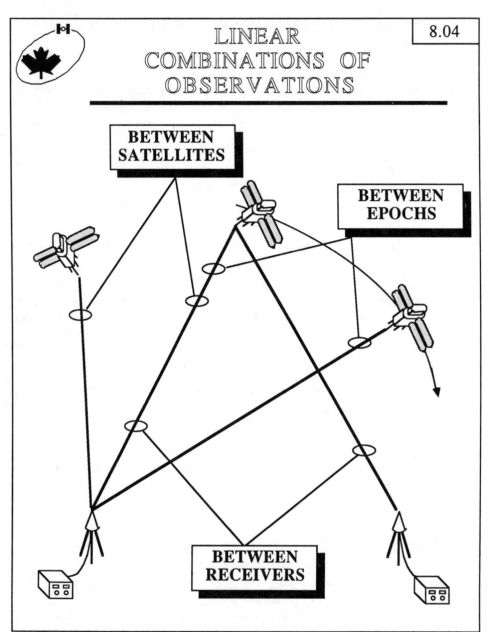

BETWEEN SATELLITES

BETWEEN EPOCHS

BETWEEN RECEIVERS

© Canadian GPS Associates, April 1986

LINEAR COMBINATIONS OF OBSERVATIONS

Depending on the type of application and the level of accuracy one seeks from GPS, there are significant advantages and disadvantages in forming certain linear combinations of the basic code pseudo-range, or carrier beat phase observables.

Using GPS data, both point and relative positioning are possible. However, because of the uncertainties in the satellite positions, clock behaviour, and propagation delays, 'absolute' point positioning will likely be obtained with accuracies of only a few metres. For most positioning requirements for geodetic and geodynamic applications, it will be necessary to use GPS in a relative mode. Of the error sources affecting the GPS signals, satellite orbit, satellite clock, receiver clock, and atmospheric propagation errors will exhibit some correlation among signals received at several stations simultaneously tracking the same several satellites. The goal of the differential process is to take advantage of these correlations to improve the accuracy of relative positions. Using the code or carrier phase measurements for relative positioning consists of taking differences between measurements. In this way, the effect of the various errors, common to the measurements being differenced, are removed or greatly reduced.

GPS measurements can be differenced between receivers, between satellites, and between epochs, or combinations thereof. Many different differencing combinations are possible. Presently, the most commonly used approach is to difference in the above order, i.e., first between receivers, then between satellites, and lastly between epochs.

The notation we use for taking these differences is intended to be mnemonic:

- Δ denotes differences between two receivers (two vertices on the bottom)
- ∇ denotes differences between two satellites (two vertices on the top)
- δ denotes differences between two epochs.

BETWEEN-EPOCH (DOPPLER) SINGLE DIFFERENCES

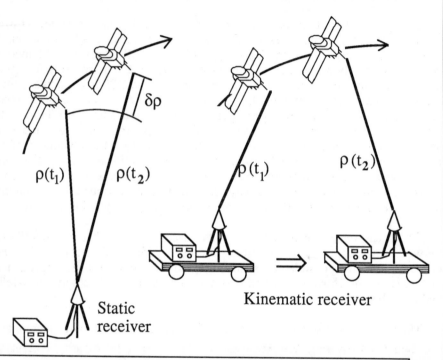

Static receiver

Kinematic receiver

$$\delta(\bullet) = (\bullet)_{epoch\ 2} - (\bullet)_{epoch\ 1}$$

$$\delta p = \delta\rho + c\cdot(\delta dt - \delta dT) + \delta d_{ion} + \delta d_{trop}$$

$$\delta\Phi = \delta\rho + c\cdot(\delta dt - \delta dT) - \delta d_{ion} + \delta d_{trop}$$

$$(\lambda N)_1 = (\lambda N)_2$$

that is why is not por
eq. in 8.3

⟵ BETWEEN-EPOCH (DOPPLER) SINGLE DIFFERENCES Jan. 27

The received frequency of a GPS satellite signal is different than the frequency transmitted by the satellite and is continually changing due to the relative motion of the satellite with respect to the receiver. This is the *Doppler effect*. The basic GPS Doppler observable is essentially the change of phase between two epochs. The corresponding *between-epoch single difference* (Doppler) equation is obtained by subtracting two equations of instantaneous phase in the form

$$\delta(\cdot) = (\cdot)_{\text{epoch 2}} - (\cdot)_{\text{epoch 1}}$$

we obtain

$$\delta\Phi = \delta\rho + c\cdot(\delta dt - \delta dT) - \delta d_{\text{ion}} + \delta d_{\text{trop}} ,$$

Note that this observation is <u>free of any cycle ambiguity</u>. since $(\lambda N)_1 = (\lambda N)_2$

Such observations can be expressed in the form $l = f(\mathbf{R}, \mathbf{r}, \mathbf{b})$, where $\mathbf{b}$ is a bias vector containing whatever terms we wish to consider as biases; $\mathbf{R}$ and $\mathbf{r}$ are contained in $\delta\rho = \|\mathbf{r} - \mathbf{R}\|_{\text{epoch 2}} - \|\mathbf{r} - \mathbf{R}\|_{\text{epoch 1}}$; and $l = \delta\Phi$, the observed phase change.

The processing technique required to correctly interpret the data is determined by the relationship among the epochs over which the change of phase is measured:

• If the Doppler count is recorded for a short interval, the counter reset to zero, and sometime later, repeatedly, another Doppler count recorded, we obtain *Intermittently Integrated Doppler* (IID) measurements. Using this technique, much potentially useful data is ignored.

• A second approach is to reset the counter to zero after each counting (integration) interval, but immediately start counting again, without losing any cycles. This type of data are *Consecutive Doppler Counts* (CDC). These measurements can be interpreted as range changes over the integration intervals.

• The third approach is to simply sum the consecutive Doppler counts throughout the satellite pass to obtain *Continuously Integrated Doppler* (CID) measurements. These measurements can be interpreted as the range changes since some initial (signal lock-on) epoch. If the initial range is considered as a range unknown (ambiguity), the Doppler observation can be considered to be a difference of two biased range observations.

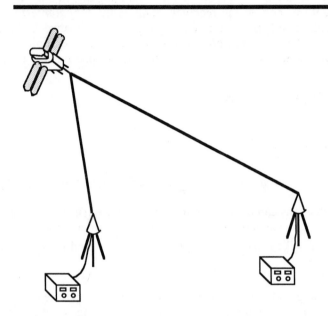

$$\Delta(\bullet) = (\bullet)_{\text{receiver 2}} - (\bullet)_{\text{receiver 1}}$$

$$\Delta p = \Delta \rho - c \cdot \Delta dT + \Delta d_{\text{ion}} + \Delta d_{\text{trop}}$$

$$\Delta \Phi = \Delta \rho - c \cdot \Delta dT + \lambda \cdot \Delta N - \Delta d_{\text{ion}} + \Delta d_{\text{trop}}$$

⋆ BETWEEN-RECEIVER SINGLE DIFFERENCES Jan 27

For a pair of stations simultaneously observing the same satellite, the mathematical model for a *between-receiver single difference pseudo-range* observable obtained from P- or C/A-code measurements can be derived by differencing two simultaneous pseudo-ranges to the satellite; in the form

$$\Delta(\cdot) = (\cdot)_{receiver\ 2} - (\cdot)_{receiver\ 1}$$

to obtain

$$\Delta p = \Delta\rho - c\cdot\Delta dT + \Delta d_{ion} + \Delta d_{trop}$$

where Δd_{ion} and Δd_{trop} are differential corrections for the ionospheric and tropospheric delays, and ΔdT is a differential correction for the receiver clock errors.

Similarly, if the two stations are collecting carrier beat phase data, a *between-receiver single difference carrier phase* observable can be derived as

$$\Delta\Phi = \Delta\rho - c\cdot\Delta dT + \lambda\cdot\Delta N - \Delta d_{ion} + \Delta d_{trop} \quad .$$

Between-receiver single differences remove or greatly reduce the effects of errors associated with the satellites:
- satellite clock errors, and ⇒ St
- to a great extent orbit errors and atmospheric delays as well (if the baseline lengths are short compared with the 20 000 km altitude of the GPS satellites).

BETWEEN-SATELLITE SINGLE DIFFERENCES

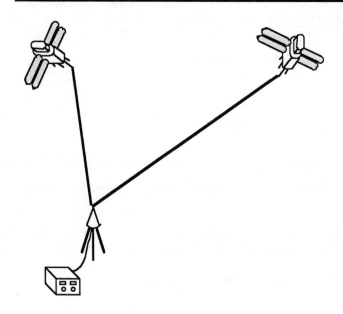

$$\nabla(\,\bullet\,) = (\,\bullet\,)_{\text{satellite } 2} - (\,\bullet\,)_{\text{satellite } 1}$$

$$\nabla p = \nabla \rho + c \cdot \nabla dt + \nabla d_{\text{ion}} + \nabla d_{\text{trop}}$$

$$\nabla \Phi = \nabla \rho + c \cdot \nabla dt + \lambda \cdot \nabla N - \nabla d_{\text{ion}} + \nabla d_{\text{trop}}$$

BETWEEN-SATELLITE SINGLE DIFFERENCES σ_{α} $2z$

Another type of difference may be formed by differencing the observations of two satellites as simultaneously recorded at a single station. Such a difference is known as a **between-satellite single difference**. The mathematical model of the between-satellite single range difference observable, in the form

$$\nabla(\cdot) = (\cdot)^{\text{satellite 2}} - (\cdot)^{\text{satellite 1}}$$

is given by

$$\nabla p = \nabla \rho + c \cdot \nabla dt + \nabla d_{\text{ion}} + \nabla d_{\text{trop}} \,.$$

The corresponding model for the between-satellite single difference carrier phase observable is

$$\nabla \Phi = \nabla \rho + c \cdot \nabla dt + \lambda \cdot \nabla N - \nabla d_{\text{ion}} + \nabla d_{\text{trop}} \,.$$

The between-satellite single difference observable is free from receiver clock errors. If the goal of a particular GPS observation campaign is eventually to form double differences, the between satellite differencing could be done at each individual receiver at the time of observation.

RECEIVER-TIME
DOUBLE DIFFERENCES

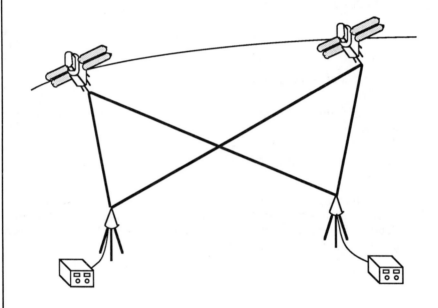

$$\delta\Delta p = \delta\Delta\rho \; - c\cdot\delta\Delta\, dT + \; \delta\Delta\, d_{ion} + \delta\,\Delta d_{trop}$$

$$\delta\Delta\Phi = \delta\Delta\rho \; - c\cdot\delta\Delta\, dT - \; \delta\Delta\, d_{ion} + \delta\,\Delta d_{trop}$$

⚹ RECEIVER-TIME DOUBLE DIFFERENCES ʃₐᵣ 27
" ʃʰₑ Mₐᵍⁱᶜ Bₑᵍⁱₙₛ"

The *receiver-time double difference observable* is the change from one epoch to the next, in the between-receiver single difference for the same satellite. This combination is particularly advantageous. The equation for the receiver-time double difference carrier beat phase observable is

$$\delta\Delta\Phi = \delta\Delta\rho - c\cdot\delta\Delta dT - \delta\Delta d_{ion} + \delta\Delta d_{trop} \ .$$

Differencing the between-epoch (δ) difference equations for two receivers results in $\Delta\delta\Phi$ identical to the above.

Note that the satellite dependent <u>integer cycle ambiguities</u> which are present in $\Delta\Phi$ are now absent from $\delta\Delta\Phi = \Delta\delta\Phi$.

This formulation allows an easier editing of cycle slips.

problem : Getting integer value

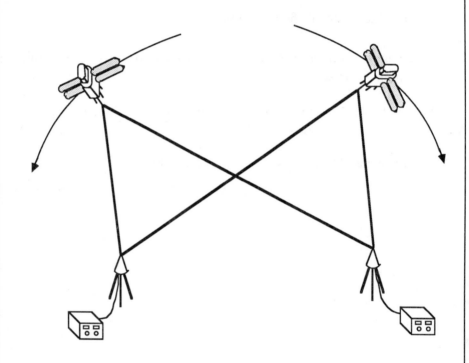

$$\nabla\Delta p = \nabla\Delta\, \rho + \nabla\Delta\, d_{ion} + \nabla\Delta\, d_{trop}$$

$$\nabla\Delta\Phi = \nabla\Delta\, \rho + \lambda\cdot\nabla\Delta\, N - \nabla\Delta\, d_{ion} + \nabla\Delta\, d_{trop}$$

"Very Nice"

↯RECEIVER-SATELLITE DOUBLE DIFFERENCES Jan 27
"Usually used"

Consider two receivers and two satellites at the same epoch. There are three possible differencing operations:
- two between-receiver single differences, each involving a different satellite,
- two between-satellite single differences, each involving a different receiver,
- one *receiver-satellite double difference*, involving both receivers and both satellites.

The receiver-satellite double difference can be constructed either by:
- taking two between-receiver single difference observables, involving the same pair of receivers but different satellites, and differencing these between the two satellites, or
- taking two between-satellite single difference observables, involving the same pair of satellites but different receivers, and differencing these between the two satellites.

The two results, i.e., $\nabla\Delta(\cdot)$ and $\Delta\nabla(\cdot)$, are identical.

The receiver-satellite double difference observation equation, for pseudo-range measurements is

$$\nabla\Delta p = \nabla\Delta\rho + \nabla\Delta d_{ion} + \nabla\Delta d_{trop} .$$

Similarly in the case of carrier beat phase measurements
integer value unknown, thus can be determined

$$\nabla\Delta\Phi = \nabla\Delta\rho + \lambda\cdot\nabla\Delta N - \nabla\Delta d_{ion} + \nabla\Delta d_{trop} .$$

Double differences remove, or greatly reduce, the effects of
- errors associated with misalignment between the two **receiver clocks,** a contributor to both of the between-receiver single differences, and
- errors associated with misalignment between the two **satellite clocks,** a contributor to both of the between-satellite single differences.

RECEIVER-SATELLITE-TIME TRIPLE DIFFERENCES

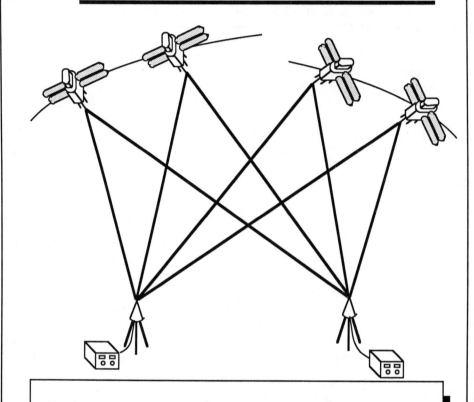

$$\delta\nabla\Delta p = \delta\nabla\Delta\rho + \delta\nabla\Delta d_{ion} + \delta\nabla\Delta d_{trop}$$

$$\delta\nabla\Delta\Phi = \delta\nabla\Delta\rho - \delta\nabla\Delta d_{ion} + \delta\nabla\Delta d_{trop}$$

⋆ RECEIVER-SATELLITE-TIME TRIPLE Jan 27
DIFFERENCES

"good for quick measurements within 20-30 cm, but is automated"
drawback ⇒ accuracy

The *receiver-satellite-time triple difference observable* is the change in a receiver-satellite double difference from one epoch to the next. The corresponding observation equations are

$$\delta\nabla\Delta p = \delta\nabla\Delta\rho + \delta\nabla\Delta d_{ion} + \delta\nabla\Delta d_{trop},$$

and

$$\delta\nabla\Delta\Phi = \delta\nabla\Delta\rho - \delta\nabla\Delta d_{ion} + \delta\nabla\Delta d_{trop}.$$

The errors which dropped out in the double difference observables are also absent from triple differences. In addition, for carrier beat phase measurements, the initial cycle ambiguity terms cancel. This is the most attractive property of this type of observable: it allows easier automatic editing of the data to remove cycle slips.

Undifferenced observations are affected by biases in receiver clocks and satellite clocks, and in the case of carrier beat phase observations, initial cycle ambiguities. These have all been eliminated from the triple differenced linear combinations. On the other hand, the number of observations has been reduced by an equivalent amount.

Double and triple difference observations remove clock errors from the model. However, often it is important to monitor the behaviour of the clocks. In such cases, it is more appropriate to use undifferenced data (to monitor both receiver and satellite clocks) or single differenced data (to monitor only receiver or satellite clocks).

CORRELATION
BETWEEN OBSERVATIONS

DOPPLER

Consecutive Doppler → **Counts are Correlated**

→ **Tridiagonal Covariance Matrix**

Continuously Integrated Doppler → **Correlation is Removed**

→ **Diagonal Covariance Matrix**

GENERAL

Differenced Observations May Be Correlated Depending on Process

CORRELATION BETWEEN OBSERVATIONS

Differenced observations are subject to *mathematical correlations*, induced by the differencing process. Regardless of the level of differencing (single, double, or triple), differenced observables can be thought of as the result of applying a **differencing operator D** to the original undifferenced observations.

Let us take the undifferenced equations

$$p = \rho + c \cdot (dt - dT) + d_{ion} + d_{trop}$$

$$\Phi = \rho + c \cdot (dt - dT) + \lambda \cdot N - d_{ion} + d_{trop} \; ,$$

any combination of the differencing operations we have considered (Δ, ∇, or δ) may be represented by an operator (matrix) **D**, which is composed entirely of the elements +1, -1, and 0 operating on a vector l of 'observed ranges' p or Φ.

If the covariance matrix of the vector of ranges l is $\mathbf{C}_l$, then the covariance matrix of the differenced range, $\mathbf{D}\,l$, is

$$\mathbf{C_{D}}_l = \mathbf{D} \; \mathbf{C}_l \; \mathbf{D^t}.$$

This provides a straightforward (but perhaps computationally inconvenient) method of accounting for the mathematical correlations introduced by differencing.

Physical correlations are more difficult to handle. Physical correlation may be spatial or temporal in nature, or a combination of both. Propagation anomalies (atmospheric inhomogeneities) are one significant source of both spatial and temporal physical correlations. To completely account for the correlations from just this one source would require a realistic model for the atmospheric parameters.

Proper accounting for the correlated nature of differenced data is necessary in order to make the differenced model equivalent to that involving the uncorrelated undifferenced data. However, correlation matrices are often computationally inconvenient. Hence, of necessity, differenced observables are often treated as uncorrelated. Excellent results have been obtained even when correlations have been neglected.

CHAPTER NINE

BIASES AND ERRORS

Guide to GPS Positioning
© Canadian GPS Associates, April 1986

BIASES AND ERRORS

BIASES

SATELLITE DEPENDENT

- Orbit representation biases
- Satellite clock model biases

STATION DEPENDENT

- Receiver clock biases
- Station coordinates

OBSERVATION DEPENDENT

- Ionospheric delay
- Tropospheric delay
- Carrier beat phase ambiguity

ERRORS

- Residual Biases
- Cycle Slips
- Multipath
- Antenna Phase Centre Movement
- Random Observation Error

BIASES AND ERRORS

Generally, the **biases** that influence the GPS measurements fall into three categories: satellite biases, station biases, and observation dependent biases.

(a) *Satellite biases* consist of biases in the satellite ephemeris (e.g., the satellite is not where the GPS broadcast data message or other orbital information tell us it is), and biases in models for the satellite clocks supplied in the broadcast message (e.g., the satellite clocks, even with the broadcast message models, are not perfectly synchronized to GPS time). These biases are thought to be uncorrelated between satellites. They affect both code and carrier beat phase measurements equally, and they depend on the number and the location of the tracking stations providing data for orbital determination, the orbital force model used, and the satellite geometry.

(b) *Station biases* usually consist of receiver clock biases and, for non-positioning types of GPS applications, such as time transfer and orbital tracking, of biases induced by uncertainties in the coordinates of the stations.

(c) *Observation dependent biases* include those associated with the signal propagation and other biases dependent on the observation type, such as, for instance, ambiguity biases inherent in the carrier beat phase observables.

The effect of biases is removed, or at least suppressed, by an attempt to model them. They are assumed to have functional relations with a variety of arguments such as time, position, temperature, etc.

Beside biases, the accuracy of positions and/or time obtained by GPS is dependent on two general influences: the geometric strength of the satellite configuration being observed, and the **errors** affecting the measurements themselves plus the remnant from the biases after the main effects have been modelled out. The former have already been discussed in Chapter 5, where it was shown that the measurement errors propagate into the position proportionally to the various Dilution of Precision factors.

Errors from each of the sources will have complicated spectral characteristics and other properties, and there will be correlations between some of these errors. However, at this stage in GPS development, the error models are usually limited to the simple approach of predicting typical standard deviations of uncorrelated equivalent range errors from each error source.

USER EQUIVALENT
RANGE ERROR

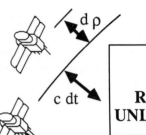

$d\,\rho$

$c\,dt$

**ALL TYPES OF BIASES
ARE FELT AS
RANGE MEASUREMENT ERRORS
UNLESS MODELLED OR ELIMINATED**

d_{ion}

d_{trop}

$c\,dT$

λN

USER EQUIVALENT RANGE ERROR

In many applications, it is useful to project the biases into the ranges. The sum of all these projected biases is then called the *range bias*, and the observed range, prior to the removal of the biases, is called the *biased range*.

The range bias can be quite sizeable, depending on what hardware and what information is used to arrive at the observed biased range. Individual contributions to the range bias may reach the following maximum values:

satellite clock bias	300 000 m (decreases to 10 m if broadcast correction is used)
receiver clock bias	10 m to 100 m (depends on the type of receiver oscillator)
orbital bias	80 m for today's broadcast ephemerides (will decrease to 10 m when operational tracking network is in place)
ionospheric delay bias	150 m at the horizon (decreases to 50 m at the zenith)
tropospheric delay bias	20 m at 10° above horizon (decreases to 2 m at the zenith)
carrier beat phase bias	anything.

Even though the individual contributions to the range bias would generally have varying signs (so that their sum would be smaller than the sum of their absolute values), it would clearly be impossible to work with these biased ranges. Thus an attempt must be made to remove the above biases by modelling or by differencing.

TIMING (CLOCK) BIASES

SIZE OF BIASES

- Satellite clocks

  1 ms ⇒ 300 km without broadcast message corrections

  30 ns ⇒ 10 m using broadcast message corrections

- Receiver clocks

  Synchronization with each other and with GPS time
  Short term stability (noise)
  Long term stability (drift and higher order terms)

OPTIONS FOR MODELLING BIASES

- Assume negligible and ignore
- Apply broadcast message correction
- Assume independent bias at each epoch for each clock
  - » Between satellite differencing
    - ◊ eliminates receiver clock bias
  - » Between receiver differencing
    - ◊ eliminates satellite clock bias
  - » Estimating independent clock biases at each epoch
    - ◊ same result as differencing
- Assume correlation between biases at different epochs
  - » Use time polynomial
  - » Treat as weighted parameters

TIMING (CLOCK) BIASES

GPS measurements are intimately connected to precise timing. GPS satellites transmit the time they begin broadcasting their individual coded message. The receiver measures the exact time each signal is received and, hence, it can compute a measure of the range to the satellite from the time elapsed from transmission of the satellite signal until its reception. This assumes, however, that both satellite and receiver clocks are keeping the same time. Any offset in time multiplied by the speed of light will result in the *user equivalent range error*. That is a one microsecond mis-synchronization between satellite and receiver clocks which results in a range bias of 300 metres. Let us first look at how well the satellite and receiver clocks can be expected to behave, and then what we can do to ensure that the mis-synchronization is nowhere near as bad as one microsecond.

GPS satellites carry both rubidium and cesium atomic frequency standards. The space environment is kind to clocks, but the clocks are physically left to drift off the standard 'GPS' time system (the less one interfers with precise clocks the happier they are). The amount by which they drift is kept within one millisecond. However, their performance is carefully monitored, and the amount by which they have drifted is accurately known. This is included in the broadcast message in the form of coefficients of a second-order polynomial

$$dt = a_0 + a_1(t - t_0) + a_2 (t - t_0)^2,$$

where t_0 is some reference epoch, and a_0 is the satellite clock *time offset*, a_1 is the *fractional frequency offset*, and a_2 is the *fractional frequency drift*. Occasionally, in transient situations mainly caused by temperature variations, satellite clocks also exhibit higher order departures which, however, can be neglected over short intervals of time. Random drift characteristics are not predictable. They only corrupt the estimation of the deterministic drifts and cause some of the higher-order terms of the drift. Any other characteristics are only observable over long periods of time. Synchronization between the GPS satellite clocks is kept to within about 20 nanoseconds by the broadcast clock corrections, and the 'GPS' time synchronized to UTC to within 100 ns.

GPS receivers generally are equipped with internal high quality (1 part in 10^{10}) quartz crystal clocks. Many receivers will also accept external timing from an atomic standard, usually either a cesium (1 part in 10^{13}) or rubidium (1 part in 10^{12}) clock. The options for modelling biases in these clocks are similar to those for the satellite clock biases. For low accuracy requirements, one may assume these biases to be negligible and ignore them altogether. Alternatively, given enough available satellites, one may choose to simply solve for an extra clock offset parameter along with coordinates. This is the usual approach used in GPS navigation; this bias is assumed to be independent at each measurement epoch. This approach makes the fewest assumptions about the clock behaviour. A polynomial clock model similar to that for satellite clocks can be used, the coefficients of which are determined as part of the parameter estimation process. This involves assumptions about clock behaviour.

ORBIT BIASES

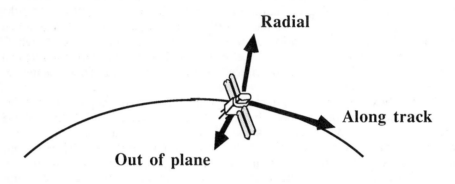

Radial

Along track

Out of plane

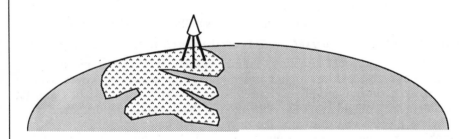

SIZE OF BIASES

- Present tracking net: 20 m typical, up to 80 m
- Operational tracking net: 5 m typical, up to 10 m

ORBIT BIASES

Satellite ephemeris errors are the most difficult to deal with. Clocks would be improved, or their undesirable effects be eliminated or greatly removed, for instance, by simultaneous tracking by two or more receivers and the use of differenced observables. **Ephemeris errors**, on the other-hand, would require a better estimation of the orbits, a process which is hampered by insufficient knowledge of the forces acting on the satellites since often these forces cannot be measured directly and adequately from the ground tracking sites. At present, using the orbital data provided by the broadcast ephemerides, satellite positions can be computed with a typical accuracy of about 20 m, with occasional errors reaching up to 80 m. When the future **Operational Tracking Network** is in place, it is anticipated that the quality of the broadcast ephemerides will be improved to the point that satellite positions will most likely be accurate to about 5 m, with occasional errors up to 10 m.

The main approach to solving the problems created by the imperfect modelling of the physical phenomena responsible for these forces has been usually directed toward their source; that is, toward developing more accurate models to begin with. Alternatively, it may be possible to use parametric models of various complexities for the ephemeris biases (i.e., with parameters that can be adjusted as part of an orbit estimation process).

ORBITAL BIAS
MODELLING

OPTION 1 - IGNORE THE PROBLEM

Assume the given ephemeris is perfect, and hold the orbit fixed.

OPTION 2 - RELAX THE ORBIT

1) Assume geometrical biases, and estimate one to six bias parameters per arc

2) Assume dynamic model, use a force model and six initial conditions

3) Assume "free orbit", and estimate independent orbital biases at every epoch

OPTION 3 - DIFFERENCE THE DATA
(RATHER THAN MODELLING THE ORBIT BIASES)

For example, between-receiver differencing reduces the effect of 20 m orbital error on baseline vector solution to 1 ppm or less.

ORBITAL BIAS MODELLING

The simplest approach to deal with these biases is obviously to ignore their existence; that is, assume that the given ephemeris is perfect. This is the approach taken, in fact, in many kinematic applications of GPS.

An alternative approach is to assume that the satellite ephemeris errors manifest themselves as geometrical biases, such as translation, rotation, etc., of the given orbital arc with respect to the true orbit. In this case, one to six **orbital bias parameters** per arc are included in the model depending on the length of the arc. Usually three biases expressed in a reference frame attached to the satellite with the axes pointing in the along-, across-, and out-of-plane directions are used for short arcs.

A physically more meaningful approach is the inclusion in the model of initial conditions (e.g., six Keplerian elements) of the satellite orbit based on an assumed **force model**.

The third alternative is to assume in the model independent orbital biases at every observation epoch. This is the **free orbit** approach.

A priori weights to the orbit bias model parameters are usually applied in all three of these approaches.

In relative positioning, the effects of certain systematic orbital errors can be removed or greatly reduced by differencing the observations from two or more sites observing simultaneously the same satellites. This is a common approach often used to date as an alternative to rigorous orbital modelling. As has already been indicated, in this approach, a 20 m orbital error, for instance, results in about 1 ppm error in a baseline vector solution.

Any estimation of orbital biases using difference observations requires that some information on orbital biases remains in the differenced observations. This means that GPS networks extending over large areas are more suitable than ones extending over smaller areas.

IONOSPHERIC DISPERSION EFFECTS

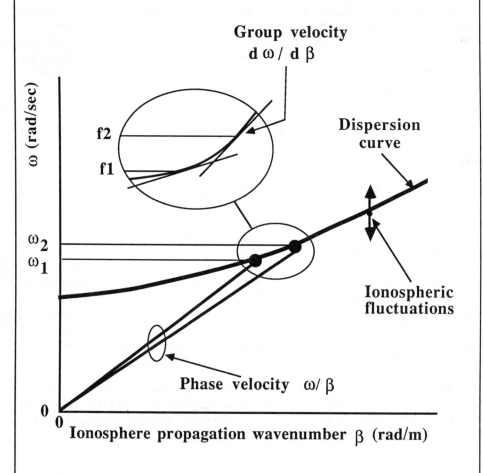

Group velocity $d\,\omega\,/\,d\,\beta$

f2

f1

Dispersion curve

ω_2

ω_1

Ionospheric fluctuations

Phase velocity ω/β

0

0

Ionosphere propagation wavenumber β (rad/m)

ω (rad/sec)

Note: $\omega = 2\,\pi\,f$

IONOSPHERIC DISPERSION EFFECTS

The *ionosphere* is generally considered to be that region of the atmosphere from approximately 50 to 1000 km in altitude in which ultra-violet radiation from the sun has ionized a fraction of the gas molecules found there, thereby releasing free electrons. GPS signals, like any electromagnetic signal propagating through an ionized medium, are affected by the non-linear dispersion characteristics of this medium, as shown on this figure. At any point in the dispersion curve, the slope of the line joining the origin to that point is the *phase velocity* $v_p = \omega/\beta$, where $\omega = 2\pi f$ is the angular frequency of the signal travelling through the ionosphere, and $\beta = 2\pi / \lambda$ is the ionospheric propagation wavenumber. The *group velocity* $v_g = \partial\omega / \partial\beta$ is given by the local tangent slope at the point. We can express v_g in terms of v_p as $v_g = v_p + \beta \, \partial \, v_p / \partial\beta$. Corresponding to the phase velocity is the *phase index of refraction* $n_p = v_p / c$, and corresponding to the group velocity is the *group index of refraction* $n_g = v_g / c$. We can express n_g in terms of n_p as $n_g = n_p + f \, \partial \, n_p / \partial f$.

The form of n_p for the ionosphere is $n_p \approx 1 - a \, N / f^2$, where N is the ionospheric electron density in electrons/m^3 at the time and place we are evaluating n_p and a is a constant (see, e.g., Bomford [1980]). Hence $n_g \approx 1 + a \, N / f^2$.

The change in path length due to the ionosphere is $\Delta\rho = \int(n-1) \, ds$, where the integration is along the propagation path. GPS code signals are dependent upon the group index of refraction, so the *ionospheric group delay* is $\Delta\rho_g = \int(n_g - 1) \, ds = + a \, N_T / f^2$. Phase measurements, on the other hand, are governed by the phase index of refraction, so the *ionospheric phase delay* is $\Delta\rho_p = \int(n_p - 1) \, ds = - a \, N_T / f^2$. Here N_T is the total electron content along the propagation path in electrons/m^2. N_T varies from 10^{16} to 10^{18} electrons/m^2. If $\Delta\rho$ is in metres and f in Hz, then $a \approx 40.28$. If we let $d_{ion} = a \, N_T / f^2$, the effect on observed code ranges is $+d_{ion}$, and the effect on observed carrier phase ranges is $-d_{ion}$. The magnitude of d_{ion} for GPS varies from tens of centimetres to tens of metres, depending on N_T.

IONOSPHERIC MODELLING

SIZE OF BIASES

- Extremal value at zenith ~ 50 m
- Extremal value at horizon ~ 3 x 50 m
- Diurnal variation: day ~ five times night
- Annual variation: November ~ four times July
- Sunspot variation: at max ~ four times at min

OPTIONS FOR MODELLING BIAS

- Dual frequency data - use dispersion

$$d_{ion} (L1) = [\rho (L1) - \rho (L2)] \{f_2^2 / (f_2^2 - f_1^2)\}$$

   » residual effect: may be at decimetre level

- Single frequency data

   » use global ionospheric prediction model
      (still in early development stage)

   » single frequency between-receiver differences

      ◊ reduces common ionospheric effect
      ◊ residual effect:
            regional baselines - typically 1 ppm
            continental baselines - not as good

IONOSPHERIC MODELLING

At GPS frequencies, the ionospheric range effect may vary from more than 150 m (at sunspot maximum periods, midday, satellite near horizon) to less than 5 m (sunspot minimum, night, satellite at zenith). Since the ionospheric effect is frequency dependent, L1 and L2 measurements can be compared to estimate the effect as

$$d\rho_{ion}(L1) = [\rho(L1) - \rho(L2)][f_2^2/(f_2^2 - f_1^2)] \ .$$

A similar approach is used to correct the observed carrier beat phase measurements by

$$d\phi_{ion}(L1) = (f_2^2 - f_1^2)/f_2^2 \ [\phi(L1) - \phi(L2) \ f_1/f_2 - (N(L1) - f_1/f_2 \ N(L2)]$$

where N(L1), N(L2) are cycle ambiguities on the L1 and L2 data. As long as the observed phases of the L1 and L2 signals are continuously counted (i.e., there are no cycle slips), the last term on the right-hand side of the equation remains constant (but unknown). Hence a time series of the linear combination of the L1 and L2 phases reflects mainly the variations of the ionospheric delay of the L1 signals.

The *dual frequency correction* removes most of the ionospheric effect in the code or carrier phase measurements. The residual effect, however, may still be significant for some applications, in particular for mid-afternoon observations, and more so during a maximum solar activity cycle.

The above technique obviously can be only applied to two-frequency data. Users of single-frequency receivers must use **ionospheric models** or rely on the ionospheric model parameters transmitted by the satellites (cf. Chapter 6). However, these types of models are still in the early stages of development and are unlikely to be more than 75% effective so that for an ionospheric effect of 50 m, for instance, residual errors of up to 15 m still remain. In fact, a study using actual data [Lachapelle and Wade, 1982] has shown that using the current broadcast ionospheric correction model actually gave worse results than not applying the correction at all.

TROPOSPHERIC EFFECTS

SIZE OF BIASES

- At zenith: 2.3 metres
- At 10 degrees above horizon: 20 metres

OPTIONS FOR MODELLING BIAS

- Ignore
- Use standard vertical refractivity profile models
  - (a) with standard atmosphere
  - (b) driven by surface weather data
  - (c) with scale parameter estimated
  - (d) both (b) and (c)
- Use local vertical refractivity profile model driven by surface weather data
- Water vapour radiometer observations for wet component
- Ray tracing (not yet attempted)

TROPOSPHERIC EFFECTS

Refraction in the neutral atmosphere—which includes the troposphere and other regions up to 80 km in altitude—is essentially independent of frequency over the entire radio spectrum. Unlike the ionosphere, the *troposphere* is not dispersive for frequencies below 30 GHz, so that group and phase delay are the same. Refraction in the neutral atmosphere may be conveniently separated into 'dry' and 'wet' components. The dry component can be approximated by

$$DTC = 2.27 \cdot 10^{-3} P_o$$

where DTC is the dry term range contribution in the zenith direction, and P_o is the surface pressure (in mbar). For an average atmospheric pressure of 1013 mbar, this corresponds to a range error of 2.3 m. The dry term contains approximately 90% of the total zenith range error, and may be estimated from surface pressure data with an accuracy of about 0.2%.

The wet component, on the other hand, depends on the atmospheric conditions all along the signal path. These conditions are not necessarily well correlated with surface conditions. There are various models available to date to model for this component taking into account such factors as the water vapour content, temperature, altitude, and the elevation angle of the signal path.

To date, the available tropospheric models, even with real-time meteorological data, appear to reduce the combined tropospheric effects by only 92% to 95% depending on the amount of atmospheric information available to the user. Users with good knowledge of the atmospheric conditions in the vicinity of their operations will have a smaller residual error than users who must rely on approximate or average data.

For differential observations, the differences of the tropospheric effects at the two ends of a baseline are also important. The available tropospheric models can be used to calculate this relative effect given the meteorological conditions at each site. In this case, one may choose the simplest approach, assuming that any tropospheric effects can be removed or greatly reduced by just differencing the observations from the two sites. This indeed may be a viable approach for most favourable cases, especially when the baselines are short. To achieve centimetre level accuracy, however, water vapour radiometers probably will need be used at both ends of the baselines to infer the integrated water vapour content along the lines of sight to the satellites. This is because the atmospheric water vapour content is likely to be quite variable in time and inhomogeneous spatially in many locations. This time variability is comparable to the time scale of the measurements at a given site. Typically, the wet component will be about 30 cm or more for observations at 20° elevation. If only surface measurements are used to estimate the total tropospheric correction, the uncertainty typically will be about 3.5 cm.

CARRIER BEAT PHASE AMBIGUITY

SIZE OF BIASES

- An integer multiple of the carrier wavelength
  - » ~ 20 cm for code correlation
  - » ~ 10 cm for squaring
- As long as receiver maintains phaselock (absence of cycle slips)
  - » same value for all epochs
  - » different value for each satellite/receiver pair

OPTIONS FOR MODELLING BIAS

- Estimate as a real number
  - » leave as real number
  - » choose nearest integer, and hold fixed
- Use combination of carrier and code measurements to estimate
- Search likely integer values for "best" values
- Difference between epochs to eliminate bias

CARRIER BEAT PHASE AMBIGUITY

Carrier beat phase measurements lead potentially to the most precise information about the receiver-to-satellite ranges one can obtain from GPS. The problem with utilizing this potential, however, is one of *cycle ambiguity.* It is quite difficult to locate accurately the exact cycle of the carrier whose phase is being measured. The present GPS receivers are capable of providing phase measurements with an integral precision of about 1 to 3 mm, with the overall accuracy of these measurements (including the influence of the atmosphere) being at the 1 to 4 cm level. However, the success of achieving this level of positioning accuracy from carrier phase measurements hinges on the capability to resolve this cycle ambiguity.

The problem is further compounded by the occurrence of frequent cycle slips. While cycle slips have to be detected and rectified before the final parameter estimation, cycle ambiguity is normally estimated together with the rest of the unknown parameters.

AMBIGUITY RESOLUTION

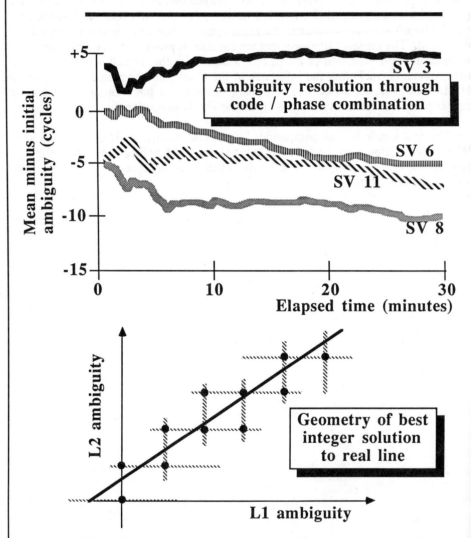

Ambiguity resolution through code / phase combination

Geometry of best integer solution to real line

AMBIGUITY RESOLUTION

One technique, usable with receivers, such as the TI-4100, which reconstruct the carrier with the knowledge of the pseudo-random noise (PRN) modulation code, relies on the **synergistic combination** of the pseudo-range and the carrrier beat phase measurements to a satellite to resolve the cycle ambiguities. It can be shown (e.g., Delikaraoglou et al. [1986]) that for each observation epoch where P-code pseudo-range and carrier phase measurements are available on the L1 and L2 frequencies, this combination allows to estimate through a recursive algorithm the cycle ambiguities on L1 and L2 as

$$N(L1) = 4.091 \, f_1 \, t_1 - 3.967 \, f_2 \, t_2 - \phi(L1) + \delta N(L1)$$

$$N(L2) = 3.967 \, f_1 \, t_1 - 4.091 \, f_2 \, t_2 - \phi(L2) + \delta N(L2)$$

with similar expressions for $\delta N(L1)$ and $\delta N(L2)$.

In practice, the success of an ambiguity resolution of the desired subcycle level hinges on the capability of reducing the effect of the instrumental errors, especially those associated with multipath errors in the code measurements. Usually such limitations can be overcome by long-term averaging leading to average ambiguity estimates with formal errors of the order of 1 to 3 cycles.

The code/phase combination over the long-term averaging process can be conveniently complemented and/or checked against alternative algorithms which search for the integer cycle ambiguities on purely geometrical principles. For instance, it can be shown (e.g., Delikaraoglou et al. [1986]) that if one assumes some approximate values for the sought integer cycle ambiguities, integer corrections to them can be found as solutions to a line equation, i.e.,

$$(f_2 / f_1)\delta N(L1) - \delta N(L2) = x \ ,$$

in the two-dimensional real space coordinated by $\delta N(L1)$ and $\delta N(L2)$, whose slope is exactly known (i.e., equal to $f_2 / f_1 = 120/154$), whereas its intercept x is affected by instrumental and other errors. The best solution (because of the errors, the equation does not generally have an exact solution when $\delta N(L1)$ and $\delta N(L2)$ are both integers) can be found through a **search on an integer grid,** (shown in the figure) for the point on this grid that lies closest to the straight line defined above.

CYCLE SLIPS

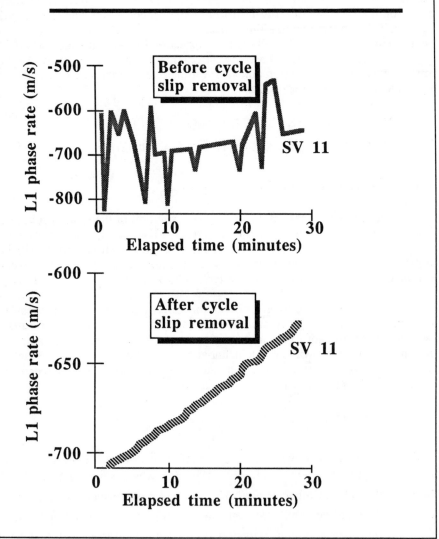

CYCLE SLIPS

When a satellite signal is obstructed in any way, it can no longer be tracked. When signal lock is resumed, the fractional part of the measured phase would still be the same as if tracking had been maintained. The integer number of cycles, however, exhibits a discontinuity or *cycle slip*. Such occurrences can be quite frequent, as shown in the figure.

There are various possible approaches to dealing with this problem. A common approach is to hold the station positions fixed (in a preadjustment), and edit the data manually by inspecting the corresponding residual series for breaks. This has been proven to work, but it can be a tedious and time consuming process. Another approach is to model the data with a piecewise continuous polynomial for each satellite. To implement this approach, however, the data have to be examined to find the times of slip occurrences (breaks) first. This again is quite tedious and, in addition, still some manual editing at the few cycles level may be necessary.

An alternative approach is to use between-receivers, satellites, and time triple difference observables to determine station locations. Once reasonably good values of station coordinates have been obtained, a search can be carried out automatically on the triple difference residuals to identify discontinuities in the double differences which form the specific triple differences [Remondi, 1985d]. Triple differences are particularly convenient to use in this connection, since they are not affected by receiver or satellite clock errors. Once such large residuals have been isolated over the whole epoch, one can easily determine which satellite is responsible for the integer cycle slips by looking at the triple difference residuals of the different satellite pair combinations.

MULTIPATH AND IMAGING

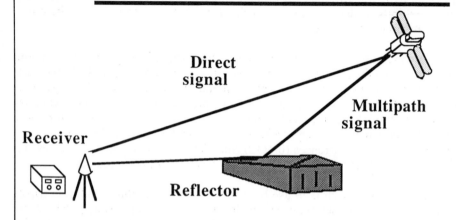

Direct signal

Multipath signal

Receiver

Reflector

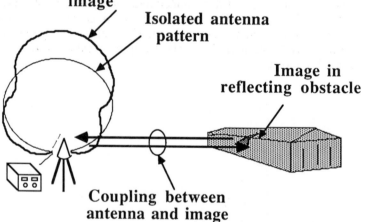

Pattern including image

Isolated antenna pattern

Image in reflecting obstacle

Coupling between antenna and image

MULTIPATH AND IMAGING

Multipath is the phenomenon whereby a signal arrives at a receiver site via two or more different paths. The difference in path lengths causes the signals to interfere at the receiver. Multipath is usually noted when operating near large reflecting obstacles, such as buildings or a ship's superstructure. The only means of minimizing multipath effects is through antenna beam shaping so as to discriminate against signals arriving from certain directions.

A related phenomenon, somewhat similar to multipath, is *imaging*, which also involves large nearby reflecting obstacles. The reflecting object produces an 'image' of the antenna and the resulting amplitude and phase characteristics are no longer those of the isolated antenna but of the combination of the antenna and its image. Of particular concern is the effect this has on the phase centre characteristics of the antenna. The method of minimizing imaging effects is to use absorbing material or, once again, beam shaping techniques to reduce the antenna-image coupling.

Multipath and imaging effects in a highly reflective environment are likely to be limiting factors for single epoch static pseudo-range applications at the 10 m level, for static carrier applications at the few centimetre level and for kinematic applications due to the higher noise level as well as to multipath induced loss of lock. Careful attention to antenna siting to minimize multipath and imaging effects is necessary when positioning accuracies at the centimetre and sub-centimetre levels are desired.

MULTIPATH EFFECTS ON CODED SIGNALS

Code chip length 'window'

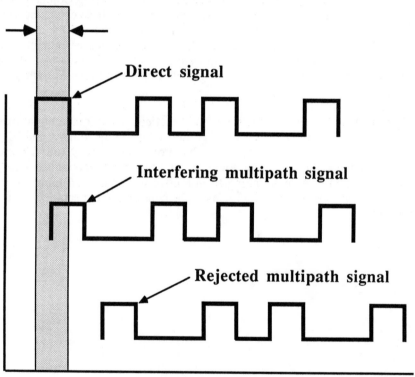

Direct signal

Interfering multipath signal

Rejected multipath signal

Time

MULTIPATH EFFECTS ON CODED SIGNALS

Coded signals, such as GPS pseudo-range messages, owing to their spread spectrum nature, have an inherent ability to discriminate against many forms of multipath. The coded signal is characterized by its **chip length** to which the receiver is synchronized. The chip length window allows the receiver to reject any other signal (including a multipath delayed version of the direct signal) which arrives outside the window, however, short delay signals which arrive within the window cannot be rejected. In this respect, coded signals offer a great advantage in multipath rejection but only outside the chip length frame. Interference within the frame (or window) may be severe. By comparison, direct phase measurements are generally equally susceptible to multipath at all practical ranges but may be less affected than pseudo-range in the presence of short-delay multipath.

Multipath may also affect carrier measurements. Multipath effects, when averaged over a long enough time for the relative phase of the direct and reflected signals to have changed by at least one cycle, will considerably reduce any biases in the measurements. This is true only for static applications. Imaging effects, on the other hand, cannot be averaged out and may leave biases in the measurements. Multipath and imaging effects are closely repeatable from day to day for the same satellite/antenna site pair, hence monitoring of changes of the antenna coordinates at the centimetre and sub-centimetre level (as required for geodynamic applications) may well be possible even in the presence of significant multipath.

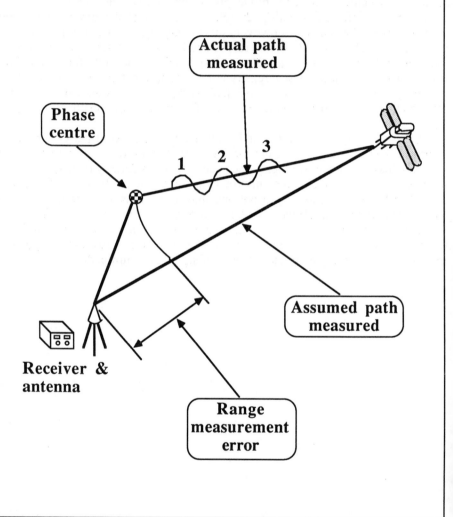

ERROR DUE TO PHASE CENTRE MOVEMENT

Actual path measured

Phase centre

1 2 3

Assumed path measured

Receiver & antenna

Range measurement error

ERROR DUE TO PHASE CENTRE MOVEMENT

Electronic radio distance measurement and positioning systems operate by determining distances from measurements performed on an electromagnetic wave which may be described by

$$F = A \, e^{j\omega t} \, e^{-jkr} \, e^{-jkd \sin\theta \sin\phi} \, e^{jkz \cos\theta} \, e^{j\alpha} \, ,$$

where the first exponential contains the time dependence and the second exponential contains the phase information due to the geometry of the source antenna, the excitation current, and the placement of the antenna and observer in a reference coordinate system. Distance measurements may be performed either by measuring the transmission time of the signal or by doing a signal phase measurement.

In a phase reference system, a single phase measurement is made and the path distance is calculated from

$$\Phi = (2\pi/\lambda)R + \alpha$$
$$R = (\Phi - \alpha)\lambda/2\pi = (\Phi - \alpha)v/\omega$$

where Φ is the indicated phase length of the path, and R is to be determined. Of course, R is a function of the geometry of the antenna and observer positions, i.e.,

$$R = z \cos\theta - d \sin\theta \sin\phi - r \, ,$$

where the true unknown distance (i.e., from the coordinate origin to the observation point) is given by r. Thus

$$(\Phi - \alpha)v/\omega = z \cos\theta - d \sin\theta \sin\phi - r$$
$$\therefore \quad r = z \cos\theta - d \sin\theta \sin f - (\Phi - \alpha)v/\omega \, .$$

The usual assumption in radiopositioning is that the unknown distance is given simply by

$$r = - \Phi v/\omega \, ,$$

which may be interpreted as the radius of a spherical wave centred at the origin (r=0), that is, the so-called phase centre of the wave coincides with the coordinate origin. The effect of the additional terms may be interpreted as moving the phase origin away from the coordinate origin by an amount which is a function of the element dimensions and the observer-source orientation (θ,ϕ).

OBSERVATION ERRORS

RULE OF THUMB

OBSERVATION RESOLUTION IS ABOUT 1% OF SIGNAL WAVELENGTH

GPS SIGNAL	WAVELENGTH λ	1% OF λ
C/A-CODE	300 m	3 m
P-CODE	30 m	30 cm
CARRIER	20 cm	2 mm

MODEL ERRORS

ERROR SOURCE		TYPICAL ERROR	WHAT TO DO ?
SATELLITE	ORBIT	20 m	difference
	CLOCK	10 m	difference
PROPAGATION	IONO	30 m	diff. + 2 freq.
	TROPO	10 m	model & diff.
RECEIVER	MULTIPATH	10 m	antenna siting
	CLOCK	300 m/ms	model in soln
	NOISE	mm $\longrightarrow$ m	

OBSERVATION ERRORS

The observed time delays to be converted to ranges will have some additional errors associated with them. These are due to the limitations of the receiver's electronics and are of a random character. As a general rule, they are proportional to the wavelength of the signal and consequently have significantly different magnitudes (standard deviations) for C/A-code ranging, P-code ranging, and carrier ranging, as shown in the table.

In addition to these truly *observational errors*, the random errors in the model have to be taken into account. The *model errors* are the residual errors that remain in the ranges and in the satellite positions after the biases enumerated in this chapter have been modelled out. These errors are generally much more damaging than the true observational errors, and no effort must be spared to reduce them.

Most of the model errors can be eliminated, or at least drastically reduced, by differencing the observed ranges between satellites, between receivers, and between times. Differencing either eliminates some of the errors because they are common to the differenced ranges (clock errors), or reduces the rest of the errors because of their spatial and temporal coherence (propagation errors, orbital errors). This reduction is more likely to be successful if the two simultaneously ranging receivers are closer together than if they are farther apart. The multipath errors can be neither modelled nor differenced out. The only protection against a multipath error is a careful siting of the antenna with the aim of avoiding reflections off surrounding structures.

STATION COORDINATES

OPTIONS FOR MODELLING BIAS

- Assume perfectly known
  (a possible case for non-positioning applications such as time transfer and orbit determination)

- Assume known with some uncertainty
  (by varying the uncertainty assumed, this approach is appropriate for all positioning and non-positioning applications)

- Assume unknown
  (the usual case for positioning applications)

EFFECTS ON ORBIT DETERMINATION

- Continental tracking network
  (to obtain 3 m orbits over the region, relative station coordinates must be known to 0.5 ppm)

- Global tracking network

EFFECTS ON TIME TRANSFER

- Each metre of error in station coordinate leads to typically 3 ns time transfer error

STATION COORDINATES

For *non-positioning applications*, i.e., orbital determination and time transfer, the positions of antennas (stations) must be assumed known either perfectly or with some uncertainty. The latter case is theoretically more appropriate because the ground positions are never known perfectly and, as such, should always be allowed to adjust even in the estimation of non-position parameters.

It should be obvious that the orbits can be predicted more accurately the better the ground positions are known. Thus, for instance, if an accuracy of 3 metres is desired in the determination of satellite positions, relative station coordinates must be known to 0.5 ppm. In addition, the spacing of tracking stations should be as wide as possible. For the time transfer, an uncertainty of one metre in the coordinates of the two stations induces an error of 3 ns in the transferred time.

Incidentally, in positioning, the accuracy of a priori knowledge of the sought coordinates also has an effect on the finally estimated coordinates. This effect gets smaller and smaller with time spent on tracking.

CHAPTER TEN

SOLUTIONS

Guide to GPS Positioning
© Canadian GPS Associates, April 1986

SOLUTIONS

POSITIONING PROBLEMS
- Main characteristics of static and kinematic positioning
- Classification of types of solutions

POINT POSITIONING USING PSEUDO-RANGES

- Satellite multi-ranging
- Least-squares solution for point positioning

RELATIVE POSITIONING

- Using pseudo-ranges
- Using phase measurements
- GPS phase measurement differencing

NETWORK SOLUTIONS

- Orbit improvement and network solution
- Weighted short-arc solution

KINEMATIC POSITIONING

- Absolute
- Relative
- Combined

POSTMISSION SMOOTHING

CONSTRAINED SOLUTIONS

SOLUTIONS

In this chapter, we look at alternative approaches to processing the observation equations discussed in Chapter 8, taking into account the biases described in Chapter 9, in order to obtain resulting positions for the tracking receivers.

We begin by considering the kinds of positioning problems that may be encountered, and the processing methods which are appropriate in each case. Generally, these problems can be divided into **static** and **kinematic** cases, in which the receivers can be considered to be stationary during the GPS observation campaign, or not, respectively.

The two approaches of **point positioning** and **relative positioning** are discussed, in which either a single receiver is used or at least two receivers are used simultaneously. Relative positioning leads naturally into a discussion of **network determination**.

Kinematic positioning can be accomplished by means of several optional approaches involving either single or multiple GPS receivers or the use of additional observations, for example, from inertial navigation systems. The effect of GPS satellite constellation outages on kinematic positioning, and the role of constraints in overcoming them, complete this chapter.

POSITIONING PROBLEMS

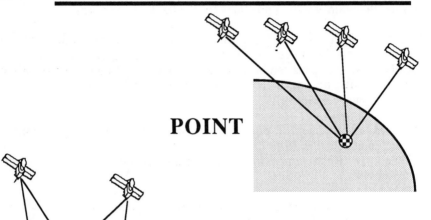

POINT

RELATIVE

NETWORK

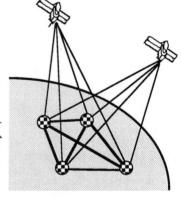

POSITIONING PROBLEMS

The three basic positioning problems to be solved are:

(1)   *point positioning* — a one point problem;
(2)   *relative positioning* — a two point problem; and
(3)   positioning a *network* of points — a many point problem.

Further, in reality these points may not be moving and thus are considered *static*, or they may be moving and thus are considered *kinematic*. Examples of the latter are a moving vehicle on land, an aircraft, or a vessel at sea.

STATIC:

- One, two, or several stationary points
- Results not needed in real time
- High redundancy, reliability and accuracy

KINEMATIC:

- One moving point
- Position relative to geocentre or
- Position relative to a second point
- Results needed in real time
- Low redundancy and thus lower accuracy
- Reliability required, thus combination and integration needed
- Improvement of results by postmission smoothing

MAIN CHARACTERISTICS OF STATIC AND KINEMATIC POSITIONING

The main characteristics of static and kinematic positioning are summarized in this figure. Static problems may involve only one point or many points. Kinematic problems, on the other hand, involve one moving point which is either defined relative to a geocentric coordinate system (absolute positioning) or another point (relative positioning).

The static class of solutions usually are performed postmission as there is normally no compelling need for real-time results. Some field preprocessing and preliminary solutions are made, however, to ensure the quality of the collected data. An abundance of data is most often available for static type solutions thereby yielding the best possible results.

Kinematic solutions, on the other hand, are characterized by a sparseness of observed data usually yielding only a unique solution. Kinematic solutions are often required in real time and the accuracies of the solutions are lower than those obtained in the static mode. Kinematic point accuracies may, however, be improved by performing relative positioning and by postmission processing, that is, 'smoothing' the data.

CLASSIFICATION OF
TYPES OF SOLUTIONS

POSTMISSION STATIC SOLUTIONS:

- **Point positioning**
- **Baseline**
- **Networks (project size)**
- **Networks (continental in size)**

KINEMATIC SOLUTIONS IN REAL TIME:

- **Instantaneous point positioning**
- **Instantaneous relative positioning**
- **Combined (p and Φ) point positioning**
- **Combined (p and Φ) relative positioning**
- **Integrated point positioning**
- **Integrated relative positioning**

POSTMISSION KINEMATIC POSITIONING:

- **Smoothing (filtering, prediction)**

CONSTRAINED SOLUTIONS

CLASSIFICATION OF TYPES OF SOLUTIONS

Another aspect which enters into defining the types of solutions possible is the type of observable used. These have already been discussed in the previous chapters. In the solutions discussed immediately below, we employ pseudo-ranges, Doppler, and single, double, and triple phase observables.

Taking the above issues into consideration, we have determined that a natural and convenient classificiation of positioning problems is the following:

(1) **Postmission Static Solutions** which include point positioning, and relative positioning (baseline) and network solutions.

(2) **Kinematic Solutions in Real Time** which includes a vast array of solutions beginning with instantaneous point positioning, instantaneous relative positioning, and integrated (range and/or phase and, e.g., inertial) relative positioning.

(3) **Postmission Kinematic Solutions** which includes smoothing algorithms.

It should be pointed out that at this stage the above stated positioning problems have been solved to various degrees of completeness. Each is now treated in succession.

POINT POSITIONING USING PSEUDO-RANGES

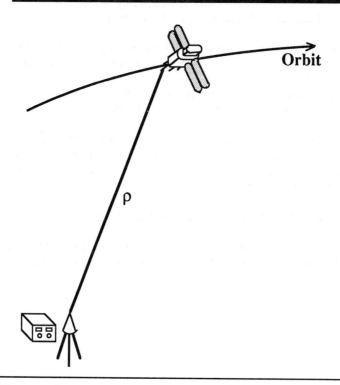

Orbit

ρ

Observation equation for pseudo-range:

$$p = \rho + c(dt - dT) + d_{ion} + d_{trop}$$

Observation equation for carrier phase:

$$\Phi = \rho + c(dt - dT) + \lambda N - d_{ion} + d_{trop}$$

POINT POSITIONING USING PSEUDO-RANGES

Point positioning utilizing pseudo-range measurements employs the following well-known GPS observation equation:

$$p = \rho + c\,(dt - dT) + d_{ion} + d_{trop},$$

where the observed range p is equal to the range ρ expressed as a function of the coordinates of the point (**R**) and the satellite coordinates (**r**). The ionospheric and tropospheric corrections to the range are applied and assumed correct. The clock bias $c(dt - dT)$ is due to the time offset between satellite and receiver clocks, and is left in the solution as a nuisance parameter to be solved for along with the position vector **R** of the point in question.

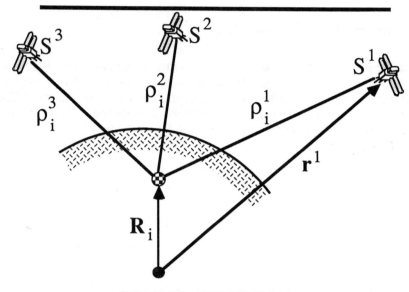

SATELLITE MULTI-RANGING

SCALAR EQUATION

$$\rho_i^j = \| r^j - R_i \|$$

— Measure LENGTHS ρ_i^j
to all satellites simultaneously

LIMITATIONS

Any error in r^j will result in an error in R_i

Propagation errors will cause errors in ρ_i^j

SATELLITE MULTI-RANGING

The mathematical model in conceptual form is

$$p = f(\mathbf{R}, \mathbf{r}, (dt - dT)) \ ,$$

where the three coordinates in $\mathbf{R}$ and $(dt - dT)$ are the four unknowns, while p is the observed quantity. It is clear from this figure that at least three p's are needed to solve for $\mathbf{R}$, and an additional p is needed so that a solution can be made for $(dt-dT)$ as well. Note that this solution is only possible if the satellite position $(\mathbf{r})$ is assumed known. This means that the ephemeris error is assumed to be zero. This assumption may degrade the accuracy of the solution.

In practice, dt is given a priori via the broadcast message, therefore the solution actually is made only for dT. The corresponding redundancy v of the solution is

$$v = n - 4 \ ,$$

where n is the total number of pseudo-ranges observed. A measure of the goodness of the accuracy of the solution is given by means of the covariance matrix $\mathbf{C}$ corresponding to $\mathbf{R}$ and dT.

In order to show how $\mathbf{C}$ is computed, we must now introduce the linearized version of the model f given above, namely:

$$\underset{n \times 1}{v} = \underset{n \times 4}{(\mathbf{A_R}\ \mathbf{A_T})} \underset{4 \times 1}{\begin{bmatrix} d\mathbf{R} \\ d\mathbf{T} \end{bmatrix}} + \underset{n \times 1}{\mathbf{w}} \ ,$$

where $\mathbf{w}$ is a vector of numbers obtained by evaluating f with approximate values of the position $\mathbf{R}$ and observed values of p; v is the vector of n residuals corresponding to the n pseudo-ranges, while $\mathbf{A_R}$ and $\mathbf{A_T}$ are the design matrices corresponding to the two sets of unknowns $d\mathbf{R}$ and $d\mathbf{T}$. Note the dimensions of the various vectors and matrices. For n equal to 4, we have the unique solution mentioned above. Also needed is the covariance matrix $\mathbf{C_p}$ of the pseudo-ranges; it is simply a diagonal matrix consisting of variances for each range.

LEAST-SQUARES SOLUTION FOR POINT POSITIONING

MODEL $\rho = f\{R, r, (dt - dT)\}$

LINERIZED MODEL

$$v = (A_R \; A_T) \begin{bmatrix} dR \\ dT \end{bmatrix} + w$$

$$\text{nx1} \quad \text{nx4} \quad \text{4x1} \quad \text{4x1}$$

NORMAL EQUATIONS

$$N \begin{bmatrix} dR \\ dT \end{bmatrix} + u = 0$$

$$N = (A_R \; A_T)^T \; C_P^{-1} \; (A_R \; A_T)$$

$$u = (A_R \; A_T)^T \; C_P^{-1} \; w$$

SOLUTION

$$\begin{bmatrix} dR \\ dT \end{bmatrix} = - N^{-1} u$$

ACCURACY OF THE SOLUTION

$$C_{R,T} = N^{-1} = \begin{bmatrix} C_R & C_{RT} \\ C_{TR} & C_T \end{bmatrix}$$

$$C_R = \begin{bmatrix} \sigma_x^2 & \sigma_{xy} & \sigma_{xz} \\ & \sigma_y^2 & \sigma_{yz} \\ & & \sigma_z^2 \end{bmatrix}, \; C_T = \sigma_T^2$$

LEAST-SQUARES SOLUTION
FOR POINT POSITIONING

The least-squares normal equations corresponding to the four unknowns is given by

$$N \begin{bmatrix} dR \\ dT \end{bmatrix} + u = 0,$$

where $N = (A_R \ A_T)^T C_p^{-1} [A_R \ A_T]$, and

$$u = (A_R \ A_T)^{-T} C_p^{-1} w.$$

The least-squares solution is

$$\begin{bmatrix} dR \\ dT \end{bmatrix} = -N^{-1} u.$$

The covariance for the three coordinates of the point and time bias as follows:

$$C_{R,T} = N^{-1} = \begin{bmatrix} C_R & | & C_{RT} \\ 3\times3 & | & 3\times1 \\ ----- & | & ----- \\ C_{TR} & | & C_T \\ 1\times3 & | & 1\times1 \end{bmatrix}$$
$$\underset{4\times4}{}$$

where C_{RT} and C_{TR} are cross-covariance matrices, and the matrices of interest are

$$C_R = \begin{bmatrix} \sigma_X^2 & \sigma_{XY} & \sigma_{XZ} \\ & \sigma_Y^2 & \sigma_{YZ} \\ \text{symmetric} & & \sigma_Z^2 \end{bmatrix},$$
$$\underset{3\times3}{}$$

and

$$C_T = \sigma_T^2,$$
$$\underset{1\times1}{}$$

which define the variances of the four unknowns. These four variances are used to define the various dilution of precision (DOP) measures. The above equations are summarized in this figure.

RELATIVE POSITIONING USING PSEUDO-RANGES

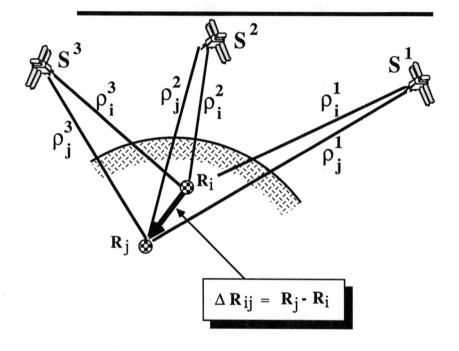

$$\Delta R_{ij} = R_j - R_i$$

Relative positions ΔR_{ij} are determined more accurately than "absolute" positions R_i and R_j, since several sources of error will be common at both receivers, and will cancel.

RELATIVE POSITIONING USING PSEUDO-RANGES

The task of determining the components ΔR_{ij} (ΔX, ΔY, ΔZ) of a baseline is a problem of relative positioning. Two (or more) receivers observe GPS signals simultaneously. Some errors are common (or similar) in the measurements made by the receivers. When solving for ΔR_{ij}, these errors cancel or are reduced.

The straightforward way of getting ΔR_{ij} is to perform two separate point position determinations R_i and R_j using, say, pseudo-ranges, and then difference the two results. It should be remembered that simultaneous measurements are needed so that errors common to each station cancel in the differencing of the two solutions.

RELATIVE POSITIONING USING PHASE MEASUREMENTS

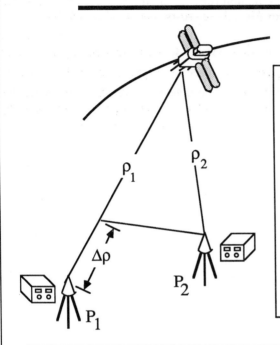

$\Delta dt \doteq 0$

(same satellite clock error in both observations)

$\Delta d\rho \doteq 0$

(effect of ephemerides inaccuracies almost identical in both observations

Observation equations:

$$\Delta p = \Delta\rho - c\,\Delta dT + \Delta d_{ion} + \Delta d_{trop} \qquad \text{(code)}$$

$$\Delta\Phi = \Delta\rho - c\,\Delta dT - \Delta d_{ion} + \Delta d_{trop} + \Delta N \quad \text{(carrier phase)}$$

RELATIVE POSITIONING USING PHASE MEASUREMENTS

Another, more accurate, way to do relative positioning is to use a single differenced phase or code measurement. Since phase measurements can be made more accurately than code measurements, its model is given below, namely:

$$\Delta\Phi = f(\Delta R, r, \Delta dT, \Delta N),$$

where two sets of nuisance parameters need be solved. The relative receiver clock bias, ΔdT, remains as the satellite clock error, dt, cancels out. The effects of ephemerides and refraction errors are almost identical at each receiver, thus, as a consequence of differencing, they are greatly reduced. Note, however, the presence of the carrier beat phase ambiguity ΔN. Hence, in relative positioning, with carrier phase observations, the inherent number of unknowns is three for ΔR, one for ΔdT, and one for the ambiguity parameter — a minimum of five equations are needed.

SATELLITE p $\quad$ Epoch t_2 $\quad$ Epoch t_1 SATELLITE q

Epoch t_1 $\qquad$ Epoch t_2

$\Phi_i^p(t_1)$

RECEIVER i $\quad$ RECEIVER j

Instantaneous	(Single) Difference over Receiver (Δ)	(Double) Difference Over Satellite (∇)	(Triple) Difference Over Time (δ)
$\Phi_i^p(t_1)$			
	$\Delta\Phi^p(t_1)$		
$\Phi_j^p(t_1)$			
		$\nabla\Delta\Phi(t_1)$	
$\Phi_i^q(t_1)$			
	$\Delta\Phi^q(t_1)$		
$\Phi_j^q(t_1)$			
			$\delta\nabla\Delta\Phi$
$\Phi_i^p(t_2)$			
	$\Delta\Phi^p(t_2)$		
$\Phi_j^p(t_2)$			
		$\nabla\Delta\Phi(t_2)$	
$\Phi_i^q(t_2)$			
	$\Delta\Phi^q(t_2)$		
$\Phi_j^q(t_2)$			

GPS PHASE MEASUREMENT DIFFERENCING

A clever technique has been developed to eliminate the ambiguity parameter, thus reducing the number of unknowns in our model to just four: three for ΔR, and one for ΔdT. This is achieved by forming two further differences to the between-receiver (Δ) difference, namely, the between-satellite (∇) and between-epoch (δ) differences.

The next model in this sequence is the so-called double difference model:

$$\nabla \Delta \Phi = f(\Delta R, r; \Delta N) \, .$$

Note that the relative receiver clock bias cancels.

The final model in the sequence is the so-called triple difference model:

$$\delta \nabla \Delta \Phi = f(\Delta R, r) \, .$$

Note that the ambiguity parameter has been eliminated.

One complication not mentioned above is that there is a price to pay for not having to solve for the ambiguity parameter. The covariance matrix for double and triple differences is non-diagonal, and the computation of its elements is given in Remondi [1985d]. A comforting note is that the solution obtained when using only a diagonal matrix is not adversely affected [Goad and Remondi, 1984]. Another disadvantage of using triple differences is that it is not possible to take advantage of the integer values of the ambiguity parameters. In some cases, however, it is not even possible to enforce the integer value; for example, for long baselines in which the atmospheric conditions are different. An important advantage of using triple differences is that cycle slips can be easily identified, however, when such slips occur, perfectly good undifferenced observations require rejection because the 'partner' observation in the difference is missing. This lack of continuity can be resolved successfully during preprocessing.

NETWORK SOLUTIONS

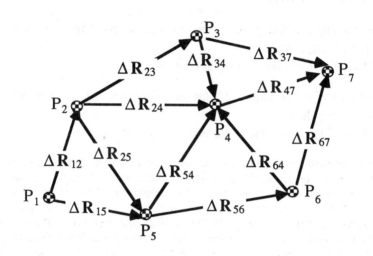

Provided all ΔR_{ij} are in the same coordinate

system as R_1 we have (for example):

$$R_7 = R_1 + \Delta R_{12} + \Delta R_{24} + \Delta R_{47}$$

NETWORK SOLUTIONS

GPS network processing techniques are still in their infancy, and at the time of writing this Guide, it is not possible to distinguish between all possibilities and state the definite way to perform this task.

Nevertheless, various researchers have followed one of two procedures depending upon the aim and extent of the network. When dealing with local networks of a few kilometres, but not larger than, say, 100 km, receiver coordinates are the main unknowns with orbit biases possibly appearing as nuisance parameters. The solution for corrections to orbital elements of GPS satellites is left to networks of regional or continental extent.

Coming back to local networks, there exist two approaches that have been used, namely:
(1) Reduce the observation campaign to simultaneous data observed from pairs of stations (baselines), and then combine these baselines into a network.
(2) Take the GPS observations observed simultaneously at all stations directly into a network adjustment where all the coordinates of the network are present as unknowns.

The baseline approach is rigorous if there are no common observations and biases between baselines. In this figure, an array of interconnected baselines is shown. If one considers one baseline as the basic unit, then the basic model for a three-dimensional adjustment is the following:

$$\Delta R_{ij} = R_j - R_i, \quad C_{\Delta R},$$

where ΔR_{ij} is the quasi-observed value of the coordinate difference with covariance matrix $C_{\Delta R}$. Note, the role played by R_j and R_i is that of unknowns to be solved for. This setup is akin to a levelling network, but in this context we get three-dimensional information instead of just height (one dimensional) information.

Another possibility is to perform a condition adjustment on the ΔRs. This means that for each independent vector polygon the sum of the vectors ΔR must be a zero vector. With the adjusted ΔRs, one is then able to compute the coordinates of any point, as indicated in this figure.

NETWORK SOLUTION AND ORBIT IMPROVEMENT

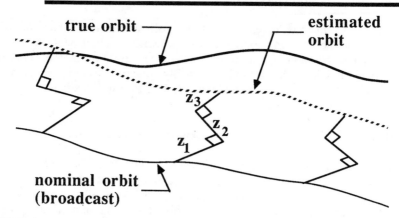

true orbit

estimated orbit

z_3
z_2
z_1

nominal orbit (broadcast)

THREE ORBIT BIASES APPROACH

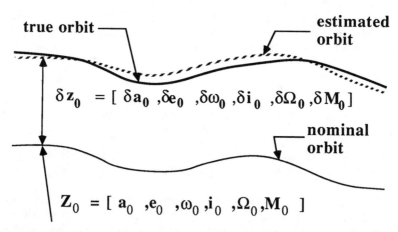

true orbit

estimated orbit

$$\delta z_0 = [\ \delta a_0\ ,\delta e_0\ ,\delta \omega_0\ ,\delta i_0\ ,\delta \Omega_0\ ,\delta M_0\ ]$$

nominal orbit

$$Z_0 = [\ a_0\ ,e_0\ ,\omega_0\ ,i_0\ ,\Omega_0\ ,M_0\ ]$$

SHORT-ARC STATE VECTOR APPROACH

NETWORK SOLUTION AND ORBIT IMPROVEMENT

One advantage of the network approach is that it is possible to expand the model to contain parameters for orbit improvement. This possibility, however, is only feasible if the networks are regional in extent.

Regional networks are those having an extent greater than 100 km and, in some applications, may be continental in extent. When station separations are of this magnitude, then it becomes both necessary and possible to improve the orbit along with the solution for the coordinates of the points in the network.

There are basically two approaches that have been developed for this purpose. One is the so-called orbit bias approach, and the second is the short-arc state vector approach. The mathematical model for both of these approaches can be written as follows:

$$f_1\,(\mathbf{R, r, b, l}) = 0, \ \ \mathbf{C}_l, \ \ \mathbf{C}_b$$

$$f_2\,(\mathbf{r, z}) = 0, \ \ \mathbf{C}_z \ ,$$

where we have a combination of models to solve. The first model contains the receiver coordinates $\mathbf{R}$, the satellite positions $\mathbf{r}$, some biases $\mathbf{b}$ (e.g., clock), and observables $\mathbf{l}$ which can be ranges and/or phase measurements. The second model represents a reparameterization of the $\mathbf{r}$s by $\mathbf{z}$ — a vector of six Keplerian orbital elements. $\mathbf{C}$ denotes a covariance matrix.

WEIGHTED SHORT-ARC SOLUTION

$$f_1 (R,r,b,l) = 0 \quad , C_1$$

$$f_2 (r ,Z_0) = 0 \quad ,C_{Z_0} \qquad \{r = BZ_0 \}$$

Z_0 - Six satellite initial conditions at reference time T_0

B - Perturbation and transformation equations relating corrections in Z_0 to corrections in r

ADVANTAGES:

- Rigorous orbit modelling provides highest possible accuracies

- Orbit characterization is physically meaningful

DISADVANTAGES:

- Increased computations

WEIGHTED SHORT-ARC SOLUTION

When f_2 is a simple coordinate transformation and z is collapsed into, say, three orbit biases (e.g., along track, radial, and out of the orbit plane), then we get the so-called orbit bias approach. When, however, f_2 represents the solutions of equations of motion and z_o is retained as a state vector of initial conditions, then we have the rigorous short-arc approach. With the latter it is possible to get meaningful orbits which are closer to the true orbits, while with the former the solved for biases simply help to absorb systematic effects [Wanless, 1985]. Further, the dynamic approach allows orbits to be predicted [Buffet, 1985]. Note the presence of the a priori covariance matrix C_{z_o} on the orbital elements which may be needed before the solution, hence explaining the name 'weighted' short-arc solution.

With a network of four station continental extent, it has been shown that it is possible to obtain orbits good to about two metres. With this in mind, the Canadian government is moving ahead with its GPS active control network scheme, which is meant to aid GPS users by supplying information on orbital and other biases to facilitate accurate relative positioning.

ABSOLUTE KINEMATIC POSITIONING

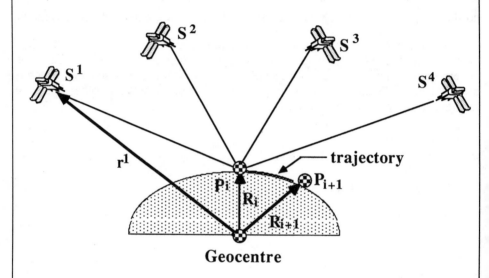

ABSOLUTE KINEMATIC POSITIONING

Absolute kinematic positioning is the determination of the position of a moving vehicle (on land, at sea, or in the air) at a specific epoch in time. The first thing this means is that the amount of data (pseudo-ranges) measured is usually just enough to get a unique solution. The mathematical model employed in this case is identical with that of static point positioning, namely,

$$p = f(R, dT)$$

with redundancy ν equal to 0 if four pseudo-ranges to four satellites are observed in order to solve for the three coordinates of R and the one clock bias parameter. Clearly, the goodness of the solution depends upon the geometrical distribution of the satellites.

RELATIVE KINEMATIC POSITIONING

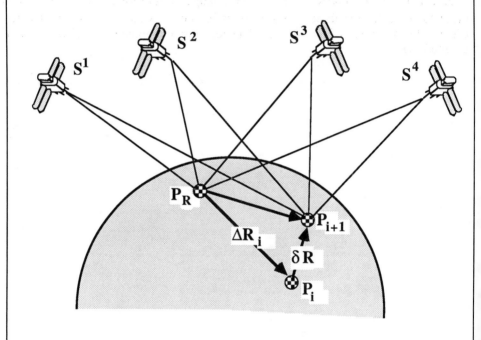

RELATIVE KINEMATIC POSITIONING

Kinematic relative positioning is the determination of the coordinates of one or more moving points relative to a fixed point. As with static relative positioning, many GPS errors (clock errors, ephemeris errors, propagation errors) are correlated between observations received at the reference station and at the moving point. As a result, to a large degree they cancel, and, hence, the relative position can be determined to a higher degree of accuracy than the absolute position.

The mathematical model for this mode is identical with the static relative positioning model. For pseudo-ranges

$$\Delta p = f(\Delta R, \Delta dT) \,,$$

where ΔR is the unknown relative position, ΔdT is the unknown clock bias of the moving receiver relative to reference receiver, and Δp is the observed receiver pseudo-range difference. Clearly, observations to four satellites are needed for a unique solution for the unknowns.

The relative model using the more accurate phase measurements has the following form:

$$\Delta \delta \Phi = f(\Delta \delta R, \Delta \delta dT) \,.$$

For real-time operations, a data link between the reference station and the moving receiver is required, in order to transmit bias information on δR. This method is valuable for 'setting out' surveys.

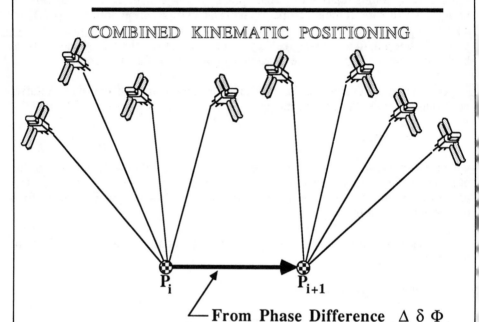

COMBINED KINEMATIC POINT POSITIONING

COMBINED KINEMATIC POSITIONING

P_i P_{i+1}

—From Phase Difference $\Delta \delta \Phi$

RELATIVE COMBINED KINEMATIC POSITIONING

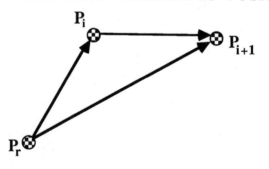

P_i

P_{i+1}

P_r

COMBINED KINEMATIC POINT POSITIONING

Kinematic point positioning involves the combination of the following two models:

$$p = f_1(\mathbf{R}, dT) ,$$

$$\delta\Phi = f_2(\delta\mathbf{R}, \delta dT) ,$$

where the first model is the standard point positioning model for pseudo-ranges, while the second contains a time differenced phase (change in phase) measurement yielding information on the change in position between contiguous epochs of pseudo-range determinations. Note the presence of the clock drift parameter, δdT.

In essence, the above model is a linkage of the discrete position determinations resulting from the kinematic absolute positioning mode described above. The solution of the above equations can be done by sequential least squares.

Kinematic relative positioning, using a combination of pseudo-ranges and phase (or Doppler) measurements, makes use of the following two models:

$$\Delta p = f_1(\Delta\mathbf{R}, \Delta dT)$$

$$\Delta\delta\Phi = f_2(\Delta\delta\mathbf{R}, \Delta\delta dT) .$$

What we have here is the same pseudo-range model for relative positioning combined with a time-difference phase measurement between the fixed and moving points. This model has all the positive characteristics of the relative positioning models (that is, biases cancel) but, in addition, we see that the time difference phase yields information on the change in relative position.

Integrated point and relative kinematic positioning take on mathematical models which, conceptually, are completely analogous to those discussed in the above two sections on the combination of GPS pseudo-range and phase data. All characteristics are the same.

It should be noted that we may integrate GPS models with other observables (systems), such as ships' log and gyro, Mini-Ranger, and even inertial systems. One must realize, however, that with inertial systems, the continuous dynamics of the trajectories are incorporated and accurate interpolation is possible. This is not possible with most other integrated systems which are intrinsically discrete operations possessing less accurate interpolation of position potential.

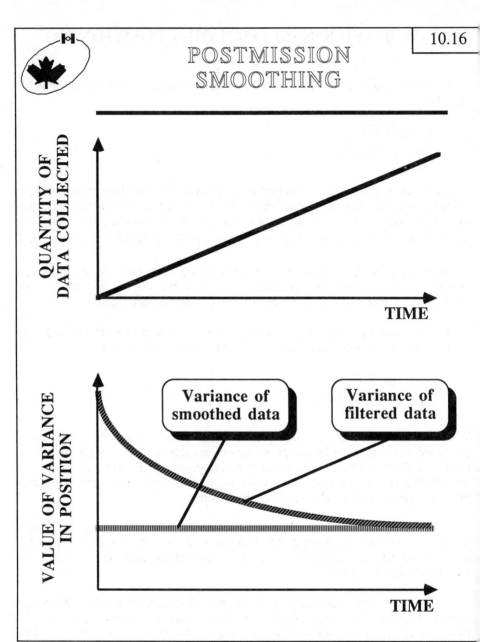

POSTMISSION SMOOTHING

QUANTITY OF DATA COLLECTED

TIME

VALUE OF VARIANCE IN POSITION

Variance of smoothed data

Variance of filtered data

TIME

POSTMISSION SMOOTHING

As already stated, kinematic positioning involves the determination of the trajectory of a moving vehicle. The amount of information (observations) on the trajectory increases with time. Positions computed in the past, however, do not benefit from the information collected in the present, and certainly do not benefit from the data to be collected in the future.

The key to being able to go backward in time and improve the results is whether the discrete time epochs have been linked in some way. This linkage has a very specific meaning, and that meaning is exemplified by those models f, discussed earlier, that involved the δ operator. These included combined point positioning, combined relative positioning, and integrated point and relative positioning. What we had in these models was the ability to predict the position at t_{i+1}, and determine (filter) the position at t_{k+1}. This task can be performed with the well-known Kalman (or Bayes) filter equations. The literature also contains the necessary equations that allows one to back solve (reverse) the filter equations and obtain updated (smoothed and improved) estimates of positions in the past from information that was collected since its filtered position was determined. Clearly, one would expect the variances corresponding to the smoothed solutions to be smaller than the filtered positions.

CONSTRAINED SOLUTIONS

WHAT OPTIONS DO WE HAVE ?

- Unconstrained solution for 3D position and time
- Height-constrained solution for 2D position and time
- Time-constrained solution for 3D position
- Height-and-time-constrained solution for 2D position

WHY CONSTRAIN OUR SOLUTION ?

- Improved geometrical strength
    - » improved position fix accuracy

WHY NOT CONSTRAIN OUR SOLUTION ?

- Must know "true" value of constrained parameter
    - » using wrong value may lead to much worse fix accuracy than the unconstrained solution

TIME CONSTRAINTS

- Useful constraints are 10 ns or smaller
    - » Only time observatories keep 10 ns time
    - » May be useful to "coast" through outage
        - » Cesium clock may keep 10 ns for one day
        - » Rubidium clock may keep 100 ns for one day
        - » Crystal clock may keep 10 µs for one day

HEIGHT CONSTRAINTS

- Useful constraints are 5 metres (15 ns) or smaller
    - » can we know our height to 5 m in a launch ?

CONSTRAINED SOLUTIONS

The geometry for a four-dimensional fix will be worse than that for a fix where we actually know one or more of the solution parameters in advance, and take this knowledge into account. We can use a technique known as **weighted constraints** — we let our solution vary from the assumed 'known' values of the weighted parameters only slightly. Constrained solutions are particularly useful to help the solution 'coast' through a rough period (that is, an outage in the geometry). However, there can be a price to pay: if the constrained parameter is weighted at an inappropriate value ('wrong' by much more than the weight constraint would indicate), then the remaining solution will be adversely affected.

Height constraints are a useful approach, for example, in the case of a conventional hydrographic survey from launches. Height constraints are quite effective at the 5 metre level, and 'knowing' our height to 5 metres, when at sea level in a survey launch, seems quite feasible. This figure shows how effective this can be in eliminating satellite outages.

In the following three figures, we consider this case study, and look at how feasible it is to constrain height to five metres realistically.

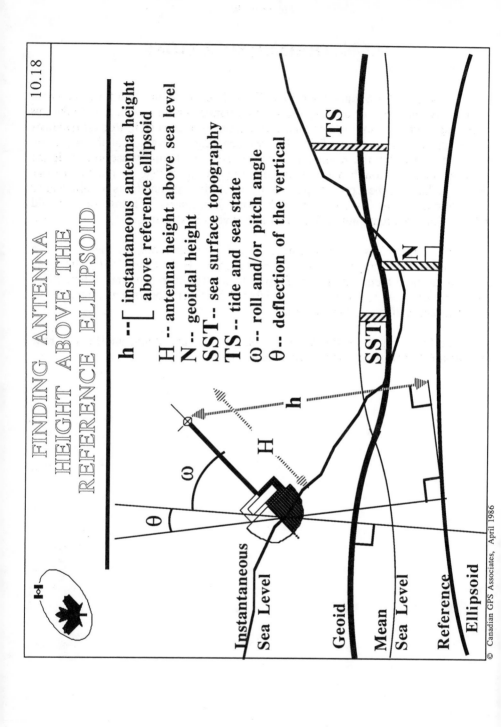

FINDING ANTENNA HEIGHT ABOVE THE REFERENCE ELLIPSOID

h -- ⌈ instantaneous antenna height
       ⌊ above reference ellipsoid
H -- antenna height above sea level
N -- geoidal height
SST -- sea surface topography
TS -- tide and sea state
ω -- roll and/or pitch angle
θ -- deflection of the vertical

Instantaneous Sea Level

Geoid

Mean Sea Level

Reference Ellipsoid

FINDING ANTENNA HEIGHT
ABOVE THE REFERENCE ELLIPSOID

This figure depicts all possible effects influencing the determination of antenna height. We need six values in order to get the **instantaneous height (h)** of the ship antenna above the selected reference ellipsoid.

- **Height (H) of the antenna above sea level:** This can be measured directly or indirectly in port to an accuracy corresponding to a standard deviation σ_H smaller than 10 centimetres. However, it will change with varying ship loading, according to the characteristics of the vessel.

- **Height (N) of the geoid above the reference ellipsoid:** The geoidal height, N, may reach as much as 100 metres. The best geoidal height information available today is good to about 2 metres (one sigma level) in an absolute sense with local relief being more accurate.

- **Roll and/or pitch angle (ω):** If we wish to account for roll, it either must be modelled in the solution, or has to be monitored; here we assume it can be monitored to an accuracy high enough so that we do not have to worry about the effect of σ_ω.

- **Tide and sea state (TS):** These have to be predicted from models. The combined magnitude may reach many metres. However, if good models are used for the prediction, its accuracy would be some 20 centimetres (one sigma level).

- **Semi-permanent sea surface topography (SST):** This is a rather difficult quantity to get hold of. Estimates exist [Lisitzin, 1974; Levitus, 1982] but it is somewhat uncertain just how good they are. Probably $\sigma_{SST} = 20$ cm would again be a fair assessment. The magnitude of SST is below 2 metres so that if the SST is considered to equal to zero, σ_{SST} would have to be raised to some 80 centimetres.

- **The deflection of the vertical (θ):** This is normally much smaller than one minute of arc and can be safely neglected.

FINDING THE GEOID HEIGHT:
ACCURACY AND DIFFICULTY

Data Source	Long Wavelength Accuracy (1 σ) With SST	Without SST	Required Data Storage	HP9816 Computation Time
Harmonic expansion of N 36 x 36 180 x 180	500 cm 150 cm	500 cm 170 cm	1,369 values 32,761 values	1 minute 5 minutes
N on 10' x 10' grid (gravimetric geoid)	150 cm	170 cm	36 values per 1x1 degree	< 1 sec
Satellite altimetry on 10' x 10' grid	150 cm	150 cm	36 values per 1x1 degree	< 1 sec

FINDING THE GEOID HEIGHT: ACCURACY AND DIFFICULTY

To be practically (99% probability) certain that h is good to 5 metres, how well do we have to know N? From the previous figure we have

$$\sigma_N = (500^2 cm^2 - \sigma_{SST}^2 - \sigma_{TS}^2 - \sigma_{H'}^2)^{1/2} = 182 \text{ cm} .$$

Where can the information about N be obtained that satisfies these accuracy requirements? There are three qualitatively different data sources readily available, summarized on this figure.

- **Geoidal heights expressed as high order and degree spherical harmonic expansion**: At least two sets of global potential coefficients that come to mind would satisfy the accuracy requirements: The Ohio State University (OSU) 180 by 180 model [Rapp, 1983] contains 32 761 coefficients. The evaluation of one N value from the OSU model takes about 5 minutes on an HP 9816 computer, once the coefficients are in the memory. A low degree expansion like the GEM 10B [Lerch et al., 1981] will not necessarily satisfy the above requirements, though its 1369 coefficients would require much less storage space.

- **Geoidal heights expressed on a regular geographical grid**: Gravimetric geoids, such as the Geodetic Survey of Canada geoid [Lachapelle, 1977] or the UNB geoid [Vaníček et al., 1986], can be precomputed on a regular grid, say 10' by 10'. Linear interpolation (very fast) between the grid nodes would suffice to give an adequately accurate N anywhere within the boundaries of the solution. The number of grid values (36 per 1° by 1° cell) to be stored would depend on the area covered by the navigating ship.

- **Satellite altimetry expressed on a regular geographical grid**: Gridded OSU SEASAT altimetry [Rapp, 1982] (heights of short period mean sea level above a reference ellipsoid) on a 10' by 10' grid and NASA 7.5' by 7.5' gridded SEASAT/GEOS-3 altimetry [Marsh et al., 1984] are available globally. These data sets would be really better suited for the antenna height determination because they automatically take care of at least part of the SST.

TYPICAL GEOID SHAPE

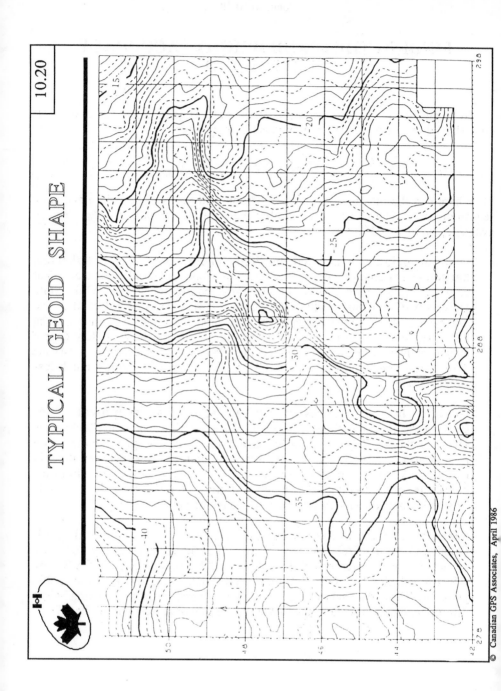

10.20

TYPICAL GEOID SHAPE

How often must the geoid height be computed?

To answer this question, let us first have a look at the horizontal gradient of N, $\partial N/\partial S$. One partial rectangle $\phi \in \langle 42°, 52° \rangle$, $\lambda \in \langle 278°E, 298°E \rangle$ from the new UNB gravimetric geoid solution is shown in this figure. This shows that changes in N are smooth, even on land. At sea the horizontal gradient is everywhere smaller than 1 minute of arc, and seldom larger than 10 seconds of arc. Normally at sea, N changes less than 1 metre in 30 km, and the changes are very smooth. Within the span of 1 hour, the changes of N can be always modelled (and forecast) as linear, and N updated as desired. At 10 knots, it would take 8 hours steaming for the geoid height to change by 5 metres, if the slope was as great as 1 metre in 30 km.

CHAPTER ELEVEN

STATIC APPLICATIONS AND RESULTS

STATIC APPLICATIONS AND RESULTS

STATIC APPLICATIONS:

- Geographical positioning applications
- Impact of GPS on control networks
- Height and geoid determination applications

QUASI-STATIC APPLICATIONS:

- Geodynamics applications
- Movement monitoring applications

RESULTS:

- Ottawa test network
- Western Canada triangle test
- Alberta township corner
- Urban tests in Québec City
- Gimli array test
- Long baseline test
- Gaithersberg test

STATIC APPLICATIONS AND RESULTS

In this chapter we consider the various applications for GPS in which the movement of the points being positioned is slow with respect to the duration of a GPS survey campaign (or perhaps there is no movement at all).

We will describe some of these applications conceptually, and will present some results which have been obtained so far with GPS in several tests, conducted mainly in Canada.

Some definitions:

• *Static* means that the points being positioned have no perceptible motion associated with them relative to surrounding points. All geographical positioning applications fall into this category in which the goal is to attach coordinates to points or features of interest.

• *Quasi-static* means that while there is perceptible relative motion among the points being positioned, it is generally so slow that it would not be noticed **during** a GPS survey campaign (a few days to weeks), but may become evident **between** campaigns (months to decades apart). Geodynamics and crustal movement monitoring applications fall into this category.

GEOGRAPHICAL POSITIONING APPLICATIONS

GEOGRAPHICAL POSITIONING

Attaching coordinates to objects of interest: e.g., control monument, gravity data point, census address, etc.

GPS AS A SURVEY TOOL

TWO RECEIVERS = FANCY "TOTAL STATION"
- No intervisibility limit
- No distance limit
- 3-D (no reference azimuth needed)

ONE RECEIVER + "ACTIVE CONTROL SYSTEM"
- Relative coordinates

COMPARISON TO OTHER TECHNIQUES

IMPACT ON LAND SURVEYING

ATTRIBUTES
- High accuracy
- Low cost
- Unified coordinate system

IMPACT ON CONTROL NETS

IMPACT ON SURVEYING PRACTICE

GEOGRAPHICAL POSITIONING APPLICATIONS

With the advent of GPS, accurate coordinates will be easily obtained for a variety of geographical applications. In addition to fulfilling the usual requirement of accurate coordinates for survey control monuments, GPS can provide equally-precise coordinates for other objects of interest, such as gravity data points, water sample points, and addresses for census purposes.

In the near term, the greatest impact of GPS in geographical positioning will be on the surveying industry. For many jobs, a pair of GPS receivers can replace a conventional total station instrument and greatly exceed its capabilities. With GPS, there is no intervisibility requirement and practically no limit to the distance between receivers. Furthermore, no reference azimuth is required as the coordinates obtained are relative three-dimensional coordinates of one point with respect to the other.

In addition to their high accuracy, GPS surveys will be carried out more cheaply than conventional surveys. For some types of surveys, this is even true at the present time with only the prototype constellation available. No line cutting or survey tower construction is required for GPS observations. It may be necessary to clear a small area surrounding a GPS antenna in order that the sky not be obscured, however, this is generally neither time consuming nor expensive. As a result, survey practice will be considerably changed with the adoption of GPS technology.

A further benefit accruing from the use of GPS is that all coordinates are in the same unique system. This characteristic considerably simplifies the use of position information in different applications and makes the creation of land information data bases that much easier.

GPS will have a particularly significant impact on survey control networks. This impact will be discussed in detail below.

IMPACT OF GPS ON CONTROL NETWORKS

WHAT INFORMATION DO COORDINATES CONTAIN?

Intrinsically - zero information

Information depends on attaching something to the coordinates

WHAT IS A CONTROL NETWORK ?

A set of monuments with attached coordinates

WHAT IS IT USED FOR ?

Transferring coordinates to other features
- **Boundary markers**
- **Map sheet corners**
- **Highways, power lines, etc.**

WHY ARE CONTROL NETWORKS INDEPENDENT FROM FEATURES OF REAL INTEREST ?

Limitations of control network survey and maintenance techniques

GPS removes some of those limitations

INDEPENDENT CONTROL NETWORKS MAY NOT BE NECESSARY !

IMPACT OF GPS ON CONTROL NETWORKS

A *control network* is a set of monumented points with coordinates (positions) attached to them. Historically, by necessity, adjacent points must have been intervisible to be able to employ the available surveying techniques. Positions were then derived through an integration (accumulation) process.

The only aim of a control network has been, and still is, to transfer coordinates to other features, that is, to allow positioning of other features with respect to the control points. With the advent of satellite positioning techniques, the role of control networks has begun to fade [Vaníček et al., 1983]. It is now possible to establish a control point anywhere without the necessity of having to connect it to already existing control points through chains of intervisible points. Intervisibility is no longer a requirement. Moreover, the necessity of having any control points at all is disappearing. It is now possible to position any desired feature directly using either a point positioning mode or relative positioning.

Direct positioning of features is naturally faster and more economical than their positioning by means of a control network. We thus believe that as soon as GPS receivers become sufficiently widespread among surveyors it will no longer be necessary or desirable to maintain a control network as we know it today. The network will then be gradually replaced by a set of GPS *foothold points*, whose main role will be to act as the fixed end of a baseline for relative positioning of any required points. An example of foothold points are the active control points discussed in Chapter 5.

HEIGHT AND GEOID DETERMINATION

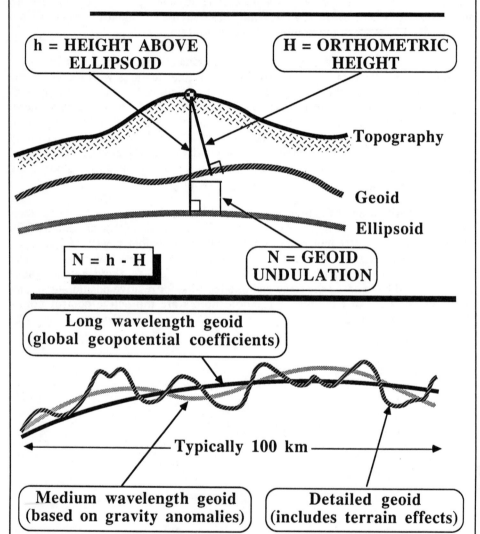

h = HEIGHT ABOVE ELLIPSOID

H = ORTHOMETRIC HEIGHT

Topography

Geoid

Ellipsoid

N = h - H

N = GEOID UNDULATION

Long wavelength geoid (global geopotential coefficients)

Typically 100 km

Medium wavelength geoid (based on gravity anomalies)

Detailed geoid (includes terrain effects)

HEIGHT AND GEOID DETERMINATION

GPS is a three-dimensional positioning system which can naturally provide heights and/or height differences above a selected ellipsoid. On the other hand, **orthometric heights** can be measured accurately by geometric levelling techniques. However, this is a slow and expensive process. If orthometric heights are known at satellite positioned stations, a direct and accurate measure of the geoid can be obtained by the following equation (see the figure):

$$N \doteq h - H.$$

Geoidal undulations (N) can also be estimated by gravimetric and other methods. Until now, it has been difficult to obtain reliable accuracy estimates for these methods. A comparison of gravimetrically-derived and satellite-derived undulations provides a reliable accuracy estimate for these quantities. For instance, this technique was used, with Transit-derived geoidal undulations, to assess the accuracy of the Canadian geoid during the late 1970s [Lachapelle, 1979]. Due to the low accuracy (50 to 100 cm) of the Transit-derived undulations, it was not possible to estimate the accuracy of the gravimetric geoid better than within the above range. The use of GPS-derived undulations nowadays permits an assessment of gravimetric undulation differences with an accuracy of the order of 5 to 10 cm. Recent tests performed in Canada (e.g., Schwarz et al. [1985]) show that the accuracy of the gravimetric geoidal height differences is currently of the order of 10 cm in the areas tested. This is very important as the various methods of computing the geoid (e.g., Lachapelle [1979], Schwarz et al. [1985], Vaníček et al. [1986]) can be more fully analysed and refined to produce a better result.

This, in turn, will lead to the combination of GPS-derived ellipsoidal heights and available geoidal undulations to derive orthometric heights in areas where geometric levelling operations are impractical. If the above gravimetric geoid accuracy of 10 cm can be confirmed over most or all of the country, it would become possible in the near future to establish orthometric heights with an accuracy of the order of 10 to 20 cm using GPS. This accuracy could be further improved by additional land and satellite-based gravimetric data and more refined geoid estimation methods.

GEODYNAMICS APPLICATIONS

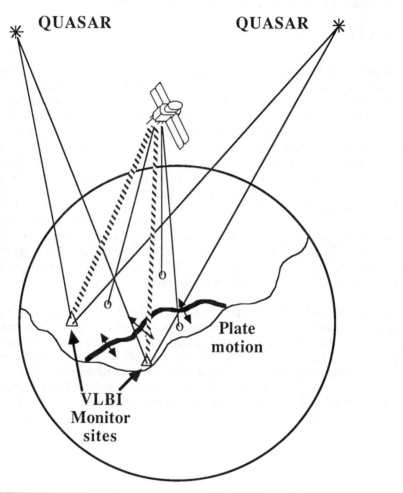

QUASAR   QUASAR

Plate motion

VLBI Monitor sites

GEODYNAMICS APPLICATIONS

The accuracy of baseline lengths determined from GPS carrier phase observations has already reached the level of 0.1 ppm. A relative error of 0.1 ppm translates to 3 cm on a baseline of, say, 300 km. This accuracy level implies that satellite orbital errors have been reduced to about 2 m. Such improved orbits can be obtained by simultaneously tracking the satellites from a network of VLBI sites, as well as from the sites of interest. With the ability to measure baselines of several hundred kilometres to an accuracy of a few centimetres, changes in baselines resulting from crustal plate motion, such as that along tectonic faults, can be monitored. GPS is therefore becoming an important tool for geophysicists attempting to understand better how the earth works.

The motions associated with plate tectonics are very small, generally of the order of a few centimetres per year. Nevertheless, such motion can be measured if a network of GPS receiver sites is established in the region of interest and the network is remeasured occasionally over a suitably long period of time. Such networks could be set up across fault zones, in areas of subsidence, or across spreading zones. The Jet Propulsion Laboratory (JPL) under the auspices of NASA has undertaken a campaign to measure the complex tectonic motion of parts of Mexico and the Caribbean using GPS [Thornton et al., 1986]. Another application of GPS in the study of geodynamics is the international campaign for monitoring the crustal motions in Iceland.

If an earthquake occurs in a region being monitored by GPS, it should be possible to accurately measure the co- and postseismic deformation. Such measurements could provide valuable clues in understanding the mechanism of earthquakes, tectonic or other.

The use of GPS to monitor the bulging of volcanos preceding eruption has also been suggested [King et al., 1985]. Although such monitoring can be done using conventional surveying techniques, it may be awkward, time consuming, and more importantly unsafe. GPS data from individual receivers placed on the flank and in the crater of a volcano could be telemetered to a central site at some distance where the volcano's deformation could be monitored safely.

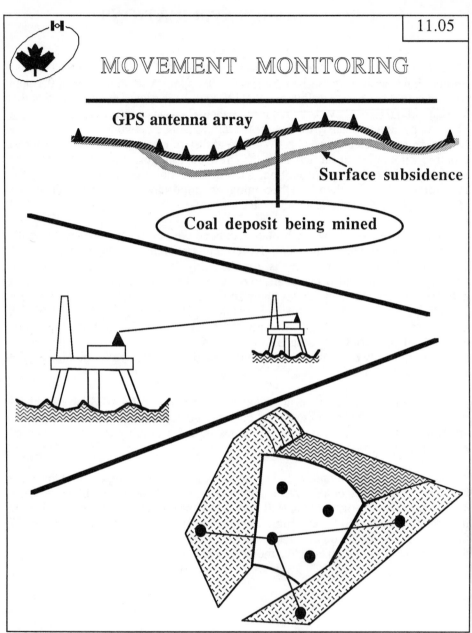

MOVEMENT MONITORING

GPS antenna array

Surface subsidence

Coal deposit being mined

MOVEMENT MONITORING

GPS, thanks to its three-dimensional accuracy, can be used for a wide variety of man-made *movement monitoring* tasks, ranging from surface subsidence caused by sub-surface mining to hydro-electric power dam deformation. Three specific applications are described herein.

Hydro-Electric Dam Deformation: This type of structure is constantly being deformed due to the load exerted on the earth's crust by the water behind the dam. In a large hydro-electric complex, the continuous monitoring of horizontal and vertical deformations may be required for safety reasons. GPS may be the most cost effective tool for this task. Firstly, it is capable of meeting the stringent accuracy requirements (1.0 to 0.1 ppm). Secondly, an array of GPS receivers could be installed permanently at proper sites and controlled remotely. In distant areas, the data could be regularly transmitted by means of an appropriate telemetry link to a processing centre for reduction and analysis.

Offshore Platform Subsidence: This GPS application has arisen in connection with the subsidence of petroleum exploration platforms in the North Sea which is due to the extraction of oil and gas [Collins, 1986]. The rate of subsidence can typically range between 10 and 50 cm per year. The platforms are periodically surveyed, say, every month to every six months. Each survey is conducted over a period of several days to insure a satisfactory short-term repeatability. The accuracy requirements being very stringent, orbital and multipath effects can be significant. Nearby platforms, assumed stable, are often used to obtain a higher accuracy through relative positioning.

Surface Subsidence: This potential application arises in connection with sub-surface mining, water, or oil withdrawal. The use of GPS can be very cost effective in such a case, since no interstation visibility is required. An array of GPS receivers can be deployed and moved quickly between sites of interest. Once the GPS constellation is complete, an array of n receivers could monitor (n-1) x 8 sites per working day (of 10 to 12 hours). Weather dependance would be decreased significantly as compared to classical survey methods.

OTTAWA TEST NETWORK

11.06

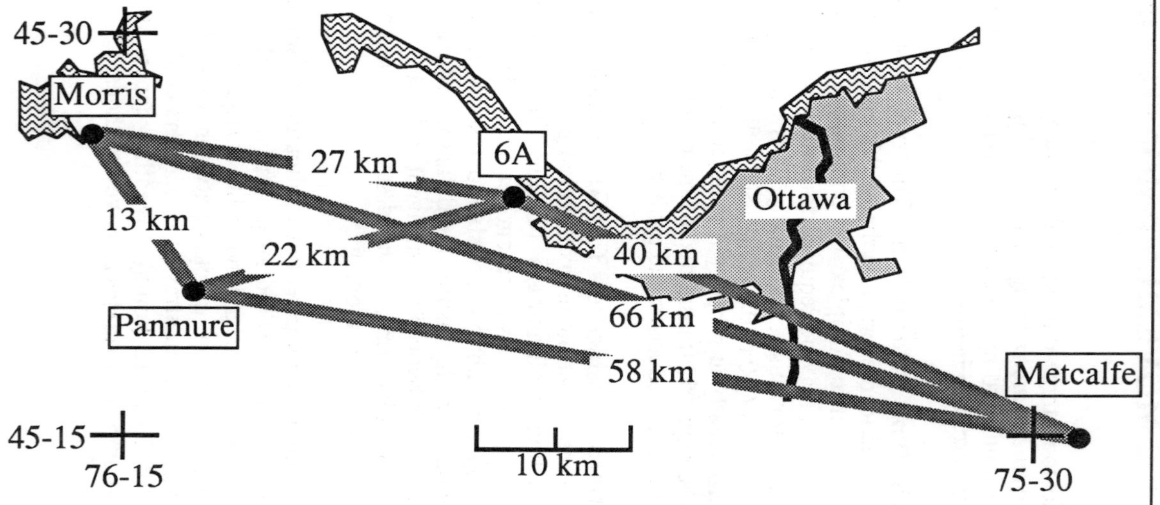

© Canadian GPS Associates, May 1987

Metcalfe
75-30

Ottawa

40 km
66 km
58 km

10 km

6A

27 km

22 km

13 km

Panmure

45-15
76-15

Morris
45-30

OTTAWA TEST NETWORK

During the summer of 1983, the Ottawa test network of the Geodetic Survey of Canada was observed using Macrometer™ V-1000 single frequency GPS receivers. Carrier beat phase data were recorded on the four stations shown here and at a few more locations close to these stations. Data were collected for up to four sessions (five hours each) per baseline. The observation sessions extended from 15:30 through 20:30 local time. In the spring of 1984, the network was re-observed with Texas Instruments TI-4100 receivers. Per baseline, up to two sessions (five hours each) were conducted between 20:00 and 01:00 local time. Relative positions resulting from these observation campaigns have been published by Beutler et al. [1984] and Kleusberg et al. [1985b]. The network has also been observed using ISTAC model 2002 receivers.

Macrometer™ V-1000 results: The carrier beat phase observations were adjusted using three different programs: Macrometrics' software for baseline vector solutions, UNB software for baseline solutions, and UNB software for network solutions (the last two being the third generation UNB software package DIPOP, used in two of its modes). All three results agreed at the 1 ppm level. The network solution is the most reliable one since it combines all observations at all stations to derive a unique set of station coordinates. Thus nonsystematic errors due to neglected ionospheric propagation delays (single frequency observations!) and other sources are reduced, at least partially.

Texas Instruments TI-4100 results: The dual frequency observations were adjusted at UNB in the network solution mode, also using DIPOP. The adjustment was done separately for the L1 carrier beat phases only and the ionospheric delay free linear combination of L1 and L2 phases. Both results agreed at the 1 ppm level.

Comparison of V-1000 and TI-4100: A comparison of the two network solutions (dual frequency result for TI-4100) showed an agreement at the 1 ppm level for the baseline lengths and height differences. The horizontal coordinate differences between the two solutions exhibited a significant rotation of about 0.5", thought to be due to orbital errors.

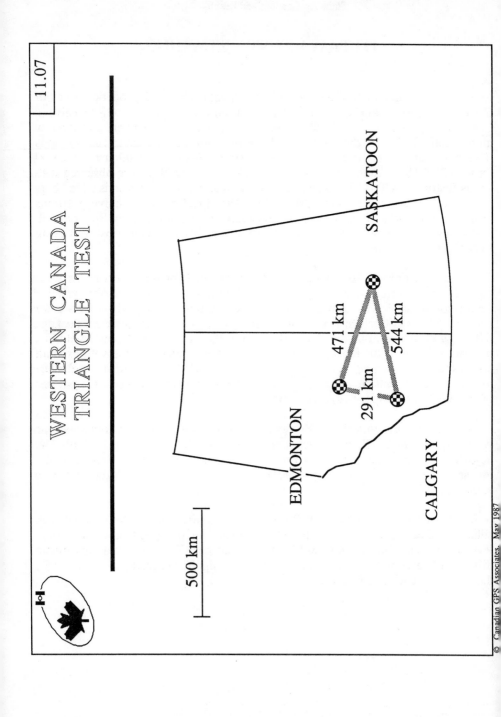

WESTERN CANADA TRIANGLE TEST

During April 1985, a triangle with baselines of 291, 471, and 544 km, respectively, was observed with 3 TI-4100 receivers over 5 days [Lachapelle and Cannon, 1986]. The primary objectives were to assess the short term repeatability of GPS determined positions and quantify the effect of the ionosphere on results using successively single and dual frequency data. The dual frequency data were used to correct for the effect of the ionosphere. Three days of dual frequency data, and two days of single frequency data, were collected. Six GPS satellites were available, and each daily observation session lasted four hours.

Each daily collected data set was processed independently using program PHASER [Goad, 1985]. The broadcast ephemerides were utilized. Carrier phase measurements at 30 second intervals were used. For the 3 days during which dual frequency observations were taken, L1 only, L2 only, and ionospherically corrected (L1/L2) measurements were successively processed to isolate the effect of the ionosphere. The stations utilized were not tied to existing networks, and the daily solutions were compared with the average L1/L2 solution based on the three days of dual frequency observations. In general, the single frequency results are consistent to within 2 to 3 ppm in terms of maximum scatter, while the dual frequency result consistency is of the order of 1 ppm. The effect of the ionosphere is thus of the order of 1 ppm. This is significant for accurate applications.

The observations took place during the middle of the night when the effect of the ionosphere is expected to be minimal. Also, the sunspot activity during 1985 was near a minimum. A maximum will be reached in 1991. At that time, the effect of the ionosphere could reach several parts per million.

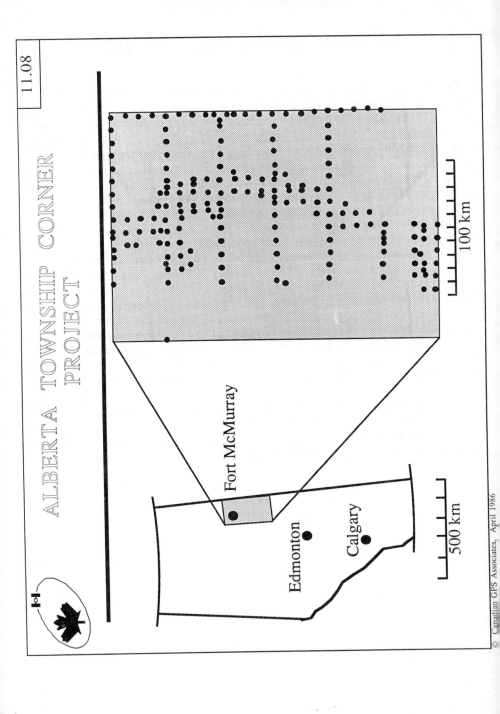

11.08

ALBERTA TOWNSHIP CORNER PROJECT

Fort McMurray

Edmonton

Calgary

500 km

100 km

© Canadian GPS Associates, April 1986

ALBERTA TOWNSHIP CORNER PROJECT

During the autumn of 1984, a 200-station network was established in an area of 135 x 230 km for the Alberta Bureau of Surveying and Mapping using four Macrometer™ V-1000 GPS receivers [Leeman and Fletcher, 1985]. The major objectives were to find and re-establish surveyed township corners and connect these to the Alberta Survey Control System. The network included 7 existing primary Doppler stations and 7 Alberta Survey Control points. The 6 (increased to 7 in the midst of the observation campaign) GPS satellites available provided 5.5 hours of observation daily. This resulted in up to 3 daily observation sessions, or up to 9 quasi-independent baselines. The distance between sites was on average 39 km. Transportation between sites was provided by helicopters.

The single baseline solutions were provided by the sub-contractor. These baselines were subsequently adjusted simultaneously by the contractor, firstly in an unconstrained mode and, secondly, in a constrained mode using the 7 existing primary Doppler stations included in the observation campaign. The number of degrees of freedom was 82 and 94 for the unconstrained and constrained adjustment, respectively. The estimated a posteriori variance factors were 1.58 and 2.69 for each of the two modes. This was considered satisfactory. Overall, the survey was estimated accurate to between 3 and 4 ppm. The field operations were completed within 71 days, averaging almost 3 points per day. The project was considered very successful.

URBAN TESTS
IN QUEBEC CITY

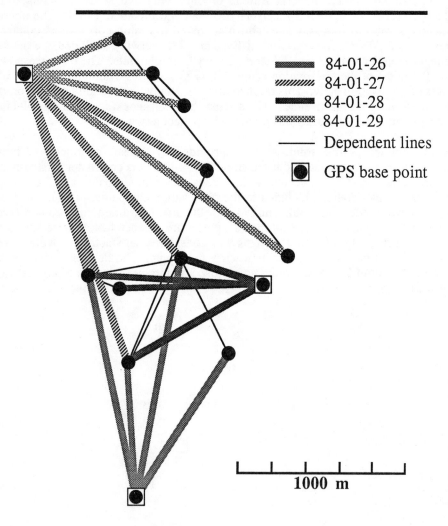

▬▬▬	84-01-26
▨▨▨	84-01-27
▬▬▬	84-01-28
▦▦▦	84-01-29
——	Dependent lines
⬤	GPS base point

1000 m

URBAN TESTS IN QUEBEC CITY

A 16-station network located in the Québec City area, with baselines ranging from 200 m to 2 km, was established in 1984 and re-observed in 1985 using successively the Macrometer™ V-1000 and TI-4100 receivers. The purpose of this project was to assess the capability of GPS to meet the Québec survey specifications for this application under a wide range of climatic and multipath environments [Moreau et al. 1985; Moreau 1986].

The Macrometer™ V-1000 test was conducted in January 1984. Three receivers were used to obtain 4 quasi-independent baselines each day. The field observations were completed in 4 days. The data were processed using both Beutler's [1984] software and that developed by the contractor; the agreement between the results was of the order of 1 mm, which was considered fully satisfactory. The external consistency of the GPS coordinate differences with the local network was of the order of 4 mm (r.m.s.) horizontally and 5 mm vertically.

The TI-4100 test was conducted in March 1985. Again, three receivers were used to obtain 4 quasi-independent baselines each day. The field observations were completed in 7 days. The data were processed by the sub-contractor. Comparison of the GPS results with the local network revealed some inconsistencies on a few baselines which were subsequently rejected from the final adjustment. After rejection of these baselines, the average agreement with the local coordinates was of the order of 1 cm. Overall, the results were not as satisfactory as the Macrometer™ V-1000 results.

The general conclusion is that GPS will become a cost effective tool for urban densification once the complete satellite constellation is available.

GIMLI, MANITOBA, ARRAY TEST

11.10

50 km

© Canadian GPS Associates, April 1986

GIMLI, MANITOBA, ARRAY TEST

During August 1984, a 22-station multi-purpose geodetic network was established under contract for the Geodetic Survey of Canada, using four Macrometer™ V-1000 receivers [McArthur et al. 1985]. The primary objective was to obtain three-dimensional coordinate differences with an accuracy of 2 ppm or better. The field observations were conducted over a 17-day period. A daily observation time period of 5 hours, based on 6 GPS satellites, was selected. Three of the four receivers were usually moved during the middle of an observation period, so that 6 quasi-independent baselines could be observed every day.

The GPS observations were reduced in single baseline mode using the contractor's software. The redundant baselines, that is, the third baseline of each triangle, was also calculated to assist the Geodetic Survey of Canada in its quality control of the single baseline reduction process. The triangle misclosures (in terms of the sum of the three baselines of each triangle), which constitute a measure of the internal consistency of the processing methodology and software, were generally better than 1 ppm wherever they could be formed. This was considered satisfactory. Some 15 baselines were measured twice, and the differences between the two sets of solutions ranged between 0.2 and 21.4 cm, with an average of 5 cm or 1.8 ppm. The single baselines were adjusted using three different methods. This was done to assess the impact of including or not including the redundant baselines in the final solution. All three methods yielded equivalent results in the statistical sense. The differences between estimated values were generally smaller than 2 cm. Overall, the 2 ppm accuracy objective was achieved, and the project was considered satisfactory.

LONG BASELINE TESTS

SPRING 1985 HIGH-PRECISION BASELINE TEST SITES

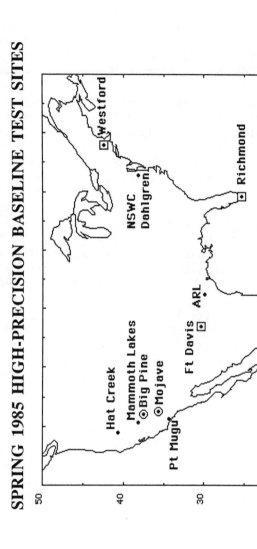

LONG BASELINE TESTS

Most results that have been obtained with GPS have been on relatively short baselines ranging from less than a kilometre in length to one or two hundred kilometres. However, several tests have been carried out with baselines as long as several thousand kilometres. Such long baseline tests are useful for separating and understanding the various biases affecting GPS observations and for accurately modelling the orbital biases of the satellites.

One such long baseline test was the Spring 1985 High-precision Baseline Test organized by JPL. Between 29 March and 5 April, dual-frequency GPS receivers were operated at 10 sites in the continental U.S. Six of the sites have permanent VLBI radio telescopes near by. Another site (Mammoth Lakes) has been visited by a mobile VLBI station. All 10 sites were occupied by Texas Instruments TI-4100 receivers. At two sites (Mojave and Big Pine), JPL's SERIES-X receivers were also operated, and at Westford, Richmond, and Fort Davis, U.S. Air Force Geophysical Laboratory dual-frequency receivers (the forerunner of the Macrometer II) were additionally operated. The receivers were used with a variety of frequency standards: hydrogen masers, cesium and rubidium frequency standards, and receiver internal oscillators. Water vapour radiometers were operated at three of the sites in California: Hat Creek, Mojave, and Big Pine.

A number of research groups have analysed the data from the test. Preliminary results of the analyses of data from all three types of receiver indicate agreement in baseline lengths with those determined by VLBI to about 0.1 ppm [University of Texas, 1986]. In order to achieve this accuracy, the satellite orbits were adjusted using the data from three or more of the stations. Use of the broadcast ephemerides alone resulted in baseline errors up to 2 ppm.

GAITHERSBURG TEST
AUGUST 12/13 1985

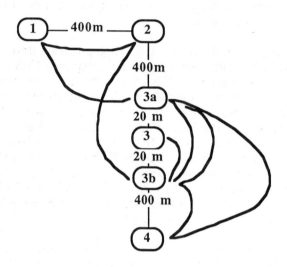

SEMI-KINEMATIC GPS POSITIONING:

- Eleven baselines
- One hour total duration
- Initial baseline in 7 minutes
- 45-105 seconds for other baselines

RESULTS:

- Worst case   3.5 cm away from reference
- Typically   1.2 cm away from reference

GAITHERSBERG TEST, AUGUST 12/13 1985

A dramatic new concept in GPS positioning was suggested by Ben Remondi of the U.S. National Geodetic Survey in early 1985, and successfully tested in August of that year. This concept has been dubbed 'semi-kinematic' GPS positioning. It has important implications for the use of GPS in such applications as setting-out surveys, aerotriangulation without ground control, and very precise positioning of moving vehicles. It drastically reduces the observing time needed to achieve the desired accuracy.

The basic idea is that the extreme accuracy of carrier beat phase measurements can be used to precisely measure **movements** of the **receiver**, as long as the carrier signal is continuously tracked, with no cycle slips. In order to extract the full accuracy from carrier beat phase measurements, the other, much larger, biases from orbit ephemeris errors, satellite clocks, and refraction must be eliminated. This is done by operating differentially. A special calibration procedure to quickly estimate the cycle ambiguity bias was also suggested by Remondi.

The procedure then is to use two receivers, one to act as a stationary monitor, the other as a roving receiver. The initial cycle ambiguity bias is determined in a matter of minutes by initially setting them up close to each other (a few tens of metres apart), and swapping their antennas. The roving receiver is then moved from point to point in such a way as to prevent shading of any satellite signals by human bodies, trees, transmission lines, etc. Care must also be taken that the receiver tracking loops are set consistently with the motion of the roving antenna. Hopefully, if both receivers are operating reliably, there will be no cycle slips, and a continuous record of carrier phase from start to finish of the operation will be achieved.

This figure summarizes the results of the first test of this method, held at the U.S. National Geodetic Baseline at the National Bureau of Standards in Gaithersburg, Maryland. Two TI-4100 receivers were initially swapped between pillars 3 and 3b, and then the roving receiver was moved (the antenna carefully held aloft by someone sitting on the roof of a truck carrying the receiver and power supply) to pillars 3a, 3b, 4, 3a, 1, 2, and finally back to 3b. At each pillar the antenna was sited on the pillar long enough to switch the receiver from 'low dynamics' to 'static' tracking loop setting. Eleven baselines were measured with an accuracy of a few centimetres. The entire operation, from ambiguity calibration to shutdown, took about one hour.

CHAPTER TWELVE

KINEMATIC APPLICATIONS AND RESULTS

KINEMATIC APPLICATIONS AND RESULTS

PRINCIPLE OF KINEMATIC POSITIONING

- **Kinematic positioning models**
- **Comparison of kinematic models**
- **Real-time vs postmission processing**
- **Accuracy and instrumentation**
- **Range of applications**

LAND VEHICLE APPLICATIONS

- **Land vehicle test traverse**
- **Land vehicle positioning results**
- **Land vehicle velocity results**

SHIPBORNE APPLICATIONS

- **Hydrographic survey test area**
- **Hydrographic survey test results**
- **3-D seismic surveys**

AIRCRAFT APPLICATIONS

- **Laser bathymetry**
- **Aerotriangulation without ground control**
- **Airborne gravimetry**
- **Helicopter applications**

KINEMATIC APPLICATIONS AND RESULTS

In this chapter, we discuss applications of GPS in which the movement of the receiver platform is so fast that for each measurement epoch an individual position has to be determined. We prefer the term *kinematic positioning* over the widely used *dynamic positioning,* since the GPS observables do not depend on the dynamics involved in the receiver motion.

The receiver movement between measurement epochs means that GPS observations over an extended period of time cannot be combined in an ordinary least-squares adjustment. Instead, either **single epoch positions** must be computed independently or the measurements observed on the receiver trajectory may be combined in a **filter/smoother algorithm**. The latter approach will generally improve the positioning accuracy compared to single epoch results and allow the inclusion of measurements obtained with other sensors (e.g., inertial survey system).

In some kinematic applications we encounter another distinct feature: the requirement of computing positions in **real time**. For real-time **relative** kinematic positioning, a data link must be established between the GPS reference station and the user. Differential data links are described in Chapter 13.

Obviously, the determination of position and velocity in real time is closely related to **navigation**.

PRINCIPLE OF KINEMATIC POSITIONING

ABSOLUTE KINEMATIC POSITIONING

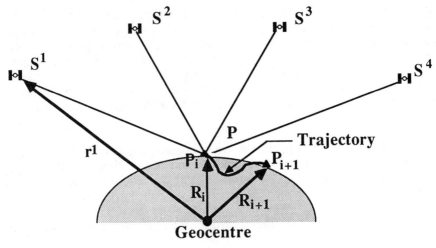

RELATIVE KINEMATIC POSITIONING

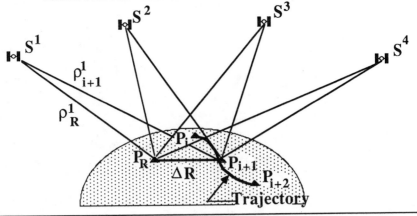

PRINCIPLE OF KINEMATIC POSITIONING

Kinematic positioning refers to applications in which the trajectory of a moving object is determined. In the applications considered here, the moving object is a GPS receiver carried by a road vehicle, a ship, or an aircraft. Slow kinematic carriers, like glaciers and tectonic plates, have been treated in Chapter 11 and will not be considered here. Kinematic positioning is closely related to **navigation**. In the first application, the positioning aspects are emphasized, while in the second application, the guidance aspects, i.e., speed and heading, are of primary interest. In addition, real-time results are required in navigation, while postmission results are quite acceptable in many kinematic positioning applications. Although the two areas overlap to some extent, the above distinctions are useful from an application point of view.

Kinematic positioning with respect to an implied coordinate system, as, e.g., the conventional terrestrial system, will be called *absolute kinematic positioning.* An alternative term often used is kinematic point positioning. Positioning with respect to one or several receivers at known positions, which track the same radiopositioning signals as the moving receiver, will be called *relative kinematic positioning.* An alternative term often used is differential kinematic positioning. Real-time relative kinematic positioning requires a radio link between the stationary and the moving receiver. The principle of absolute and relative kinematic positioning is shown in this figure. Because of the simultaneity of the measurements and the resulting reduction of satellite errors, relative positioning is more accurate than absolute positioning. This should be understood such that the vector ΔR can be determined more accurately than the vector R.

GPS measurements used for absolute and relative kinematic positioning are pseudo-ranges and phase measurements or a combination of both. GPS measurements can also be combined with observations coming from other sensors. The resulting models will be briefly reviewed in the next section.

KINEMATIC POSITIONING MODELS

ABSOLUTE KINEMATIC POSITIONING

PSEUDO-RANGE ONLY: $p = f_1 \{R, dT\}$

COMBINED: $p_i = f_1 \{R_i, dT\}$

$$\delta\Phi = f_2 \{\delta R, \delta dT\}$$

INTEGRATED: f_1 and f_2 as above

$$\delta l_v = f_3 \{v, \delta v\}$$

RELATIVE KINEMATIC POSITIONING:

PSEUDO-RANGE ONLY: $\Delta p = g_1 \{\Delta R, \Delta dT\}$

PHASE ONLY : $\Delta\delta\Phi = g_2 \{\Delta\delta R, \Delta\delta dT\}$

COMBINED: g_1 and g_2 as above

INTEGRATED: g_1 and g_2 as above

$$\delta l_v = g_3 \{v, \delta v\}$$

KINEMATIC POSITIONING MODELS

Let us review the major features of the kinematic positioning basic models and solution approaches (details of which are contained in Chapters 7, 8, and 10).

The two major subgroups are absolute and relative positioning models, each of which is further subdivided into four measurement-dependent categories: pseudo-range, phase, combined, and integrated. The first uses pseudo-range measurements only; the second uses linear combinations of phase measurements; the third employs a combination of pseudo-range and phase measurements; the fourth integrates pseudo-range and/or phase measurements with the output of other sensors, typically an inertial system. Either C/A-code or P-code pseudo-ranges may be used.

• In the absolute mode, *pseudo-range kinematic positioning* uses pseudo-range measurements p to at least four satellites to determine the receiver position R and the clock bias dT. In the relative mode, measurements are differenced over receivers, and p, R, dT are replaced by Δp, ΔR, ΔdT.

• *Phase kinematic positioning* is intrinsically a relative method [Remondi, 1985b]. It uses phase measurements to at least four satellites from both receivers to determine coordinate differences with respect to the known initial position of the moving receiver and the clock drift $\Delta \delta dT$ between the two receivers.

• *Combined kinematic positioning* uses a minimum of four pseudo- ranges p and four phase measurements Φ to determine the receiver positions R_i and R_{i+1}, the receiver clock bias dT, and its drift δdT [Kleusberg, 1986]. Absolute and relative positioning are handled as outlined above.

• *Integrated kinematic positioning* adds a dynamic component g_3 to the measurements, resulting in the determination of a practically continuous trajectory [Wong and Schwarz, 1983]. In case of an INS, for instance, velocity measurements 1_v are available about every 50 milliseconds, and thus the kinematic point density improves dramatically. This has considerable advantages if precise interpolation is required.

COMPARISON OF
KINEMATIC MODELS

GPS ALONE:

- **PSEUDO-RANGE KINEMATIC POSITIONING**
  - » No vessel dynamics
  - » Trajectory as string of independent position fixes
  - » Equivalent to static case
  - » Absolute mode makes for simple system
  - » Relative mode reduces errors

- **PHASE KINEMATIC POSITIONING**
  - » No vessel dynamics
  - » Trajectory as sum of δ vectors
  - » Sequential least squares
  - » Relative mode reduces errors
  - » Problems with cycle slips

- **COMBINED KINEMATIC POSITIONING**
  - » Similar to phase method trajectory as combination of position fixes and δ vectors

INTEGRATED SYSTEMS:

- **INTEGRATED KINEMATIC POSITIONING**
  - » Full vessel dynamics (INS)
  - » Practically continuous trajectory
  - » Kalman filter and smoother for dynamic system
  - » Best accuracy and reliability
  - » Complex system

COMPARISON OF KINEMATIC MODELS

All models, with the exception of the integrated one, use **GPS measurements only.** This makes for a simple measurement system which is usually also advantageous in terms of costs. Compared to the more elaborate integrated systems, however, it has drawbacks in terms of accuracy, reliability, and interpolation.

In the simplest case, **absolute pseudo-range positioning,** only one receiver is needed. The trajectory is modelled by a string of independent point fixes which currently are seconds apart. The vessel dynamics are not taken into account, and simplifying assumptions are necessary for interpolation. The accuracy is basically the same worldwide and is sufficient for most navigation purposes. It is, however, not adequate for many geodetic and geophysical applications. The simplicity of the measurement system is thus paid for in terms of accuracy and reliability. The other absolute positioning models (combined, integrated) will give a smoother but not a more accurate trajectory.

The accuracy is considerably better for **relative pseudo-range positioning.** Although the modelling technique is the same, the elimination of a number of common error sources improves the accuracy of the results. However, the accuracy now becomes dependent on the distance between stationary and moving receivers, and the simplicity of the original configuration is gone.

An even better accuracy is possible with **relative phase positioning.** Differenced phase measurements provide a measure for the receiver position change between epochs. Since the noise of the phase measurements is much lower than that of pseudo-ranges, the accuracy of this positioning method is potentially higher. It requires, however, the absence of cycle slips.

Relative combined positioning goes one step further in terms of modelling and operational reliability. Combining pseudo-range and phase measurements by a filtering mechanism makes the detection of large cycle slips possible as long as they are not correlated with errors in the pseudo-range measurements.

Finally, **relative integrated positioning** has the potential to provide higher accuracy, improved reliability and precise dynamic information, albeit at the price of more system complexity and higher costs. The addition of an inertial system, for instance, gives a more accurate interpolation between GPS fixes, helps to eliminate cycle slips, increases relative positioning accuracy, provides precise velocity information, and improves overall system reliability.

REAL-TIME VERSUS POSTMISSION PROCESSING

REAL-TIME PROCESSING:

- **ADVANTAGES**
    - » **Results available immediately (navigation, guidance)**
    - » **No data storage problems**

- **DISADVANTAGES**
    - » **Less accurate**
    - » **Measurements often not stored (for post-mission computation)**
    - » **Blunder detection difficult**
    - » **Real-time link needed for relative methods**

POSTMISSION COMPUTATION:

- **ADVANTAGES**
    - » **More accurate**
    - » **Blunder detection easier**
    - » **Detailed analysis of residuals possible**
    - » **Model identification**
    - » **No real-time data link needed**

- **DISADVANTAGES**
    - » **Results cannot be used in the field**
    - » **Data storage problems**

REAL-TIME VERSUS POSTMISSION PROCESSING

Real-time processing is usually required for navigation applications, while postmission processing is often sufficient for kinematic positioning applications. In many cases, a considerable improvement in accuracy and reliability can be achieved by using the real-time results as input to a postmission smoother.

The comparison on this figure shows that **real-time methods** have two major advantages. They provide information that can be immediately used, and they are often an ideal way of data compression. This is especially true for methods, like Kalman filtering, which condense the huge amounts of satellite and inertial data into a state vector with a small number of components and a covariance matrix containing the statistical information. Without firmware filters of this type, an operational system would be difficult to build and storage requirements would be staggering. The real-time advantage of these processing methods can, however, turn into a postmission drawback. Since real-time filters can only use data up to the filtering epoch, their estimates are optimal only for the data subset available at that time. Thus, better results can be obtained postmission when the complete data set is available [Schwarz, 1983]. This requires, however, the storage of intermediate results. If this is not done, real-time efficiency can result in a loss of valuable information needed for postmission analysis. Such an analysis is not only important from an accuracy point of view but is also needed for the detection of blunders, such as, e.g., cycle slips, which are difficult to eliminate in real time.

Postmission processing eliminates most of the problems that trouble real-time processing and adds some interesting features for model verification and improvement. It can be done by a variety of methods of which optimal smoothing seems to be the most appropriate for the problems at hand. The higher accuracy of the results, especially in cases where a dynamic model is used, makes blunder detection much easier. In addition, residuals can be analysed and the identification of unmodelled error sources becomes possible. With the storage capabilities available today, one of the major drawbacks of postmission methods, namely, the need for considerable storage space, becomes less and less important. Thus, postmission methods should be used as the standard procedure in all cases where real-time results are not absolutely necessary.

ACCURACY AND INSTRUMENTATION

MODEL	ACCURACY (1σ IN M)	INSTRUMENTATION REQUIREMENTS
ABSOLUTE		
Pseudo-range	20-30	1 C/A-code receiver
	15-20	1 P-code receiver
Combined	15-20	1 receiver
Integrated	15-20	1 receiver plus inertial system
RELATIVE		
Pseudo-range	5-10	2 receivers
Combined	0.5-1.5	2 receivers
Integrated	0.2-0.3	2 receivers plus inertial system

Current (1986) satellite coverage has been assumed

ACCURACY AND INSTRUMENTATION

The difference in accuracy between the different kinematic positioning models goes hand in hand with differences in the instrumentation requirements. In general, the rule that higher accuracy is more expensive is also true here, although the reverse is not the case. This figure gives an overview of the **accuracies achievable** and lists the instrumentation requirements. The numbers are typically given for postmission results, although the difference between real-time and postmission results is immaterial for the absolute methods. Not all of the accuracy estimates have been confirmed by actual test runs, but there is little doubt that they show the right order of magnitude.

The first important conclusion is that adding relative position information, either in the form of phase differences or in the form of inertial velocity measurements, does not change the **absolute positioning accuracy** to any great extent. The reason for this is obvious. The major error sources in absolute kinematic positioning are, at present, orbital errors and ionospheric refraction effects. Both are not eliminated using carrier phase or inertial system measurements. The increase in accuracy for the combined and integrated method using a C/A-code receiver comes from a smoothing of the noisy data by the information provided by the inertial system or carrier phases, not from an elimination of the above errors. The same effect is present in the P-code receiver results but is so small that it does not change the accuracy estimates.

The dramatic **improvement in accuracy** achieved by relative kinematic positioning shows the potential of these methods for geodetic applications. It is remarkable that, at present, no real difference between P-code and C/A-code results exists. This will change, however, once SPS is degraded. The accuracy estimates for the combined kinematic method have been obtained under the assumption that cycle slips can be satisfactorily eliminated from the data. Although higher accuracies have been predicted by several authors, test results at present do not confirm these predictions. The results for the integrated kinematic method are taken from a simulation study and need further confirmation.

RANGE OF APPLICATIONS

ACCURACY (1σ)

APPLICATION

30m ——

MOST NAVIGATION APPLICATIONS
MANY LAND VEHICLE APPLICATIONS
AS, E.G., POSITIONING AND GUIDANCE
OF TRUCKS, AMBULANCES AND TAXIS

10m ——

HYDROGRAPHIC SURVEYING
AIRBORNE BATHYMETRY

3-D SEISMIC
AEROTRIANGULATION
1m —— GRAVITY VECTOR MAPPING SYSTEM
AIRBORNE GRAVIMETRY
AIRBORNE LASER

RANGE OF APPLICATIONS

Although the full impact of GPS will only become apparent in a decade or so, many new and interesting applications are envisaged right now and are being actively pursued by research groups in many countries. The following overview is not complete. It concentrates on work that is currently in progress in Canada. Following this figure, the applications will be subdivided into **three major groups.** In the first group, low accuracy applications will be treated which require positioning at the 20 to 30 m (1σ) level and can be handled by absolute kinematic positioning. In the second group, medium accuracy applications in the 5 to 10 m (1σ) range will be treated which can make use of the relative pseudo-range model. In the third group, high accuracy applications in the 0.5 to 2.0 m range will be discussed which require the use of either relative phase, relative combined, or relative integrated kinematic positioning.

Low accuracy applications will be sufficient for most conventional marine and airborne navigation tasks and will simplify to a considerable degree the positioning methods used in airborne geophysical surveys. New applications are emerging in the land vehicle mode where the positioning and guidance of truck fleets, ambulances, and taxis pose interesting problems. These applications will become economical once the price of C/A-code receivers drops to a few thousand dollars.

In *medium accuracy applications,* GPS will most likely replace a number of hydrographic survey systems currently in use. Launch positioning and bathymetry are two of them. Since real-time results are usually required, the development of a reliable radio link is important for these applications.

In *high accuracy applications,* GPS, in the phase, combined, and integrated mode, will give rise to a variety of dedicated systems which will solve problems which could not be adequately handled by conventional methods. Among them are aerotriangulation without ground control, airborne gravimetry and gradiometry, and direct gravity and geoid determination from a moving land vehicle. It will also facilitate a number of applications for which present survey technology is marginal or cumbersome, such as, e.g., three-dimensional seismic and airborne laser profiling. The decision whether to use GPS alone or the integrated method will, to a large extent, depend on how well the cycle slip problem can be solved.

LAND VEHICLE
APPLICATIONS

LOW ACCURACY APPLICATIONS

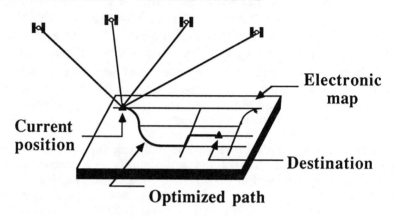

Electronic map

Current position

Destination

Optimized path

HIGH ACCURACY APPLICATION

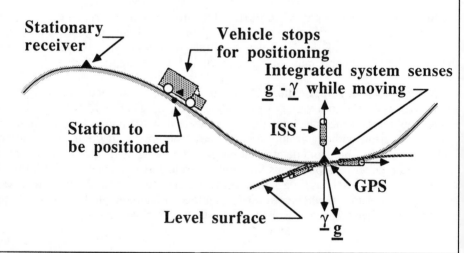

Stationary receiver

Vehicle stops for positioning

Integrated system senses $\underline{g} - \underline{\gamma}$ while moving

Station to be positioned

ISS →

Level surface

GPS

$\underline{\gamma}$ $\underline{g}$

LAND VEHICLE APPLICATIONS

Land vehicle uses of GPS are mainly in the low and high accuracy group of applications. A brief description of some proposed applications will be given here before test results are reported in the remainder of this section.

In *low accuracy applications,* the receiver is one component of a system which integrates the real-time positioning capability of GPS with stored map information to either display the current position of the vehicle on an electonic map or to guide the vehicle to a specific location along a traffic optimized path. Realization of such a system is dependent on low cost receivers and is currently envisaged for ambulances, truck fleets, taxis and, perhaps, railway cars.

High accuracy applications are currently discussed for precise positioning and for gravity field determination. In the first application, GPS will be used in the relative phase mode. The survey operation will be similar to that used in inertial surveying, i.e., the vehicle will start from a known position, drive to the unknown position, and stop there for a short period of time before driving on to the next unknown position [Remondi, 1985a; 1985b]. Gravity vector mapping is possible by using an integrated INS/GPS. In this application, the relative combined GPS mode is used to feed precise position information to the INS. The inertial sensors can then be used to detect changes in the gravity field and to plot a continuous profile of gravity, deflections of the vertical, and the geoid [Schwarz, 1986].

LAND VEHICLE
TEST TRAVERSE

TEST COURSE
FOR
TRUCK TESTS

N

43 km

← regular zero
velocity updates

18 km

← given coordinate
control

DYNAMICS
Accelerations of up to 3 m/s^2
Velocities of up to 135 km/h
Total test time: almost 3 hrs

CONTROL
Regular zero velocity updates at two minute intervals
15 second-order control points

KINEMATIC CHECK POINTS
Number : 360
Accuracy : 0.3 to 0.8 m (1σ) in position
1 to 3 cm/s (1σ) in velocity

LAND VEHICLE TEST TRAVERSE

Testing the different kinematic positioning models **in the land vehicle mode** has several advantages. First of all, it is the only mode that supplies sufficiently accurate control information. In airborne and shipborne applications, the inaccuracy of the control data usually leaves some doubt as to the quality of the results achieved. Second, it usually is much less costly in terms of mobilization and vehicle costs. Third, results give a good indication of what can be achieved in the air and sea environments because the dynamics of the land vehicle mode are more varied than those of the other two environments.

Results of two tests will be reported in the following. **The first test** was performed on a test route close to Calgary, which is depicted on this figure. The L-shaped line has a total length of about 60 km with 13 intermediate points which have been surveyed in by conventional methods and usually have second-order accuracy. Two TI-4100 receivers with Phase II software were used in this test as well as a time-synchronized Ferranti Inertial Survey System (FILS). The tests consisted of a forward and a backward run with the first receiver stationary at Calgary, about 65 km away, and the second receiver and the inertial system on the truck. The operating mode was that used in inertial surveying, i.e., zero velocity update stops were made about every two minutes and at all known stations. Dynamic conditions showed large variations, with accelerations of up to 3 ms^{-2} and velocities of up to 135 km h^{-1}.

The second test was done on a much shorter baseline and under more benign dynamic conditions. Twelve reflectors were mounted on poles along a 5 km course. Coordinates of the poles were obtained by conventional methods. An infrared detector, pointing perpendicular to the truck axis in both directions, received reflection pulses which were timed to about one millisecond. The truck moved at constant speeds of 20, 50, and 100 km h^{-1} along the test course. Again two T1-4100 receivers were used, one on the truck and one stationary in Calgary, about 20 km away.

LAND VEHICLE
POSITIONING RESULTS

COMPARISON OF MODELS

MODEL *	ERROR IN	RESULTS	
		Mean (m)	RMS (m)
Absolute Pseudo-range	φ	-4.0	6.4
	λ	6.2	9.5
	h	6.6	13.2
Relative Pseudo-range	φ	0.4	6.6
	λ	0.9	6.3
	h	-2.0	7.2
Relative combined	φ	0.3	0.8
	λ	-0.4	1.2
	h	-1.0	1.3

* All results are for P-code receiver.

LAND VEHICLE POSITIONING RESULTS

In the first test, the inertial output was used to compute 360 'kinematic reference points' along the traverse. This was done by processing the inertial data through a Kalman filter/optimal smoother using all zero velocity and coordinate updates available. Smoothed velocity and position information was then computed at time intervals of 30 seconds. It is estimated that the position information thus obtained has an accuracy of about 0.3 to 0.8 m (1 σ) for each coordinate, while the velocity information is good to about 1 to 3 cm s^{-1} (1 σ).

The GPS measurements were then used with the **pseudo-range and the combined model** to derive positions and velocities at the same time marks. Results for the forward run are shown in this figure. The accuracies achieved in the absolute and relative pseudo-range mode are comparable to those published by other authors, although the absolute results seem to be exceptionally good in this case. The reduction of orbital and atmospheric errors by the relative method shows clearly in the decrease of the mean errors. The most interesting results are those achieved with the relative combined method because they give, for the first time, actual results for a large and dynamically varied reference data base. They show clearly that **accuracies at the 1 m level** can be achieved [Cannon et al., 1986]. Considering the accuracy of the control data and the unavoidable interpolation errors for the GPS measurements, the overall accuracy is probably close to 0.5 m (1σ). The processing also showed that cycle slips are a real problem and occur more frequently than expected. They are clearly acceleration dependent and happen even in this low dynamic environment. Only if a reliable solution to this problem can be found will the combined method be useful in practice.

In the second test, the kinematic positioning results were compared to the reference positions of the poles. The RMS of these differences was at the 2 m level [Lachapelle et al., 1986]. A major portion of these differences is due to errors in the reference pole positions. The RMS of differences in position obtained in repeated runs along this test route was below 1 m [Kleusberg et al., 1986].

LAND VEHICLE
VELOCITY RESULTS

STATIONARY RECEIVER ESTIMATES

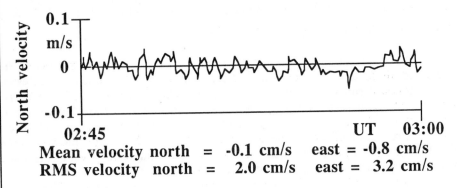

Mean velocity north = -0.1 cm/s   east = -0.8 cm/s
RMS velocity north = 2.0 cm/s   east = 3.2 cm/s

MOVING RECEIVER: DIFFERENCES BETWEEN
GPS 1-MINUTE AVERAGES, AND INS

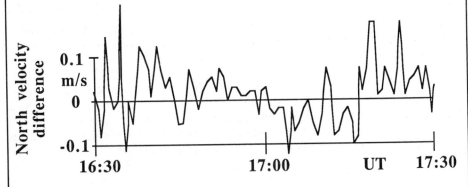

Mean velocity difference north = 2.9 cm/s east = 9.3 cm/s
RMS   velocity difference north = 7.6 cm/s east =13.4 cm/s

LAND VEHICLE VELOCITY RESULTS

The accurate **determination of velocity** is needed in applications like airborne and shipborne gravimetry, ocean current studies, and precise position interpolation. The reason to test the GPS capability for these applications in land vehicle mode, again has to do with the difficulty to get sufficiently accurate velocities for comparison. It is much easier to get reference velocities from an independent source on land than it is at sea or in the air. The only GPS measurement accurate enough for these applications is the phase observation; therefore, all methods proposed so far are based on time differenced phase measurements.

Two routes have been taken to evaluate the accuracy of GPS derived velocities. One is the **processing of static data in the kinematic mode,** which is effectively a zero velocity test; the other is the comparison with independently derived velocities. Results of the first approach show that differencing pairs of L1 carrier phase measurements 0.16 seconds apart gives velocities with a noise level of 3 to 5 cm [Wells et al., 1985]. At present, such measurements can be obtained every few seconds. They represent a best case situation because the static case has a lower noise level than the dynamic case.

Independent reference velocities are best obtained from a high accuracy inertial system which is constrained by frequent zero velocity measurements. Thus, the land vehicle tests [Cannon et al., 1986], reported upon earlier, are well suited for this purpose. The velocities obtained from the filtered and smoothed inertial data have accuracies between 1 and 3 cm (1σ). Comparison with time differenced GPS phase measurements show a standard error of about 10 cm for the GPS derived velocities. This confirms results which have been obtained in shipborne tests using one minute averages of GPS and INS derived velocities [Kleusberg et al., 1985a].

SHIPBORNE APPLICATIONS

APPLICATIONS:

	ACCURACY REQUIREMENTS
• Navigation in open waters	1 km
• Navigation in coastal channel	50-100 m
• Hydrographic surveying	2-5 m
• Three-dimensional seismic surveys	2-5 m
• Gravity surveys	<10 cm s^{-1}

PROBLEMS:

- Antenna motion
- Multipath effects

SHIPBORNE APPLICATIONS

Marine uses of GPS cover the whole range of accuracies achievable with the system. In this section, only shipborne applications will be treated, while airborne marine applications will be discussed in the next section. One problem common to most shipborne applications is the **mounting of the antenna** high above the centre of gravity of the vessel. This results in large antenna accelerations which may result in frequent cycle slips. Thus, the use of the phase method in this environment depends on an operational solution to the cycle slip problem. In addition, the antenna movements make it difficult to determine a precise trajectory of the vessel. Therefore, the high accuracies that can be achieved in land vehicles and aircraft require additional instrumentation in shipborne applications.

Low accuracy applications of GPS in the marine environment comprise most navigation tasks in open waters. For this, GPS in the absolute positioning mode is an ideal system. Its accuracy and global availability make it superior to the systems currently used for this purpose, and the development of rather inexpensive C/A-code receivers will soon make it very economical as well.

Medium accuracy applications of GPS using the relative pseudo-range mode are of considerable interest to hydrographic surveying. Real-time accuracies of 5 m or better are required in real time. Tests have shown that the relative pseudo-range mode is marginal in this case and that the use of phase measurements is required. This would result in the difficulties mentioned above or require the use of a simple inertial strapdown system to smooth the noise in the relative pseudo-range measurements.

High accuracy applications are, at present, mainly needed in marine geophysical exploration. Positioning accuracies of 2 to 5 m (1σ) are required for three-dimensional seismic surveying, while velocity accuracies of 10 cm s^{-1} or better are needed in marine gravity surveys to keep the error in the Eötvös correction below 1 mGal.

HYDROGRAPHIC SURVEY TEST AREA

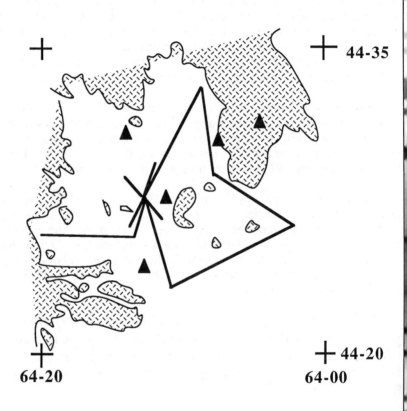

44-35

44-20

64-20   64-00

HYDROGRAPHIC SURVEY TEST AREA

Hydrographic surveys comprise a number of different tasks which have a variety of accuracy requirements. To evaluate the suitability of GPS for these tasks, the Canadian Hydrographic Survey has conducted a number of tests in 1982 and 1983 in the **Mahone Bay area** on the southeast coast of Nova Scotia. These experiments were undertaken at a relatively early stage of GPS development and do not always reflect the current state of user equipment. They are important, however, because many of the concepts, specifically, integrated and relative kinematic positioning, were put to the test for the first time. The experience gained during these campaigns was used in the planning of subsequent airborne tests and for the design of reliable operational procedures.

The test area is shown in this figure. It also indicates the tests conducted on a typical day during the 1982 campaign. The solid line indicates the ship's track showing a polygon ending with a buoy test. The reference trajectory in this case was obtained from a **Mini-Ranger system** on board the ship. The shore stations for this system are shown as black triangles. The total time for each test was restricted to about four hours due to satellite availability. The tests were mainly used to evaluate absolute pseudo-range and absolute integrated positioning.

The tests in 1983 were conducted to assess both absolute and relative pseudo-range positioning with fast switching single channel receivers. In this case, the reference trajectory was obtained from a **Syledis radionavigation system**, whose accuracy was estimated to be in the 3 to 5 m range. The baseline length, i.e., the distance between stationary and moving receivers, was about 10 km on the first day and about 50 km on the next two days. The total time available for each test was again about four hours.

HYDROGRAPHIC
SURVEY TEST RESULTS

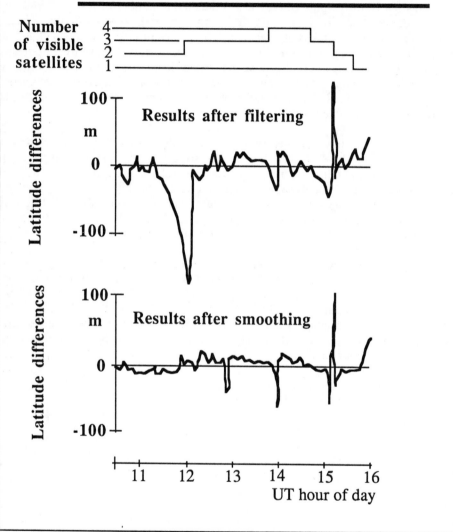

Number of visible satellites

Results after filtering

Latitude differences

Results after smoothing

Latitude differences

UT hour of day

HYDROGRAPHIC SURVEY TEST RESULTS

The equipment for the **first test** [Schwarz et al., 1984b] consisted of a slow switching STI 5010 receiver, a modified Ferranti Inertial System (FILS), a cesium clock, and an HP 1000 computer, in which all measurements were integrated by means of a real-time Kalman filter. The filter was designed to read a set of uncorrected coordinates and velocities from the FILS every 1.28 seconds and to accept pseudo-range updates from the STI 5010. Since this receiver required approximately 60 seconds to lock on to a satellite and about six seconds to determine a pseudo-range, results are not comparable to today's multiplexing or multichannel receivers. However, they are still of interest because they show very clearly the dependence of real-time results on satellite geometry (results after filtering) and the elimination of these effects by postmission smoothing (see this figure). The remaining spikes after smoothing are most likely due to errors in the Mini-Ranger system. Overall results are a real-time positioning accuracy of 25 m (1 σ) and a postmission accuracy of 15 m. Estimated velocity results are 5 cm s^{-1} for real time and 3 cm s^{-1} for postmission. All results refer to a three or four satellite coverage.

The equipment for the **second test** [Lachapelle et al., 1984b] consisted of two T1-4100 multiplexing receivers, performing dual frequency P-code pseudo-range and phase measurements on up to four satellites. Pseudo-range measurements, recorded at intervals of 3 to 6 seconds, were used for the tests. Results showed that absolute pseudo-range positioning using the precise positioning system (P-code) is possible at the 15 m (1 σ) level given good geometry for three or four satellites. Under similar circumstances, the 5 to 10 m (1 σ) range was achieved for relative pseudo-range positioning. Another important result from these tests is that the use of the L1 pseudo-range only produces better differential results than ionospherically corrected data. This implies that similar results can be achieved with C/A-code receivers. This was confirmed by later tests.

3-D SEISMIC SURVEY

PRINCIPLE

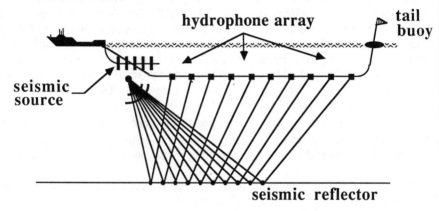

hydrophone array

tail buoy

seismic source

seismic reflector

BOUNDARY DELINEATION

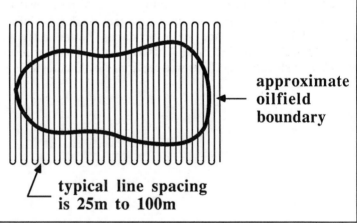

approximate oilfield boundary

typical line spacing is 25m to 100m

3-D SEISMIC SURVEYS

Three-dimensional seismic surveys are one of the more demanding offshore applications [Morgan, 1983] where GPS may be used to advantage. The **principle** is shown in this figure. An array of hydrophones, called a streamer or a cable, is towed behind a survey vessel along a predetermined course. A seismic source is activated at intervals of about 10 seconds, i.e., about every 25 m, and the reflected energy received by the hydrophones is digitized and stored for future processing. The final product is a detailed three-dimensional picture of the sea bottom subsurface. In most cases, three-dimensional seismic surveys are not conducted for original exploration but are performed after oil or natural gas has been found. They are used to delineate the extent of the reservoir and to provide better resolution of important geological structures. The positioning requirements are higher than for the usual exploratory survey because the line spacing has to be much denser (25-100 m) and more accurate to achieve the resolution wanted.

In terms of positioning, three different tasks have to be distinguished:
- positioning of the survey vessel
- positioning of the seismic energy source
- positioning of the hydrophone array.

It should be noted that only the first and part of the last problem can be solved by GPS because the seismic source and the hydrophones are submerged. **Positioning of the survey vessel** with respect to the shore stations is needed with an accuracy of 10 to 15 m (1 σ), while its real-time position along track and across track is required with precisions of 3 m and 10 m, respectively. While relative pseudo-range positioning will meet most of these requirements, it is marginal for the 3 m accuracy. However, any of the other relative kinematic methods is capable of achieving it. Although the submerged seismic source and the hydrophones cannot be positioned by GPS, an antenna could be mounted on the tailbuoy of the streamer. Since the streamer is 3 to 5 km long, the tracking of the buoy with respect to the survey vessel will give an important constraint to the magnetic heading sensors attached to the streamer. The accuracy required is 5 to 10 m (1 σ) and can be achieved by relative pseudo-range positioning.

AIRCRAFT APPLICATIONS

MODES:

- **Fixed wing aircraft**
- **Helicopter**

APPLICATIONS:

• **Laser bathymetry**	**15-20 m**
• **Buoy positioning**	**10-15 m**
• **Aerotriangulation**	**1-2 m**
• **Airborne gravimetry**	**2 m in h, 10 cm/s in velocity**
• **Control point positioning**	**< 0.5 m**
• **Laser profiling**	**< 0.5 m**

PROBLEM:

- **Mounting of antenna**

AIRCRAFT APPLICATIONS

Airborne applications of GPS again cover the whole range of achievable accuracies. However, much interest is at present directed towards high accuracy methods at the level of 1 m (1 σ) or below because they open the way to new applications in photogrammetry, geodesy, and geophysics which could not be considered up to now. Among them are aerotriangulation without ground control, airborne gravimetry and gradiometry, and airborne laser profiling.

From an operational point of view, fixed wing applications and helicopter applications should be distinguished. **Fixed wing aircraft** operate in a rather stable dynamic environment and are well suited for most of the above applications which require constant flight altitude and regularity of procedure. Cycle slip problems may occur during takeoffs and turning manoeuvres. On the other hand, **helicopters** experience a more varied dynamic environment and, therefore, may be more prone to cycle slip problems. Their flexibility in terms of hovering, landing, manoeuvering and velocity, results in a wide range of GPS positioning applications.

In both cases, the **mounting of the antenna** on the aircraft requires special consideration. On fixed wing aircraft, it is usually installed on the upper part of the fuselage in a location which minimizes shading and multipath effects. Permanent modifications to the aircraft are usually made. The problem is more difficult for helicopters. If the antenna is installed under the main rotor, signal interference will inevitably cause frequent losses of the GPS signal. On large helicopters, it may be possible to install the antenna on the top of the main rotor shaft, above the rotor. However, these types of helicopters are relatively expensive to operate. On smaller types of helicopters, the upper extremity of the vertical tail fin may be well suited for a GPS antenna due to its location above the vertical tail rotor of the helicopter. The site is horizon clear on many types of helicopters and losses of signal can be avoided altogether. The modification of the vertical tail fin is, however, relatively complex.

LASER BATHYMETRY

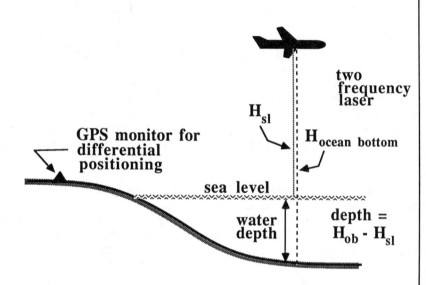

ACCURACY REQUIRED :   15 m horizontally

METHOD :   relative pseudo-range positioning

LASER BATHYMETRY

One of the airborne systems that has been developed for remote depth sounding of shallow waters is the **Lidar bathymeter**. It consists of a dual frequency laser with one frequency chosen such that it is reflected at the surface of the water, while the other penetrates the water and is reflected at the ocean floor. The water depth thus can be derived as the difference of the two elevations measured in the airplane. To locate the measured depth profile, the horizontal position of the aircraft is needed as a function of time. Although navigation systems are presently available which will give the required accuracy of 15 to 20 m, the GPS was tested for this application because of its availability in remote areas.

The experiment took place in 1983 in the Lake Huron test area of the Canadian Hydrographic Survey [Lachapelle et al., 1984a]. Two TI-4100 were used, one installed in a DC-3 aircraft, while the second was set up about 100 km away. The accuracy of the results was assessed using four transponders of a **Del Norte Trisponder System** (UHF), which provided reference positions with an accuracy of 1 to 3 m (1 σ) depending on geometry. Aircraft speeds during the test were between 210 and 300 km h^{-1}.

Results for **absolute** pseudo-range positioning using the precise positioning system (P-code) were 10 to 15 m (1σ) for the horizontal coordinates and 20 to 25 m in height when using ionospherically corrected data. When using L1 data only, i.e., when not applying the ionospheric correction, the noise level dropped but biases of up to 50 m showed in the results. In the **relative** pseudo-range mode, which eliminates a large part of the ionospheric propagation effects, results using L1 only were usually better giving standard errors of 10 m or better for the horizontal coordinates and 15 m for height. In this case, biases were almost completely eliminated by using the differential technique.

AEROTRIANGULATION WITHOUT GROUND CONTROL

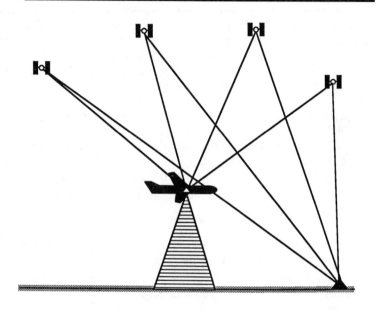

ADVANTAGES

- Homogeneous control
- No targetting or access problems
- Free choice of flight patterns
- Instantaneous positioning (repeated flights)

AEROTRIANGULATION WITHOUT GROUND CONTROL

The use of ground control is, at present, the standard procedure in aerotriangulation. However, ground control is costly, time consuming to establish, and often introduces inhomogeneities in the transformation between model coordinates and control coordinates. Replacing ground control by control at **flight level** is an attractive alternative because it provides a set of homogeneous control points at flight level, avoids targetting and access problems, gives complete freedom in the choice of the flight pattern, and makes instantaneous positioning possible. Accuracies required for medium scale mapping are 1 to 2 m (1 σ) in all coordinates at ground level. A feasibility study [Schwarz et al., 1984a] showed that the same accuracy is required at flight level.

Three approaches to solve this problem have been proposed. The first one is a straightforward application of the relative phase method. It has the potential to achieve the desired accuracy if the cycle slip problem can be overcome. Judging by the results of the land vehicle tests reported earlier, this is difficult with present receiver technology. However, recent results of an airborne test have been successful in maintaining lock during maximum takeoff accelerations [Mader, 1986]. The other two methods use an integrated approach combining GPS with an inertial navigation system [Goldfarb and Schwarz, 1985]. The first of the two strategies uses a high accuracy INS to smooth the noise in the relative pseudo-ranges. The model is that of relative integrated positioning using pseudo-ranges only. Achievable accuracies, obtained from simulations, are better than 0.5 m. The second strategy uses a low precision INS as an interpolator to detect and eliminate cycle slips in the phase data. In this case, the accuracy is obtained from relative phase measurements and is at the level of 0.3 m (1 σ). The model used is that of relative integrated positioning using phase measurements only. These two methods have not yet been tested in the airborne environment.

AIRBORNE GRAVIMETRY

gravity anomaly vector
(magnitude measured)

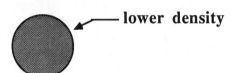

lower density

ADVANTAGES OF AIRBORNE METHOD:

- Fast coverage of large areas
- Regular profiles
- Attenuation of "surface noise"

AIRBORNE GRAVIMETRY

Gravity measurements are one of the major data sources for geodesy and are also an important reconnaissance tool used in geophysics. Terrestrial gravity measurements are done at discrete points. Although very accurate, the measuring procedure is slow and rather difficult to use in remote and mountainous areas. Attempts to make the method airborne have been made, therefore, more than once during the last 30 years but have so far not met with success, at least not in the fixed wing aircraft mode. This failure was due to at least three causes: The difficulty to position the aircraft with an accuracy of 2 m in height, the difficulty to obtain the aircraft velocity to 10 cm s^{-1}, and the difficulty to separate gravitational and inertial accelerations. GPS has the potential to provide solutions to the first two problems.

In order to secure 1 mGal accuracy for the gravity anomalies, the orthometric height of the aircraft must be known to better than 3 m, while the horizontal position is required to within 50 m. The latter requirement can be easily met by any of the absolute GPS methods. The **height accuracy** is not as easy to achieve. Since the orthometric height is composed of the ellipsoidal height obtained from GPS and the geoidal height, errors in both components must be considered. In general, the geoidal height can be computed with an accuracy of 1 to 3 m (1 σ). This means that the ellipsoidal height is required with an accuracy of about 2 m (1 σ). This accuracy can be achieved by the relative phase and the relative combined method assuming that cycle slips can be eliminated. If that is not possible, only the relative integrated method will give the necessary accuracy. The additional measurements can be either pressure altimeter data or, again, inertial data. **Aircraft velocities** have to be known to 10 cm s^{-1} or better in order to keep the error in the Eötvös correction below 1 mGal. This is achievable with time differenced phase data or through the use of an integrated system.

The third problem mentioned above can be rigorously solved by airborne gradiometry. However, a practically sufficient solution is perhaps also possible by airborne gravimetry. It requires the smoothing of high aircraft accelerations and the **separation of gravitational and inertial effects** by a priori statistical information. The resulting smoothed gravity data would be sufficient for geodetic purposes and may have enough short wavelength information for reconnaissance gravity surveys. Major advantages of the method would be the rapid data acquisition even in remote areas, the coverage of large areas, and the possibility of flying gravity and aeromagnetic surveys on the same mission.

HELICOPTER APPLICATIONS

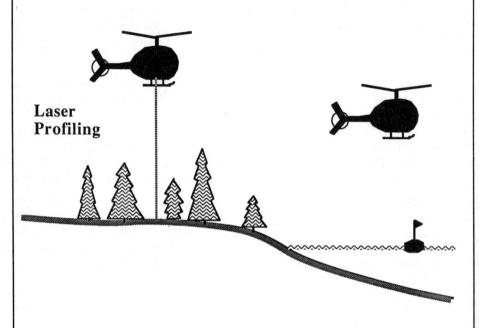

Laser Profiling

ADVANTAGES:

- **Hovering**
- **Manoeuvering flexibility**
- **Minimal landing space**

HELICOPTER APPLICATIONS

The major advantage of using helicopters instead of fixed wing aircraft is their greater flexibility. The hovering mode, the capability for quick manoeuvres, and the small space required for landing opens up a whole new range of applications which are not possible with fixed wing aircraft. The hovering mode, for instance, is used to position objects or sites where landing is impossible; examples are positioning of buoys and objects in heavily forested areas. The manoeuvering flexibility makes detailed laser profiling possible in areas of rugged topography. Landing flexibility makes establishment or resurvey of large numbers of control points in forest-free regions very cost effective. Many helicopter-borne inertial surveying techniques currently utilized should be replaceable by GPS techniques once GPS satellites are available on a continuous basis.

A series of tests was conducted in 1984-85 to assess the accuracy of helicopters for **buoy positioning** and Loran-C calibration. A Bell 206B helicopter and two TI-4100 receivers were used for the tests. The GPS antenna was installed on the upper extremity of the vertical tail fin. The tests in 1984 suffered from frequent loss of the GPS signal due to the tracking software used. They indicated, however, that latitude and longitude can be determined with an accuracy of about 10 m when using the relative pseudo-range method while hovering. Tests with the improved Phase II tracking software, conducted in 1985, showed clearly that the signal loss problem had been overcome.

For **control point positioning and laser profiling,** accuracies at the half metre level are needed. This requires the use of phase data or an integrated system approach. While the relative phase or the relative combined method will be adequate for the first application, an attitude reference and thus an integrated system is needed in the second application. Test results are not available yet, but extrapolating the results obtained in road tests shows that the potential to achieve these accuracies is certainly there.

CHAPTER THIRTEEN

DIFFERENTIAL DATA LINKS

DIFFERENTIAL DATA LINKS

DIFFERENTIAL GPS REQUIREMENTS

COMMUNICATION LINK REQUIREMENTS

- **What factors must be considered when designing a real-time differential GPS data communication link?**

GPS CORRECTION MESSAGE FORMAT

- **Words 1 and 2 content**
- **Type 1 message**
- **Type 2 message**

COMMUNICATION METHODS

- **What signal propagation modes are available?**

SYSTEM OPTIONS

- **What options are actually available?**
- **How do we choose one?**

SYSTEM COMPONENTS

- **What do we need at the monitor?**
- **What do we need at the remote user site?**

DIFFERENTIAL DATA LINKS

This chapter describes the operational requirements of a differential GPS communication link by first considering the constraints imposed by both static and kinematic applications. To these operational constraints are added the factors which govern the type of equipment and service which will ultimately be used. These factors include such considerations as range of operation, signal propagation mode, cost, and system maintenance.

Attention is given early in this chapter to the actual GPS correction message, the kind of information it contains, the variety of different message types, and examples of two of these messages. The GPS correction message has been defined in the recommendations of the Radio Technical Commission for Marine Services [1985] (RTCM SC-104). The variety of message types of interest and the update frequency of these messages are factors which affect the data rate over the communication channel.

Additional factors which must be considered in designing a communication link are also presented, including a survey of possible communication methods and options spanning the range from older developed technologies, such as high frequency radio, to much newer methods, such as direct satellite broadcasting and spread spectrum channelling.

The chapter concludes by describing the basic system components of a differential GPS communication link at both the monitor and remote sites.

DIFFERENTIAL
GPS REQUIREMENTS

STATIC APPLICATIONS

- May use postprocessing
- Data may be buffered or stored
- Communication need not be in real time
- Link equipment may not be power or range limited

KINEMATIC APPLICATIONS

- Real-time processing desirable
- Strict correction message timing, bandwidth, and content
- Allowed processing time is determined by the vessel dynamics and the control response time
- Link equipment must be designed to tight power and range specifications
- Very high data link reliability required

DIFFERENTIAL GPS REQUIREMENTS

The purpose of the communication link in a differential GPS application is to relay correction messages from the monitor station to the field user. Applications may be classified as either static or kinematic, depending upon the dynamics of the user. Each type of application will place constraints on the communication link.

In *static* applications, the field user is either not moving or is able to remain stationary for as long as desired. This would be the case in determining a precise land position. Under these conditions, the GPS correction may be applied after all the measurements have been taken and recorded (postprocessing) or the correction message may be temporarily stored or buffered for later transmission and processing. For this reason, there is no need for the communication channel to remain in operation at all times. Also, there will usually be more flexibility in the available transmitter power (and, hence, range) for stationary sites.

In *kinematic* applications, the field user may be an aircraft, ship, or other mobile platform. Postprocessing is not always possible in these cases since the GPS data are being used at least partially for real-time navigation. Under these conditions, the correction message must follow strict length and timing specifications, and the receiver processing time (and message updating interval) are determined by the vessel dynamics and control response time. The communication link equipment must be carefully selected or designed to rigid power and range requirements with emphasis on reliability and redundancy.

COMMUNICATION LINK REQUIREMENTS

Range

Type of Service

Duty Period

Propagation Constraints

Dynamic Constraints

Cost

Service & Maintainability

Number of Users

COMMUNICATION LINK REQUIREMENTS

In all differential GPS applications, we assume that the RTCM SC-104 recommendations will be adhered to, and that any further particular application requirements will be in addition to these. In this section, we address the scope of these additional requirements. The specific application requirements may be summarized in the following categories.

- **Range:** What is the operational distance between the monitor station and the user? What is the tradeoff between channel bandwidth, range, and equipment cost?
- **Type of Service:** We may select from a variety of communication methods and system configurations, each having its own constraints, advantages, and disadvantages.
- **Duty Period:** The communication link may be required to operate continuously, on demand, or only at specified intervals. The duty cycle will be determined by the positioning accuracy requirements at hand. Kinematic applications, such as hydrographic surveys, may require continuous operation, whereas static applications may only require periodic fixing. The duty period may place additional constraints on the communication link data rate.
- **Propagation Constraints:** Different methods of radio propagation present different limitations in terms of cost, reliability, range of operation, and equipment complexity.
- **Dynamic Constraints:** The degree of movement of the user will have a great influence on the possible equipment choices. Available equipment space, shock loading, receiver tracking capability, and antenna beam coverage are factors which must be considered. The motion of the user will also determine the duty cycle of the communication link.
- **Cost:** What is the tradeoff between system complexity, reliability, and unit cost? What is the operational cost of a unit failure? How many units are in the system? Will new technology introduce cost benefits? Will new technology make the present system obsolete, or can the system be expanded easily to take advantage of new components without sacrificing existing units?
- **Service and Maintainability:** What are the ambient operating conditions? Will the equipment require specially trained operators or maintenance technicians? What is the expected service lifetime of the units? How and where will units be repaired or replaced? Are the units interchangeable either in whole or in part? Can the monitor be operated unattended?
- **Number of Users:** How many users will the system support? Are the user units fully interchangeable at all ranges? Can the system be easily expanded to accommodate additional users? Can two or more such systems be operated side-by-side without interference? Can the fixed monitor station be easily adjusted to serve different networks of users?

GPS CORRECTION MESSAGE FORMAT

word 1	word 2	message

general message information

16 MESSAGE TYPES

1	Differential corrections
2	Delta differential corrections
3	Station parameters
4	Surveying
5	Constellation health
6	Null frame
7	Beacon health
8	Pseudolite health
9	High rate differential corrections
10	P-code differential corrections
11	C/A-code L1,L2 differential corrections
12	Health message
13-15	To be decided
16	Special messages

GPS CORRECTION MESSAGE FORMAT

According to RTCM SC-104 recommendations, the correction transmission consists of a selection of 16 different message types. Obviously not all message types are broadcast in each transmission, and some of the messages require a high update rate, while others require only occasional updating. For example, for navigation users the only information requiring a high update rate is the Type 1 message. Its rate is determined by the typical frequencies of the error sources. The selective availability (SA) procedures are expected to introduce the largest of the errors. Based on degraded data available to the RTCM SC-104 study group, transmission rates between 1/(6 sec) and 1/(15 sec) for 4 and 11 satellites in view, respectively, were found appropriate to keep SA errors below 3 metres. As the other message types can be transmitted at intervals of minutes rather than seconds, the overall data rate need not exceed 50 to 75 bps.

The GPS correction transmission consists of two leading words (each 30 bits long) followed by the actual correction message of which there are 16 different types. The two leading words are common to all message types and contain information on which message type follows, station identification, timing information, message length (not all message types or messages are the same length), and the station health status.

The actual correction messages contain a wide variety of information of use to the surveyor or navigator. These messages relay extensive information on monitor station position and health, satellite constellation health, and corrections to be applied to the direct GPS observations. The most commonly used message will be Type 1 which contains the actual pseudo-range correction. The Type 2 message, for example, will be used to augment the Type 1 data in the event that new orbital or clock parameters are introduced by the monitor station.

CONTENT OF
WORDS 1 and 2

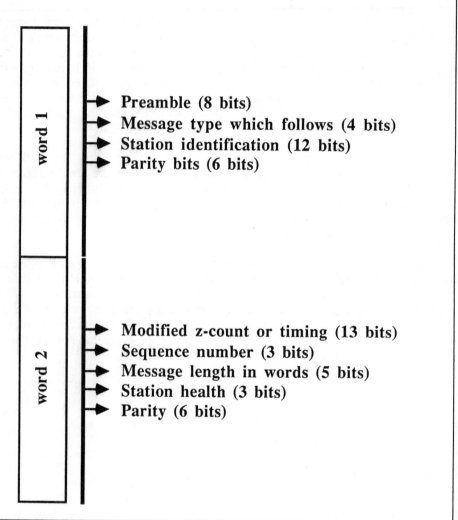

word 1
- Preamble (8 bits)
- Message type which follows (4 bits)
- Station identification (12 bits)
- Parity bits (6 bits)

word 2
- Modified z-count or timing (13 bits)
- Sequence number (3 bits)
- Message length in words (5 bits)
- Station health (3 bits)
- Parity (6 bits)

CONTENT OF WORDS 1 AND 2

The two leading words of each transmission contain message type and station identification information. In addition, the message length is given, since not all messages are of the same length nor are all messages of the same type of equal length. Station health status is also provided, as well as several parity bits for checking.

TYPE 1 MESSAGE

Corrections to GPS pseudo-ranges in the form

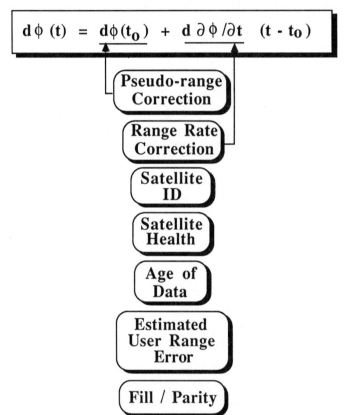

$$d\phi(t) = d\phi(t_0) + d\,\partial\phi/\partial t\,(t - t_0)$$

- Pseudo-range Correction
- Range Rate Correction
- Satellite ID
- Satellite Health
- Age of Data
- Estimated User Range Error
- Fill / Parity

TYPE 1 MESSAGE

This is the primary message type which provides the pseudo-range corrections. The message contains the correction term, as well as the range rate correction, to enable application of corrections at any time. Timing information for this adjustment is taken from the second word in the message header. The message also contains the satellite identification number for which these corrections apply, satellite health summary, age of the data, and the estimated user range error. The type 1 message is transmitted separately for each GPS satellite.

TYPE 2 MESSAGE

Corrections to Type 1 data in the form

$$d\phi(t) = d\phi(t_0) + d\,\partial\phi/\partial t\,(t - t_0) + \underline{d\phi_{data}}$$

Delta Correction

Fill / Parity

Always used to augment a Type 1 message

Does not contain satellite ID, health or data age

$d\phi_{data}$ **is used only when the broadcast message parameters being used by the monitor station change. It will correct for the difference between the old and new broadcast messages, until such time as the remote has begun using the new set also. The remote uses "age of data" in Type 1 as a flag to use Type 2.**

TYPE 2 MESSAGE

The reference station will transmit a Type 2 message whenever it starts using new GPS navigation data, i.e., when the station switches from one set of orbital and clock parameters to another. If the user does not switch to the new orbital and clock parameters at the same time, the Type 1 data which he has received will be useless to him. Therefore, the Type 2 data gives corections to the Type 1 data for use by those who have not yet switched to the new orbital and clock parameters.

COMMUNICATION METHODS

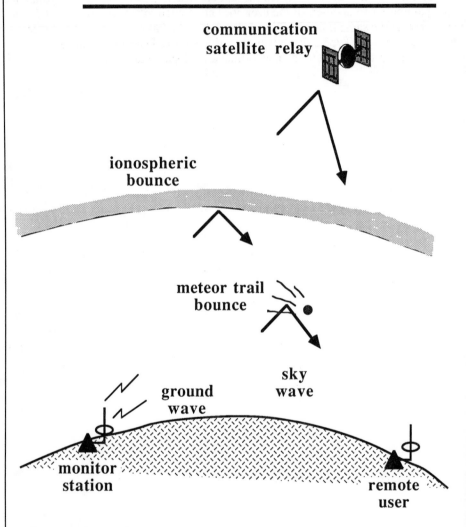

communication
satellite relay

ionospheric
bounce

meteor trail
bounce

sky
wave

ground
wave

monitor
station

remote
user

COMMUNICATION METHODS

Many differential applications may allow a choice of the method of communication, and in other cases the choices may be extremely limited. The principal characteristics of several methods are as follows:

- **Ground wave propagation:** At low frequencies, the range may extend to several hundred kilometres. The wave is 'bound' to the earth-air interface and may require large transmitter antennas.

- **Sky wave propagation:** Includes direct and tropospheric refracted waves. At HF frequencies, the range may extend to a few hundred kilometres, and at higher frequencies the range becomes reduced to near horizon.

- **Ionospheric bounce:** Service is sporadic and varies from day to night, as well as from season to season. The bounce distances tend to be much larger than the typical differential GPS ranges, and no service is available at short ranges of under a few hundred kilometres.

- **Meteor trail bounce:** Provides burst service at continuous ranges out to several hundred kilometres.

- **Communication satellite relay:** Power limitations of the satellite restrict this usage to remote users who can mount steerable directional antennas. The communication satellite must be geosynchronous so as to provide continuous operation. True mobile satellite communication service is anticipated by the year 2000.

SYSTEM OPTIONS

Piggyback

Frequency Hopping

Satellite Broadcasting

Direct Dedicated Radio Service

Meteorite Scattering

Pseudolite

Single Link
or
Relay Service

Real Time
or
Postprocessing

SYSTEM OPTIONS

The implementation of the communication channel link allows further considerations as follows.

• **Piggyback operation:** Can the differential correction message be added to some presently used radio service?

• **Frequency hopping**: A technique employed to avoid some propagation limitations. Such systems may be range-limited, and the remote units may not be interchangeable. The system may be complex and expensive but operationally sound in certain applications.

• **Satellite broadcasting**: Not practical for direct mobile service, but may be used as part of a split link.

• **Direct dedicated radio service**: Establishing and licensing a radio service for differential message handling independent of existing radio services.

• **Meteor scattering**: Commercial systems are available but may require a costly transmitting station to serve the region.

• **Pseudolite service**: Provides useful features in some applications (e.g., terminal air navigation), and may be practical as the final leg of a long-range system assuming that interference will not occur with normal GPS operation.

For each of the choices above, we must consider whether the system will be designed to offer **real-time or postprocessed** correction. Further, the system may be designed to provide direct correction messages to the user, or an intermediate **relay link** may be used.

SYSTEM COMPONENTS

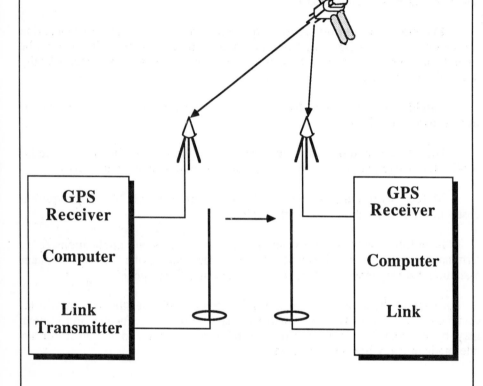

GPS
Receiver

Computer

Link
Transmitter

GPS
Receiver

Computer

Link

Monitor Station

Remote User

SYSTEM COMPONENTS

Monitor Station

The monitor station consists of a GPS receiver, a computer to calculate the pseudo-range and range rate errors and to compose the correction message, a modem, and a radio frequency (RF) transmitter with its associated antenna assembly and coupler. The computer/modem should include the provision for an error correction scheme for the RF link. This is in addition to any error correction or checking schemes which may be built into the GPS message.

Application requirements may dictate that the monitor station be easily transported by, e.g., a helicopter, and operated unmanned. It may also be necessary to select a radio transmitter which can be easily adjusted to serve different user networks on different frequencies.

Remote User

The remote user equipment consists of a GPS receiver, a computer for decoding the correction message and incorporating it with the GPS message, a modem, and a radio link receiver with its associated antenna assembly. The emphasis of the communication equipment selection criteria should be on reliability, simplicity of operation, and servicability. Ideally, all user units should be fully interchangeable. Unit cost for the communication equipment should be low enough to use spares to guarantee backup, particularly where equipment failure would involve very costly mission failure.

Application requirements may place further restrictions on equipment choices in order to meet ambient and dynamic performance standards (e.g., marine spray, arctic, airborne, small launch).

CHAPTER FOURTEEN

GPS SURVEY DESIGN

GPS SURVEY DESIGN

DESIGN PARAMETERS IN GPS SURVEY DESIGN

DATUM DEFINITION

GEOMETRICAL DESIGN

SELECTION OF OBSERVING ACCURACY

SATELLITE CONFIGURATION SELECTION

STEPWISE DESIGN OF A NETWORK

LOGISTIC DESIGN

FOOTHOLD OPERATION

PROCESSING SOFTWARE

OUTAGES

CONSTRAINTS

GPS SURVEY DESIGN

In this chapter, we show the concepts involved in designing a GPS survey to achieve the highest accuracy. Also, we address the related problem of minimizing the cost of a GPS field campaign while adhering to the prescribed accuracy for the resulting positions. To obtain geodetic results from a GPS field campaign, the collected data must be postprocessed. Aspects concerning the selection of appropriate computer software are brought to light here as well.

A certain amount of design is involved even when planning to use GPS for navigation. Two particular aspects involved in such a design are discussed here: the effect of outages, and the effect of constraints.

DESIGN PARAMETERS IN GPS SURVEY DESIGN

PARAMETER GROUP	PARAMETERS
Station geometry	• number of stations • configuration of stations • baselines
Satellite geometry	• number of satellites • configuration of satellites • mask angle
Receivers	• type(s) of receiver to be used • number of receivers available • configurations for each session • weather observations to be made ? • manual, remote control, or preprogrammed ?
Time considerations	• time of day (ionospheric effects) • observing window and duration • sampling rate (preprocessing)
Ranging mode	• code (C/A or P) or carrier or both • L1 or L2 or both
Processing mode (software)	• datum • ranges or range differences • network or baseline by baseline • broadcast or precise ephemerides • bias modelling
Auxiliary	• number of personnel • method of transportation • leased or owned equipment

DESIGN PARAMETERS IN GPS SURVEY DESIGN

In this chapter, we consider only the case of a general network of points to be positioned. A *baseline* can be regarded as the most simple network consisting of only a pair of points. Hence, any statement valid for a network is equally valid for a baseline.

The aim of a survey design is to maximize the accuracy of positions to be determined. This is always true, although we usually will have considered some other design criteria first; for example, cost, manpower, observing time, number and type of equipment required, logistics. In mathematical terms, this means that the trace of the covariance matrix C_x of the position unknowns is to be minimized with respect to whatever variables are to be considered. But C_x is merely a properly scaled inverse of the matrix of normal equations N. Consequently, we really seek the minimum of $Tr(N^{-1})$, where different configurations and different observing accuracies give different matrices N, and thus different values of $Tr(N^{-1})$.

Whereas there are infinitely many choices of configurations, both of the ground (receiver) stations as well as satellites, and of observing times, for practical reasons, only a finite number of many combinations of configurations, observing times, and other design parameters can be tried. The design is then reduced to a **trial and error process**. Once a selection of a set of design parameters is made, elements of the N matrix can be evaluated with relative ease. Under those circumstances, the criterion of max $Tr(N)$ instead of min $Tr(N^{-1})$ would lead to the same **optimal selection of design parameters** and, therefore, to the same design.

In the rest of this chapter, we shall treat three particular subproblems to the above general problem of design.
• We shall show the choices available for controlling the accuracy of ranging/range differencing.
• We shall discuss the concepts involved in the ground station configuration design.
• We shall describe the principles used in selecting optimal satellite configurations.

DATUM DEFINITION

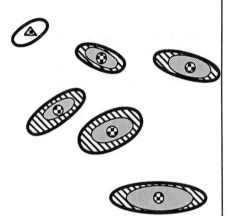

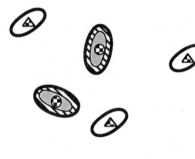

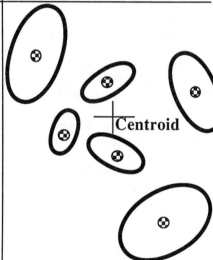

△ **Fixed or weighted point**

⊗ **Estimated point**

RESULTING CONFIDENCE REGIONS FOR

Fixed point scenario

Weighted point scenario

Centroid

Pseudo-inverse solution

DATUM DEFINITION

When constructing the design matrix for the survey network it is necessary to describe how to position and orient the network on the earth's surface. This procedure is often known as *datum definition*. (Note that this is a looser use of the term **datum** than its mathematical definition, which is that a *datum* is a particular coordinate surface.) This can be done in several ways:

• holding one point fixed (placing an infinite weight on the known position of the point),

• holding one point properly weighted (placing the appropriate weight P_X on the one known position),

• holding no point fixed and using a generalized inverse to invert the (singular) N,

• holding several points fixed,

• holding several points properly weighted by P_X.

The first three approaches use the minimum necessary number of **positional constraints** and are therefore known as *minimum constraint adjustments*. The last two belong to a family of **overconstrained adjustments.** Other techniques also exist.

All minimum constraint adjustments yield identical results for the *network configuration* (relative positions among the points). It is said that network configuration is invariant with respect to the choice of the minimal set of constraints. The placement of the network on the earth's surface, though, would generally be different. Also, the relative confidence ellipsoids will be the same for all minimum constraint adjustments, whereas absolute confidence ellipsoids will vary. Different situations are shown in the figure in a two-dimensional fashion; the concepts are analogous, however, in three dimensions.

It should be emphasized that the only statistically rigorous way of selecting the datum is to take all the known positions into consideration by putting appropriate weights on them. If a position of only one point is known — this includes the case when only a very approximate position (good to only one kilometre) of the network is available — and if we are not particularly interested in learning where exactly the network is located, in an absolute sense, then any minimum constraint adjustment will do the job. This should be borne in mind when realizing that GPS determined relative positions are inherently superior to the GPS point positions.

The concepts involved in the *foothold technique* (used, for example, in the Active Control System), will be treated separately in a subsequent section.

GEOMETRICAL DESIGN

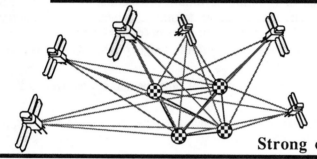

Strong configuration

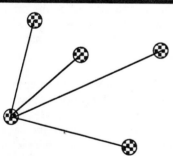

Weaker configuration

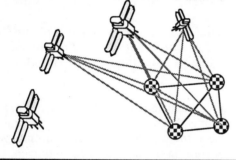

No geometrical redundancy

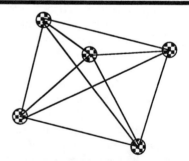

Maximum geometrical redundancy

GEOMETRICAL DESIGN

Often the survey design problem to be solved includes the geometry of both the satellites to be used and the network of ground stations. The aim then is to design the geometrically strongest combined configuration. Clearly, if time and expense are of no importance and receivers capable of tracking any number of satellites are available, then the use of all visible satellites and all possible baselines that can be created within the network will result in the **strongest configuration** and will give the best accuracies of relative positions. This is, however, never the case and limitations must be considered.

The number of satellites to be tracked simultaneously is limited by the number of receiver channels, real or simulated. Most receivers are capable of tracking four satellites simultaneously, and the selection of the best four satellites is thus the most often posed problem.

Baseline length and orientation affect the accuracy of estimated baseline components — relative positions. The selection of baselines within the network can either reduce or enhance *geometrical redundancy*, i.e., the number of conditions that sums of baselines must satisfy to make a consistent collection (so that all loops made of individual baselines close to zero).

SELECTION OF OBSERVING ACCURACY

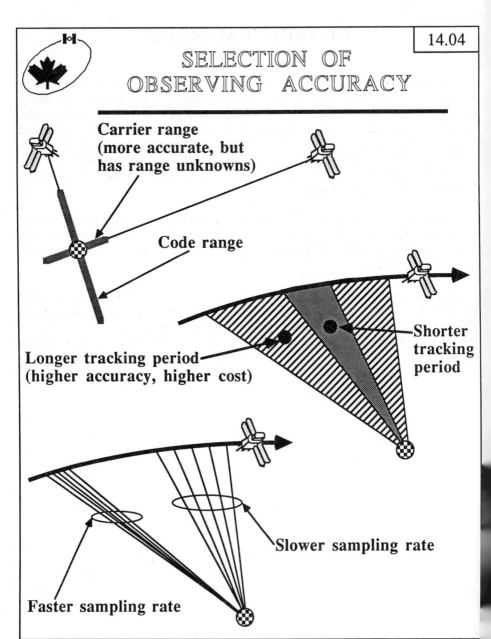

Carrier range (more accurate, but has range unknowns)

Code range

Longer tracking period (higher accuracy, higher cost)

Shorter tracking period

Slower sampling rate

Faster sampling rate

SELECTION OF OBSERVING ACCURACY

The accuracy of observed ranges is one of the most crucial parameters which control the overall accuracy of determined positions. Thus ranging by means of one of the carriers is, as we have seen, much more accurate than ranging using either of the PRN codes even though one has to solve for the range unknowns (the ambiguities). Consequently, most GPS surveying has been done with carrier ranging.

Generally, the longer we track the selected set of satellites the more accurate the resulting position differences. This is due to a more extensive sampling of the atmosphere (and resulting randomization of atmospheric delays) and more varying geometry of the satellite set (and resulting randomization of orbital errors) rather than to more ranges being collected. Dependence of accuracy on range sampling speed is very weak since frequent sampling drives down only the random part of the error but does nothing to reduce biases.

To reduce biases introduced by incorrect modelling of tropospheric delays, the mask angle (vertical angle cutoff) during tracking should be kept reasonably large (8° to 15°). Observed values of weather parameters are likely to reduce further suspected biases in tropospheric modelling. If the utmost accuracy is desired, then water vapour radiometers may have to be used. All these precautions are, of course, much more important for long baselines where range differencing is less likely to difference away biases present in the observations.

Selection of the appropriate time of day for the observations reduces the effect of the ionosphere, and keeping the antenna away from reflective structures reduces the danger of multipath problems. Finally, when carrier ranging is employed, potential accuracy decreases with every new range unknown that has to be solved for. Hence, switching to a marginally more favourable set of satellites for a brief period of time would not be a good strategy because it would result in decreased accuracy.

Reasonable and practical combinations of choices should be tested in constructing the $\mathbf{N}$ matrices. We note that the selection of observing period will have the most significant effect on the internal structure of $\mathbf{N}$. The rest of the variables will affect only the scale σ_o^2 of $\mathbf{N}$.

SATELLITE
CONFIGURATION SELECTION

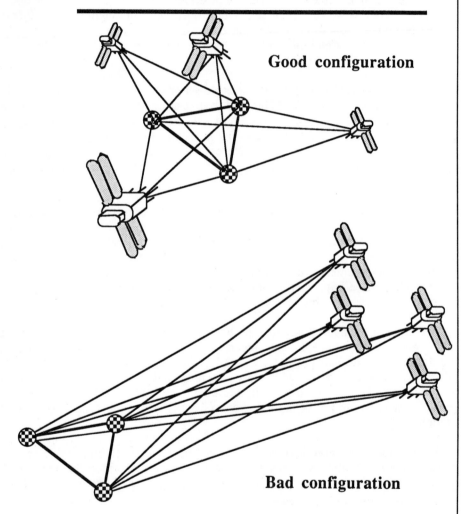

Good configuration

Bad configuration

SATELLITE CONFIGURATION SELECTION

When we use receivers which are not capable of tracking all the available satellites, it is important to ensure that the set of satellites to be tracked makes the best configuration for the task to be performed. This can be done rigorously by selecting such a set that gives the minimal trace of N^{-1} but selection algorithms based on the idea of minimizing the appropriate DOP may be quite adequate. This would be the case when a shorter observing interval is contemplated for the duration of which the satellite constellation does not change significantly. Then the best configuration for the centre of the observing interval can be sought.

For short baselines, it is reasonable to assume that the most suitable configuration for relative positioning is identical to the most suitable configuration for point positioning. This implies that, for instance, for the usual selection of four satellites the criterion of the maximum volume of the tetrahedron made out of the four satellites can be used. Since processing mode makes no difference as far as final results are concerned [Lindlohr and Wells, 1985], then it has no effect on the optimal configuration either. It is of interest to note that if across satellite differences are used in the processing, results are invariant with respect to the selection of *reference satellite(s)* [Lindlohr and Wells, 1985].

Minimization of the effect of orbital errors, **dr**, in a satellite configuration is a much more difficult proposition. To study the effect we may use the following vector equation [Vaníček et al., 1985]

$$\mathbf{b} \ \mathbf{dr} = \rho \ \mathbf{e} \ \mathbf{db}$$

formulated for a single baseline **b**, where **e** is the mean unit vector in the direction of the satellite. For several satellites we get

$$\mathbf{b} \ \Sigma_i \ \mathbf{dr}_i = \Sigma_i \ \rho_i \ \mathbf{e}_i \ \mathbf{db}$$

and all we can ascertain is that for small overall bias $\Sigma_i \ \mathbf{dr}_i$ the effect **db** will be either small or tend to be perpendicular to $\Sigma_i \ \rho_i \ \mathbf{e}_i$, which in turn, for the optimal satellite configuration, will tend to be directed perpendicularly upwards from the baseline.

Needless to say, we have to make sure that all the satellites in the selected configuration are visible simultaneously to all the tracking receivers.

STEPWISE DESIGN
OF A NETWORK

Step 1
Session 1

Step 2
Session 2

Step 3
Session 2

Step 4
Session 3

Step 5
Session 3

Step 6
Session 4

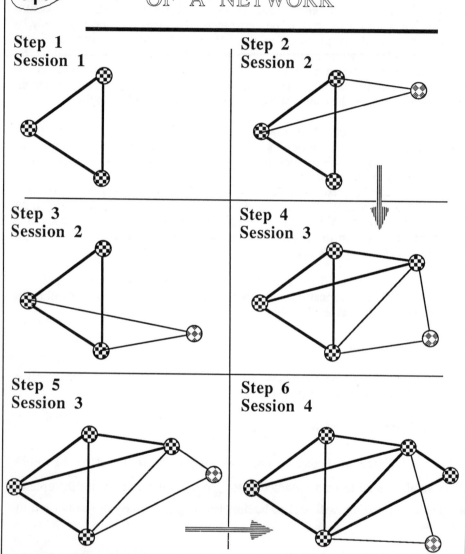

STEPWISE DESIGN OF A NETWORK

In designing an optimal configuration of ground points, including the selection of baselines (simultaneously observed pairs of points), we assume the satellite configuration as given, while varying the ground station configuration. Since for a large network the inversion of the matrix of normal equations N needed for each tested configuration can be quite laborious, it is advisable to use an efficient inversion algorithm. Stepwise updating of N^{-1} seems to be a sensible technique to adopt in this context. It is based on the idea of inverting expressions of the following kind:

$$N + \Delta N,$$

where the economy comes from the fact that ΔN will have relatively few non-zero elements. For instance, removal of one baseline will affect only two points resulting in ΔN having only a 6 by 6 non-zero submatrix imbedded in a zero matrix. The addition of a baseline renders a similar result.

The use of an incremental matrix ΔN cuts down the number of operations necessary to evaluate the individual elements of N. Since each observation gives an independent contribution to all the affected elements of N, the number of operations needed to assemble each element may be quite large. Denoting by E the number of contemplated sessions (receiver location permutations), by N the number of observations during each session, by S the number of tracked satellites, and by R the number of simultaneously operating receivers, we have to deal with the total of either ENS(R-1) independent single differences, or EN(S-1)(R-1) independent double differences, or E(N-1)(S-1)(R-1) independent triple differences. This represents, for instance, 10 800 observed double differences even for a relatively modest case of 20 sessions of 60 observations each using four satellites and four receivers.

When the stepwise updating of N is used, then for the deletion of one baseline only EN(S-1) observations of double differences have to be considered in assembling ΔN.

This figure is based on the use of three receivers to position six points. We start with a three-station setup (step 1); try two alternative expansions to a fourth station (steps 2 and 3), and decide that the former is better; try two alternative expansions to a fifth station (steps 4 and 5), and decide that the latter is better; and finally expand to the sixth station.

LOGISTIC DESIGN

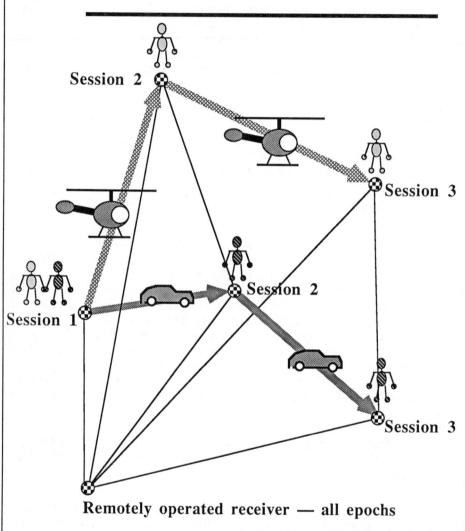

Session 2

Session 3

Session 2

Session 1

Session 3

Remotely operated receiver — all epochs

LOGISTIC DESIGN

From the practical point of view, it is usually desirable to minimize the cost of field work while adhering to the prescribed accuracy. The components in this minimization problem are all or a selection of the following:

- personnel
- transportation means and their deployment
- number and type of receivers
- use of own or rented receivers
- use of remotely controlled or preprogrammed receivers.

The cost associated with the individual components generally varies from company to company, from place to place, and from job to job. It is, therefore, impossible to give a generally valid prescription here, and a solution should be sought for each case separately.

Mathematically, it is possible to work out the exact solution using linear and quadratic programming. Software for these so-called economic problems is commercially available. Most of the time, an approximate solution works out satisfactorily.

The choice of economically appropriate software for processing the collected observations should be considered in the logistic design.

FOOTHOLD OPERATION

CASE OF TWO ROVING RECEIVERS

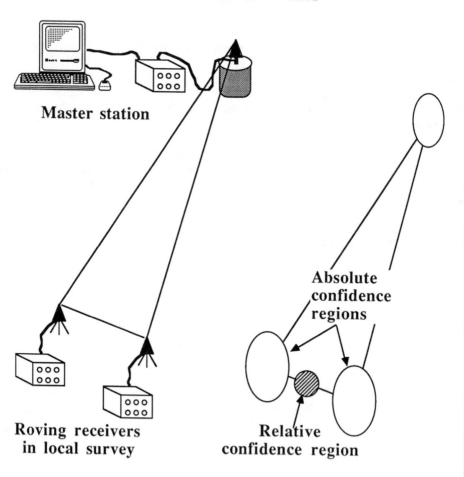

Master station

Absolute confidence regions

Roving receivers in local survey

Relative confidence region

FOOTHOLD OPERATION

In the *foothold mode* of operation, when a permanent **master station** is operated and maintained by a service organization, the survey design would have a different character. The service organization may or may not be equipped to design the survey procedures for the user. If not, then it would be up to the user/surveyor to do it himself.

The foothold mode can be used with either one or several **roving receivers**. In either case, the master station serves as the datum point whose coordinates would be weighted relatively highly, because the accuracy of its position would be quite high.

The distance of roving receiver(s) from the master station would normally be much longer than distances between roving receivers. As a result, the integrity of the relative positions of roving receivers will be quite high, whereas their location with respect to the master station (in metric units) would be less well known.

If the user must carry out the design by himself, the steps to be followed are analogous to those described earlier.

PROCESSING SOFTWARE

GENERAL PURPOSE SOFTWARE

- Not restricted to GPS observations
- Solutions for station coordinates, satellite orbit, force model and nuisance parameters
- Mainframe computer

BUILT-IN RECEIVER SOFTWARE

- Real-time position and velocity solution
- Code receiver only

RECEIVER MANUFACTURER'S SOFTWARE

- Dedicated to operate on output of a particular receiver type
- Baseline and/or network mode
- Personal computer

3rd PARTY SOFTWARE

- Not restricted to particular receiver type
- Baseline and/or network mode
- Mainframe, mini, or personal computer

OBSERVATION CAMPAIGN PLANNING SOFTWARE

PROCESSING SOFTWARE

Even though with proper formulation the results are invariant with respect to the processing mode (ranges, range differences, double differences, triple differences, etc.), there are still a number of other features that deserve a thought from the point of view of selecting the appropriate software for processing the collected data.

First, the available software varies considerably as far as bias modelling is concerned: orbital biases, clock biases, range biases, atmospheric biases. Secondly, not all software is able to process data in the network mode. If only individual baselines can be processed, then a separate program has to be used subsequently to adjust the baselines within the network.

Modelling of tropospheric and ionospheric delays may also vary significantly. Some software allows input of actual weather parameters; others do not. Data rate reduction (normal point formation) is treated differently in different programs and so are cycle slips. Lastly, different pieces of software provide different kinds of output, particularly in the error estimates.

Not all software is available for all categories of computers. If only a personal computer is available, then the choices may be fairly limited. Also computer time consumption may have to be taken into account, since the performance of different programs varies appreciably.

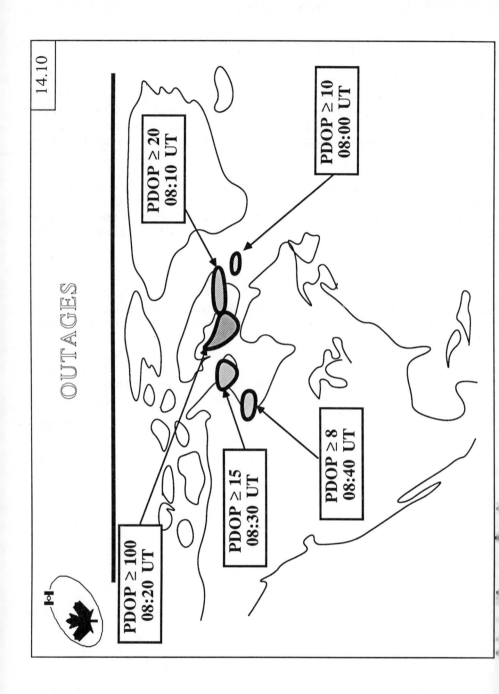

OUTAGES

PDOP ≥ 20
08:10 UT

PDOP ≥ 10
08:00 UT

PDOP ≥ 100
08:20 UT

PDOP ≥ 15
08:30 UT

PDOP ≥ 8
08:40 UT

14.10

OUTAGES

The geometry provided by GPS satellites changes continually, as the satellites move in their orbits, and as the user moves from place to place over the surface of the earth. For certain times and at certain places the geometry can become very bad. Such cases are referred to as *outages*. An outage is the occurrence (in time and space) of GPS satellite geometry so bad that the GPS position accuracy is worse than some predefined level. Full information about the accuracy of a GPS position is contained in the covariance matrix associated with that position. It is often useful to separate the accuracy estimate into two factors: that due to range measurement errors, and that due to geometry, as represented in a simple way by the *Dilution of Precision (DOP)*. This single number describes the geometrical strength of the GPS satellite constellation at any point in time and space, and is defined as the factor by which GPS range errors should be multiplied to yield the corresponding positioning error (see Chapter 4).

Outages are usually defined in terms of DOP values. For example, we may specify that an outage occurs whenever GDOP exceeds 6 — that is, whenever the r.m.s. solution error exceeds six times the range measurement error. For range errors of, say, 2 metres, this would yield an r.m.s. solution error of 12 metres. If we take the full covariance matrix information into account, we may find each of the position coordinates and time to have to quite different accuracies. But as a simple measure of the effect of geometry, the DOP value is quite useful.

Once the full GPS constellation is in place, outages will still occur, but briefly (typically for less than 10 minutes, once per day), and only in specified locations on the surface of the earth. This figure shows the occurrence in time and space of outages near Baffin Island for the 18 + 3 constellation. In this case, the outage is specified in terms of PDOP.

Outages depend strongly on mask angle: larger mask angles will cause more serious outages, both in extent and duration. For the mask angle of 5°, considered in this figure, outages last typically for about 15 minutes, and are of limited extent. At a mask angle of 20°, this outage expands to cover most of North America.

Outages are of primary concern in navigation and real-time point positioning, where during an outage other positioning systems must be used. In surveying, they are a minor nuisance, causing only a forced extension of time needed for field observations thus making the GPS survey more expensive.

This figure was prepared with the help of program **MacGEPSAL**, available from the Geodetic Research Laboratory, Department of Surveying Engineering, University of New Brunswick.

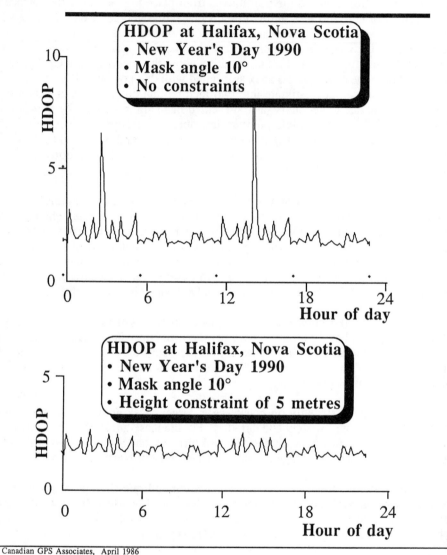

EFFECT OF HEIGHT CONSTRAINT

HDOP at Halifax, Nova Scotia
- New Year's Day 1990
- Mask angle 10°
- No constraints

HDOP at Halifax, Nova Scotia
- New Year's Day 1990
- Mask angle 10°
- Height constraint of 5 metres

EFFECT OF HEIGHT CONSTRAINT

The geometry for a four-dimensional position will be worse than that for a position where we actually know one or more of the solution parameters in advance. There will be many applications for which we really do need to solve for all four parameters (latitude, longitude, height, and receiver clock offset). In these cases there is not much we can do to improve the geometrical strength.

Investigating the effect of various constraints on expected results for the remaining parameters is an important aspect of GPS survey design. Since we will never know our position coordinates or time perfectly ahead of time, it is important that we use a technique known as **weighted constraints**, discussed earlier. We still solve for the constrained parameters, but we let our solution vary from the assumed 'known' value only slightly. For example, if we assume that we know the height to 5 metres, we can instruct the GPS software to prevent the height value in the solution from varying more than 5 metres from the 'known' value we specify for height going into the solution.

What do we gain from a constrained solution? Improved geometrical strength, and enhanced redundancy, and hence improved accuracy for the solution for the remaining, unconstrained, parameters. The tighter the constraint (that is, the more accurately we know the constrained parameters) the greater this improvement in geometrical strength. What do we risk by using a constrained solution? This depends on whether we actually know the constrained parameters as well as we have told the algorithm we do. For example, if we constrain the height to 5 metres, but use a 'known' value for height which is wrong by 50 metres, we will have a much worse horizontal position than if we had assumed we knew nothing about the height and had solved for it. How much worse depends on the geometry again, but would typically be of the same order as our height error—50 metres. The trick is to match the constraint to the accuracy with which we know the constrained parameter.

This figure shows the results of a GPS hydrographic survey planning exercise in which the application of height constraints to improve GPS geometry was investigated. The top plot in this figure shows the variation in HDOP at Halifax, Nova Scotia, on New Year's Day 1990, assuming the 18-satellite constellation and a 10° mask angle. Two outages are evident, where HDOP approaches a value of 10. The bottom plot shows the result for the same case, but with a 5 metre height constraint applied. This constraint eliminates the outage. We conclude that, if the shipboard GPS receiver ellipsoid height can be predetermined to 5 metres (requiring accurate geoid maps, estimates of tide and swell, height of antenna above the water level, and the effects of roll and pitch), then constraining it will improve the geometrical strength enough to eliminate outages.

This figure was prepared with the help of program **MacGEPSAL**, available from the Geodetic Research Laboratory, Department of Surveying Engineering, University of New Brunswick.

CHAPTER FIFTEEN

PRACTICAL ASPECTS
OF GPS SURVEYING

PRACTICAL ASPECTS OF GPS SURVEYING

PROCEDURES

- Planning
- Field operation
- Data processing

STANDARDS

- GPS survey standards
- Field procedure standards
- Data processing standards

MONUMENTATION

PRACTICAL ASPECTS OF GPS SURVEYING

At this time of GPS equipment and software evolution and relatively high prices, it is safe to say that GPS is primarily used for large survey control projects. GPS techniques are more efficient and cost effective than alternative methodologies, such as inertial systems, Transit satellite receivers, and conventional techniques.

Unfortunately, standards and specifications for GPS surveys do not yet formally exist, so it is difficult to establish GPS procedures. Little practical information is available, except from papers written primarily by government agencies [U.S. Federal Geodetic Control Committee, 1986] and progressive survey firms regarding various GPS survey control projects.

Perhaps the next few pages, although not providing an exhaustive description of GPS surveying, will at least provide a sketch of the procedures to be followed and some of the criteria which may soon make up the GPS surveying standards.

PLANNING

DESIGN

- **Project layout / network design**
- **Redundancy**

OBSERVATION SCHEDULE

- **Satellites available**
- **Time per station**
- **Stations per day**

INSTRUMENTATION

- **Codeless or code correlation**
- **One frequency or two**
- **Data recording system**

LOGISTICS

- **Transportation**
- **Personnel**
- **Power**

RECONNAISSANCE

- **Obstructions**
- **Accessibility**

PLANNING

Until the cost of GPS receivers drops and a full satellite constellation is available, careful planning of GPS surveys is critical for a successful project [Hothem et al., 1984].

The initial planning stage involves the project layout and network design which are primarily dependent on accuracy requirements, satellite constellation, and geometry (as already discussed in a previous chapter). Consideration must be given to the number of receivers, redundancy, time per station, number of stations per day, observation window, and whether one station will be used as a base for the whole project or a leap frog approach will be used.

Accuracy requirements will determine whether or not an L1/L2 receiver is required and whether or not precise ephemerides need be arranged for. Choice of receiver will affect the type of recording system and media which will be required. Codeless receivers will require that receivers are physically synchronized often during a project. Other receiver characteristics which affect logistics are whether power requirements are AC, 12 or 24 v DC, whether the equipment is portable and ruggedized or merely transportable, and what antenna cable lengths are available.

Terrain and station accessibility will determine whether car, truck, or helicopter is used to transport the receivers and the number of personnel required.

Planning cannot be finalized until site reconnaissance is completed. Sites must be inspected for vehicle access, cable length requirement, obstructions, foliage and, if necessary, the monument itself must be found. While receivers are expensive and the operating window is short, few operations can afford surprises during the observation campaign.

FIELD OPERATION

BEFORE LEAVING BASE
- Receiver synchronization (if required)

EN ROUTE TO OBSERVING STATIONS
- Maintain power to receiver

SETTING UP AT OBSERVING SITES
- Antenna - set-up, centre, measure phase centre height
- Receiver - initialize, select satellites (if required)
- Recorder - ensure data is being recorded
- Perform any required calibrations

OPERATION AT OBSERVING SITE
- Monitor receiver operation
- Collect temperature, humidity, and pressure data
- Enter the following in the log book
    - » Weather
    - » Receiver problems
    - » Operator errors
    - » Obstruction diagram

COMPLETION OF OBSERVING SESSION
- Remove and label data tape (disk, etc.)
- Repeat calibration checks (if possible)
- Next site or return to field office

FIELD OPERATION

The daily operations in the field office, wherever it may be, include [Beck, 1985]: synchronization of receivers when codeless techniques are used, charging of batteries, fuelling generators and vehicles, and initializing data storage media. Before heading out to the stations, receivers are often placed in standby mode to warm up the internal oscillator.

Once at the site, the antenna is centred above the station on a tripod and the height to the antenna phase centre is measured. All cables are connected and the receivers are initialized so that visible satellites are acquired. For receivers that do not track all satellites in view, it is important that all receivers used in the project are simultaneously tracking the same satellites. When tracking has begun, the operator must ensure that the recording device is functioning properly and that both measurements and broadcast ephemeris (if applicable) are recorded. The operator then monitors tracking performance by watching receiver signal quality indicators. Switching satellites and making pressure, temperature, and relative humidity measurements may also be required.

Log books are maintained to record any operator errors, receiver problems, tracking problems, obstruction diagrams, and weather data.

When the predetermined amount of data has been collected, the antenna height and centring is checked, the antenna taken down, and the equipment moved to the next site or back to the field office or camp.

DATA PROCESSING

IN THE FIELD

- **Data verification**

PREPROCESSING

- **Smoothing**
- **Editing (cycle slips, etc.)**
- **Ambiguity resolution (first step)**
- **Ephemeris representation**

ADJUSTMENT

- **Ambiguity resolution (second step)**
- **Baseline relative positioning computation**
- **Three-dimensional network adjustment**

POSTPROCESSING

- **Data analysis**
  - » **Repeatability**
  - » **Accuracy**
- **Archive results**

DATA PROCESSING

The first stage of data processing is transferring the data to (usually) diskette for backup and/or further processing. There is a trend toward using transportable microcomputers for the data processing which allows processing for most applications to be completed in the field (where no external ephemeris source is needed). Re-observation can be scheduled before demobilizing as required by the processing output.

Data is verified to ensure data quantity and quality. Preprocessing also includes measurement editing and smoothing, such as correction or flagging of cycle slips and differencing of phase data between stations, satellites, and epochs as required. The collected broadcast ephemeris must be decoded and interpreted; precise ephemeris can be obtained from the Canadian Geodetic Survey or the U.S. National Geodetic Service but at best two weeks later. In either case, the ephemeris representation is usually altered by, e.g., fitting a curve through consecutive broadcast segments to form a contiguous representation or by computing satellite coordinates for each satellite at each transmission epoch.

One approach to the adjustment stage of the processing is as follows. Accounting for horizontal and vertical antenna offsets and weather data, three-dimensional geometric relative positions using non-differenced or differenced phase and range observations are computed. The processing scheme and software choice can vary depending on accuracy objectives. The results of this single baseline, or session (multi-baseline) or network (multi-session) processing, consisting of coordinate differences and associated covariance matrices are then input into a minimally constrained three-dimensional network adjustment program in order to generate reliable statistics and detect any remaining errors.

An alternative adjustment approach is to input the preprocessed observations from a multi-session network campaign directly into a network adjustment package.

This approach forces the adjusted coordinates to be consistent over all observations in the campaign, rather than only on a session by session basis as above. In this way, biases which are strongly deterministic with one session but to some extent random between sessions (e.g., orbital biases and ionospheric biases) will be able to contribute to the estimation of a more realistic network covariance matrix. This latter approach is taken by DIPOP, the third-generation differential GPS positioning program package developed at the University of New Brunswick for the Geodetic Survey of Canada.

Data analysis includes checking whether the internal consistency of results and the results of repeated baselines meet the desired accuracy. Residuals are examined and the variance factor tested to ensure proper weighting

The final processing step is to present the results, and to archive all text, diskettes, tapes, etc., in an orderly manner.

GPS SURVEYING STANDARDS

GPS
RELATIVE POSITIONING ACCURACIES
EXCEED
CURRENT STANDARDS

CURRENT STANDARDS
ARE TWO DIMENSIONAL

GPS IS THREE DIMENSIONAL

NEW SPECIFICATIONS MUST ADDRESS
- **Various accuracy requirements**
- **New parameters**
- **Receiver and software calibration**

GPS SURVEYING STANDARDS
WILL EVOLVE WITH EXPERIENCE

GPS SURVEYING STANDARDS

Accuracies approaching 0.1 ppm are currently achievable with GPS which considerably exceed current standards. The accuracy requirement, be it 1:5000 or 1:1 000 000, will determine the specification of time required, instrumentation, methodology, etc., and also the cost; current costs vary between $100 and $4000 per point surveyed using GPS.

No published government standards for GPS surveys formally exist yet. New parameters will require definition in these forthcoming standards. Some of the issues are [Hothem, 1985]:

- GPS provides three-dimensional capabilities requiring ties to bench marks
- satellite geometry and ephemeris accuracy constraints need definition
- geoid slopes and accuracies need definition
- different measurement types and accuracies are available
- baseline, session, or network solutions are possible
- redundancy can come from the number of occupations per stations, repeat baseline observations, measuring antenna height twice.

Even when standards are defined, two major problems will remain: instrumentation calibration/compatibility, and software calibration. To compare results of instrumentation or combination of receivers and to evaluate realism of statistics and results generated by GPS processing software and to ensure compatibility and confidence in results generated from different software packages, three-dimensional calibration networks akin to current EDM baselines are being established, and test data sets are being provided for software calibration.

At least 100 GPS survey sets are currently being used in Canada and the U.S. alone. The rapidly increasing number of receivers is imposing a need to establish surveying standards for both field and office procedures. The following pages address some of these but are by no means near complete. GPS surveying standards will evolve as experience with GPS grows.

FIELD PROCEDURE STANDARDS

INSTRUMENT CALIBRATION STANDARDS

- Antenna
- Receiver
- Clock

SURVEY DESIGN STANDARDS

- Number of horizontal control points
- Number of bench marks
- Minimum number of receivers
- Number of occupations per station (redundancy)
- Minimum & maximum station separations
- Connections between stations
- Observing period per point
- L1 only, or L1 & L2
- Meteorological data acquisition

FIELD PROCEDURE STANDARDS

At this time, the only sure way to evaluate receiver accuracy and performance is by testing the receivers on a known baseline or network, as has already been done by the Federal Geodetic Control Committee of the United States and by the Canadian Geodetic Survey with receivers including, e.g., Macrometer™ V-1000, TI 4100, ISTAC Model 1991, Trimble 4000S, and WM101.

Specifications for field procedures must include (beyond those existing for conventional techniques) as a function of desired accuracy:

- number of existing horizontal control points to be occupied
- number of bench marks to be occupied
- minimum and maximum station spacing
- time per occupation as a function of satellite geometry
- one or two frequency instrumentation
- number of receivers
- data rates
- number of occupations per site
- cutoff elevation
- quantity and quality of meteorological data
- number of repeated baselines
- antenna setup specifications

Very preliminary values, for the above parameters as a function of accuracy, can be obtained from USNGS for use as a guideline.

DATA PROCESSING STANDARDS

SOFTWARE PACKAGE CALIBRATION STANDARDS

- **Standard data sets**

INPUT OPTION STANDARDS

- **Elevation cutoff (mask angle)**
- **Offset antenna capability**

DATA STANDARDS

- **Ephemeris source and accuracy**
- **Measurement rejection criteria**
- **Maximum acceptable measurement rejection rate**

POSTPROCESSING ANALYSIS STANDARDS

- **Repeatability tolerances**
- **Result of minimally constrained adjustment**
- **Loop misclosures**

DATA PROCESSING STANDARDS

As with instrumentation, the only way of ensuring realistic results with confidence is to use data reduction software which has been tested on a three-dimensional calibration network or with a standard test data set.

Specifications for processing data might include (as a function of accuracy desired)

- how the antenna offsets are applied
- satellite elevation cutoff
- ephemeris source and age
- measurement data quality and quantity
- measurement data rejection criteria
- measurement residual maximums
- baseline or session adjustment specification

After computing vectors or baselines, any baselines observed more than once would have to meet repeatability criteria for each of the three-dimensional vector components as a function of baseline length.

A minimally constrained three-dimensional adjustment would reveal whether realistic observation weights were used and what the standard errors (precision) of the three-dimensional vector component are. A constrained adjustment using existing control coordinates accounting for scale, orientation, and undulation relationships between the GPS satellite and the control network datums would provide proper integration of the GPS relative positioning results (obviously at a level corresponding to the control network accuracy).

Specifications for the display and storage of results and variance-covariance information will also be required.

MONUMENTATION

ESTABLISHING CONTROL POINTS AS REQUIRED,
USING GPS RELATIVE POSITIONING TECHNIQUES,
IS BECOMING MORE COST EFFECTIVE
THAN MAINTAINING MONUMENTATION

EVENTUALLY
MONUMENTATION MAY BE UNNECESSARY
AND BE REPLACED BY A NATIONAL NETWORK
OF A FEW GPS MONITOR STATIONS

MONUMENTATION

The need for stable expensive long term monumentation at often difficult to access sites might soon disappear except in urban areas where GPS satellites are not readily visible and for very high precision geodynamic studies networks. With GPS, re-establishing points is becoming less expensive then monumenting. Because there is no intervisibility requirement, new points established should be accessible by land transport and should be placed where they will be most useful.

Azimuth reference marks may need be added for local survey orientation. These can be established using GPS, from star observations using a theodolite, or by observations using a gyrotheodolite.

Continuously tracking GPS monitor stations, as proposed by the Texas State Department of Highways and the Canadian Geodetic Survey, could satisfy most monumentation requirements and provide additional benefits to the surveyor [Steeves et al., 1986]:

- no physical access to control points required
- no descriptions of control points required
- may be able to use fewer receivers
- automatic access to latest control point coordinates
- single datum
- automatic integration of information into the national framework.

Development and testing of such systems has already begun.

APPENDIX A

CHARACTERISTICS OF VARIOUS GPS RECEIVERS

WHICH GPS RECEIVER ?

APPLICATION
- **Real time or postmission**
- **Static or dynamic**
- **Differential or point positioning**
- **Accuracy requirement**

TYPE
- **One or two frequencies**
- **Code dependant or codeless**
- **Multichannel, switching, hybrid**
- **C/A- or P-code**
- **Fully integrated system or sensor only**

FEATURES
- **Carrier phase**
- **Data logging**
- **Physical characteristics and portability**
- **Power requirements**
- **Software**

COST

WHICH GPS RECEIVER?

When deciding on which receiver to buy or use, several key selection criteria must be addressed:

- the application for which it will be used;
- the accuracy requirement;
- the type of signal processing required;
- the necessary features and options required to suit the application; and, of course,
- cost.

The more applications a receiver will fulfill, the greater its flexibility, the fancier the features and options, the greater the cost. Real-time applications may only require displayed positions, velocities, and waypoint navigation, whereas postmission applications obviously require data logging devices and interface ports. Static receivers for point positioning or time transfer do not require a fast sequential or multi-channel receiver configuration, whereas one mounted in a helicopter might. Defining the accuracy requirement to 50 m, 15 m, 5 m or submetre determines whether differential techniques are required, C/A- or L1/L2 P-code is needed, and whether carrier beat phase measurements must be available. The environment in which the receiver will be used dictates the antenna type and mount, receiver size, portability, and degree of ruggedness. Sometimes only a GPS receiver sensor, as part of a multi-sensor integrated navigation system, is required, as opposed to a complete self-contained receiver system.

GPS receiver technology is rapidly evolving. What follows is essentially a catalogue of commercially available GPS receiver products. The information has been gleaned from company brochures, manuals, phone conversations, and proceedings. (Where no reference is given, information was obtained from brochures.) Due to the dissimilar type and quantity of information available, the discussion format for each receiver varies.

DISCLAIMER: An attempt has been made to include most known, commercially available GPS receivers; however, some may have been overlooked or insufficient data was available. Trademarks used belong to the respective manufacturers. Specifications, prices, availability, and material which follows are for information only and are subject to change without notice. For specific and current information, GPS receiver manufacturers should be contacted. No endorsement is hereby intended or implied.

CMA-786   (C-SET)

MANUFACTURER: **Canadian Marconi Company**

APPLICATIONS: **Low dynamics air, sea, and land navigation**

FEATURES:

- **2 channel L1, C/A-code, multiplex**
    1 channel tracks up to 8 satellites
        pseudo-range and pseudo-range rate
    2nd channel to acquire satellites, collect almanac and ephemeris data
- **1/2 ATR short**
- **Standard interface ports for external sensor aiding and relative positioning**
- **3-D navigation function**
- **Optional low profile antenna (0.8 x 13 x 13 cm)**

AVAILABILITY:

- **1986**
- **$ to be determined**

CMA-786 (C-SET)

Manufacturer: Canadian Marconi Company
                     415 Leggett Drive
                     P.O. Box 13330
                     Kanata, Ontario
                     Canada K2K 2B2

Canadian Marconi is taking advantage of experience gained in producing the military CMA-774 (D-Set) P- and C/A-code L1/L2 medium dynamics receiver in its development of a commercial GPS receiver initially intended for air navigation applications [Canadian Marconi Company, 1985]. What makes this navigation receiver different from any other is its dual channel C/A-code L1 multiplexing architecture. One of the channels is dedicated to tracking all of the up to 8 acquired satellites to generate pseudo-ranges and Doppler measurements. The second channel performs utility functions including:
• satellite acquisition (and re-acquisition as necessary);
• data bit synchronization and almanac and ephemeris data collection.

The advantages of tracking all visible satellites, as opposed to the minimum of four required for three-dimensional positioning, are:
• no need to acquire new satellites during satellite shading;
• no requirement for GDOP calculation;
• redundant measurements and therefore improvement in navigation accuracy.

In its final design, the CMA-786 will accept (optionally) external aiding through various standard interfaces (ARINC 426 I/O, RS-232C and RS-422) from sensors such as altimeter, Omega, and Doppler and a data link to support differential mode of operation. Operational features include automatic signal acquisition and tracking and typical three-dimensional waypoint navigation functions.

Physically, the CMA-786 is housed in a 1/2 ATR short unit weighing 8 kg, drawing 50 W maximum from 24 VDC or 115 VAC. Full temperature range components are optional. The CDU can be an off-the-shelf CMA-823. Two choices of antenna are available; either a 4 cm diameter by 13 cm helix cylinder type for ship or helicopter, or a crossed-slot low profile 8 x 13 x 13 cm antenna for commercial aircraft.

JMR SATTRAK

MANUFACTURER: **EDO Canada Ltd.**

APPLICATION: **Point positioning, low dynamics navigation**

FEATURES:

- **4 satellite sequencing on 1 L1, C/A-code channel**
- **Single piece (30 x 40 x 17 cm) ruggedized receiver/processor, CDU, and thermal printer**
- **Operates at -10°C to +50°C**
- **11-15 VDC (1 hour internal battery)**
- **No ephemeris or measurement data output**
- **30 waypoint navigation**
- **Compact (6 x 35 cm) antenna**
- **Usable in relative positioning mode (static)**
- **30 m single point mode (r.m.s.)**
- **5 m relative positioning static (after 5 min.)**
- **0.1 m/s (r.m.s.) speed**

AVAILABILITY:

- **$35,000; 30 days delivery**

JMR SatTrak

Manufacturer:
EDO Canada Ltd.
8-6320 11th Street S.E.
Calgary, Alberta
Canada T2H 2L7

As of early 1986, EDO Canada Ltd. had available a portable GPS positioning instrument transportable in a single package (including antenna) of 30 x 40 x 17 cm weighing about 10 kg. This L1 C/A-code single channel sequential receiver is for low dynamic and static positioning applications. The system functions on its own internal 12 VDC battery or can be connected to an external power supply.

The displayed (or printed) output consists primarily of two-dimensional or three-dimensional positions, speeds, waypoint information and time. The best four satellites to track are automatically selected.

In recent tests, 30 m r.m.s. accuracies for both static and dynamic positioning were achieved [Ayers and Gonthier, 1986]. By taking 5 minute averages at two static sites and performing a *translocation*, three-dimensional relative positioning accuracies of 5 m r.m.s. were achieved.

ASTROLAB II

MANUFACTURER: **Interstate Electronics Corp.**

APPLICATION: **Low dynamics navigation, time transfer, research and development training set**

FEATURES:

- **1 channel 4 satellite sequencing L1, C/A-code**
- **Interfaces DECCA, ARGO, Syledis, Mini-Ranger, Speed Log and Gyro**
- **48 x 14 x 44 cm (rack mounted) 18 kg**
- **19-32 VDC, 110-220 VAC (± 30 V)**
- **Waypoint navigation**
- **Relative positioning capability (option)**
- **Resident user software**

AVAILABILITY:

- **90 days delivery**

ASTROLAB II

Manufacturer: Interstate Electronics Corporation (IEC)
                       1001 E. Ball Road
                       Anaheim, California 92805
                       U.S.A.

IEC has had many years of GPS experience, primarily for the military in support of the Trident I and II programs. Their experience won them the contract for development of GPS hardware for a new range application program, involving differential GPS and integrated low cost INS.

In 1984, IEC had available commercially the model 4200, a C/A-code L1 time transfer and positioning receiver. Since that time they have acquired additional GPS technology and now have available the Astrolab II, again a C/A-code L1 sequential receiver for time transfer, low dynamics navigation and relative positioning. This rack mount non-ruggedized unit is intended as a training set for users wishing to learn about GPS through experience. The system has both IEEE 488 and RS-423 interfaces which allow interfacing to print and plot devices along with surface radio-location systems, such as DECCA, ARGO, Syledis, and Mini-Ranger, with available software packages. It also has an optional speed-log and gyro interface. Software also allows for relative positioning, controlling input/output to radio links. Several waypoint navigation functions are included.

The 48 x 14 x 44 cm, 18 kg receiver is tolerant of a wide range of power inputs: 19-32 VDC or 110, 220 V (±30 V) AC.

ISTAC-SERIES GPS POSITIONER MODEL 2002

MANUFACTURER: **ISTAC, Inc.**

APPLICATION: **Precise relative positioning**

FEATURES:

- **L1, all visible satellites, codeless pseudo-range**
- **Consists of 3 pieces**
    Antenna/receiver (7 kg)
    Rubidium clock interface unit with internal power (18 kg)
    Data analyser/recorder/computer (7 kg)
- **External ephemeris source required**
- **Not restricted to GPS satellites**
- **Accuracy:**
    10 cm in 15 min
    30 cm in 3 min

AVAILABILITY:

- **45 days delivery**
- **$US 57 000 per unit complete with all processing software**
- **L1/L2 and carrier phase processing options may be available in 1987**

ISTAC-SERIES GPS POSITIONER MODEL 2002

Manufacturer: ISTAC, Inc.
                        444 North Altadena Drive, Suite 101
                        Pasadena, California 91107
                        U.S.A.

SERIES is an acronym for Satellite Emission Range Inferred Earth Surveying. The technology originated at the Jet Propulsion Laboratory (JPL) and evolved to a configuration of 'codeless' pseudo-ranging in 1980 [MacDoran et al. 1985a], which will not be affected by the U.S. Department of Defense (USDoD) selective availability policies. The first commercial version of the product, the Model 1991 Land Surveyor marketed by GEO/HYDRO of Rockville, Maryland, was introduced in 1985. Since then, a more portable and efficient version, the GPS Positioner Model 2002, has been introduced. Both systems are best used in relative positioning modes.

The Model 2002, in its three piece portable configuration of a total of 32 kg, can achieve accuracies at the 30 to 10 cm level in 3 to 15 minutes, respectively (with good geometry). Like other 'codeless' receivers, an external ephemeris is required. ISTAC makes orbit determination software available along with an ephemeris service.

The unique features of the ISTAC products are that they track all visible GPS satellites without knowledge of their orbit, and that the receiver could be tuned to track other satellites, such as GLONASS satellites. The system configuration is different from most GPS receivers, consisting of the antenna/receiver assembly (23 x 42 cm), connected to the clock interface unit which houses the rubidium atomic clock and timing electronics connected to the field portable computer/data analyser/recorder (46 x 33 x 13 cm) for data collection and verification. This computer can also be used in the field for baseline postprocessing using ISTAC supplied software.

ISTAC-SERIES MARINE POSITIONING SENSOR MPS-1

MANUFACTURER: **ISTAC, Inc.**

APPLICATIONS: **Low dynamics relative positioning for marine environment (e.g., seismic surveys, inland harbour navigation)**

FEATURES:

- **Under development**
- **As Model 2002 but L1/L2 for marine application**
- **< 10 knots**
- **Communication cross-link required**
- **1 second update interval**
- **Accuracy:**

    5 m @ 500 km
    10 m @ 1000 km

AVAILABILITY:

?

ISTAC-SERIES MARINE POSITIONING SENSOR, MPS-1

Manufacturer: ISTAC, Inc.,
444 North Altadena Drive, Suite 101
Pasadena, California 91107
U.S.A.

Using the same receiver technology as employed in the Model 2002, the two frequency SERIES marine positioning sensor (MPS-1) is under development for real-time marine relative positioning applications at speeds of < 10 knots [MacDoran et al., 1984; MacDoran et al., 1985b]. In order to achieve real-time position, communication cross-links must be supplied between the receivers. Accuracies of 5 m to 10 m are expected at receiver separation distances of 500 to 1000 km, respectively. Applications include offshore survey vessel location, seismic vessel and streamer location, and harbour navigation.

JLR-4000
GPS NAVIGATOR

MANUFACTURER: Japan Radio Corporation

APPLICATION: Low dynamics navigation

FEATURES:
- C/A-code 1 channel L1, sequential receiver
- 30 waypoint memory
- Cross-track error, distance, bearing, time to go, etc.
- No raw data available
- Outputs positions, time, velocities
- 1 second cycle rate
- Antenna: 35 x 6 cm; < 1 kg; -25°C to +70°C
- Receiver/Processor/Display: 32 x 25 x 12 cm; 6 kg; 0°C to +50°C; 110/115/220 VAC or 24 VDC, < 30 watts
- Optional interface to remote display, printer, plotter
- Accuracy: (as at April 1986)
  30 m r.m.s. position
  0.1 m/sec r.m.s. speed

AVAILABILITY:
- $CAN 32 000

JLR-4000 GPS NAVIGATOR

Manufacturer: Japan Radio Corporation (JRC)
                          17-22, Akasaka
                          2-Chome, Minato-Ku
                          Tokyo 107
                          Japan

JRC has been developing a GPS receiver since 1979. They completed the prototype JLR-4000 in 1982 and announced its availability in 1984. This sequential C/A-code, L1, compact, single channel receiver is designed solely for low dynamics navigation of, e.g., marine vessels and automobiles [Japan Radio Corporation, 1985; Tomioka and Yamada, n.d.]. It is designed to provide 30 m (r.m.s.) position accuracy and 0.1 m/s r.m.s. velocity accuracy each second with the current GPS constellation. This information is available to the control display unit of the receiver and optionally to a remote display, colour plotter and printer. Navigation functions, such as 30 waypoint storage, distance, bearing, time to go, cross track error, arrival alarm, etc., are included. Because it is solely for navigation, broadcast message data and measurement data are not available for output.

The compact receiver/processor/display unit is powered from external 10-40 VDC or 110/115/220/230 VAC consuming on average less than 30 watts. It is operational in non-hostile environments at temperatures of 0°C to 50°C. The 6 cm diameter 35 cm quadrifilar helix omnidirectional antenna can withstand temperatures of -25°C to +70°C. The maximum antenna cable length is 50 m.

In Canada, the JLR-4000 is available through the Canadian Marconi Company, 2442 Trenton Avenue, Montréal, Québec, Canada H3P 1Y9.

LTN-700

MANUFACTURER: Litton Aero Products

APPLICATION: Commercial aviation to medium
dynamics

FEATURES:

- L1 C/A-code 1 channel fast sequencing
- Approx. 3/4 ATR short (32 x 19 x 19 cm); 9 kg
- Receiver/processor
    -15°C to +70°C
    115 VAC (400 Hz)
- Access to data and measurements
- Interfaces:
    ARINC 575 to CDU
    ARINC 429 auxiliary
    RS-232 for testing, etc.
- Marine/land applications options
    Ruggedized antenna/preamp assembly
    Various power supply options
    Differential GPS interface

AVAILABILITY:

- $US 50 000 antenna, CDU, receiver

LTN-700

Manufacturer: Litton Aero Products
6101 Condor Drive
Moorpark, California 93021
U.S.A.

The Litton Aero Products LTN-700 GPS Navigation Set, designed primarily for the commercial aviation market, has been available since 1984. Although it is a GPS sensor, it is usually sold as a system consisting of the L1 C/A-code, 4 satellite fast sequencing receiver/processor, control display unit and antenna.

What makes this receiver unique is how it sequences through the satellite signals [Sturza, 1984].   During acquisition mode, the receiver sequentially acquires the satellites (through a slow sequencing scheme).   Then during tracking a fast sequencing scheme is implemented—each 20 ms is divided into five, 4 ms intervals. Carrier tracking of four satellites and code tracking on one (of the four) satellite takes place every 20 milliseconds. A complete cycle of code and carrier tracking of 4 satellites requires 80 ms, easily allowing the receiver to update navigation outputs every 1 second. This scheme also allows for simultaneous data demodulation.

The system has also been designed to be used as a developmental tool allowing both raw and processed measurements and data to be accessed via RS-232 ports. Optional configurations allow the system to be used in marine and land navigation applications including a differential GPS interface, ruggedized antenna/ preamplifier assembly, and various power supplies.

The next Litton Aero Products GPS air navigation receiver system will incorporate a two-card receiver system to enable 'all-in-view' satellite tracking.

MACROMETER™ V-1000

MANUFACTURER: **Litton Aero Service**

APPLICATION: **Precise relative positioning only**

FEATURES:

- **6 channel L1 only**
- **Carrier phase squaring (codeless)**
- **No broadcast ephemeris decoding**
- **Both 12 VDC and 115 VAC (350 watts) required**
- **91 kg without generator**
- **3 mm antenna phase centre accuracy**
- **Synchronization of receivers required**
- **Ephemeris available through contract**
- **Antenna/preamp operable at -50°C to +70°C**

AVAILABILITY:

- **No longer for sale**
- **Still widely used (services can be leased)**
- **Minimum configuration includes:**
    - **2 field units**
    - **1 processing system and software**
    - **1 GOES satellite time receiver**
    - **1 time interval counter**

MACROMETER™ V-1000

Manufacturer: Litton Aero Service
       8100 Westpark Drive
       P.O. Box 1939
       Houston, Texas 77251-1939
       U.S.A.

Early versions of Macrometer technology were introduced to the survey community in 1982. Since the January 1983 tests by the (U.S.) Federal Geodetic Control Committee (FGCC), the Macrometer V-1000 has been used extensively for precise relative surveying.

In spite of its size (58 x 56 x 64 cm) and weight (73 kg), exclusive of the antenna (18 kg), the system is transportable and has been successfully used in both small 4 wheel vehicles and helicopters. Because the units use codeless carrier phase 'squaring' techniques, no broacast ephemeris data decoding is done and no clock synchronization using the GPS signal is possible. This scheme requires that the receivers be synchronized to each other and also to UTC via, e.g., a GOES (Geostationary Operational Environmental Satellite) satellite time receiver, and that power is maintained continuously to the internal oscillators. Ephemeris for postprocessing is available within 3 to 5 days under contract with Litton Aero Service or within several weeks through the U.S. National Geodetic Survey (USNGS).

The antenna pre-amplifier design is such that the unit can be operated between -50°C and +70°C. The antenna phase centre uncertainty is estimated to be 2 to 3 mm regardless of orientation, and the attached large ground plane is effective in reducing multipath.

The data are recorded in the non-volatile bubble memory unit of the receiver unit and transferred to a small data cartridge after the recording session, which can last from 10 minutes to 6 hours depending on accuracy requirements and geometry. The data are processed postmission with the Aero Service-supplied processing system and software.

Macrometer™ is a registered trademark.

MACROMETER II™

MANUFACTURER: Litton Aero Service

APPLICATION: Precise relative positioning

FEATURES:

- As V-1000 plus L2 frequency
- 3 portable units per system
- 27 kg (less antenna)
- 12 VDC (200 watts)
- 1 to 2 ppm currently achievable using provided ephemeris
- 10 min to 6 hrs depending on desired accuracy

AVAILABILITY:

- $US 240 000
- Approximately 6 months delivery
- Complete system
    2 Macrometer II portable field systems
    1 data processing system and software
    1 GOES satellite time receiver
    1 HP time interval counter

MACROMETER II™

Manufacturer:
Litton Aero Service
8100 Westpark Drive
P.O. Box 1939
Houston, Texas 77251-1939
U.S.A.

The Macrometer II, conceptually identical with the V-1000, has been redesigned to consist of three portable waterproof units weighing a total of 27 kg. This dual frequency version of Macrometer technology allows for ionospheric calibration and high accuracy relative positioning on long baselines even after the U.S. Department of Defense implementation of denial of P-code access. Operationally, the Macrometer II is used like the V-1000 except an AC generator is no longer required, just a 12 V battery (200 watts) will suffice.

Accuracies of 1 to 2 **ppm** have been readily achieved with the Macrometer system, as indicated in the many papers written by a variety of users.

In the future, Litton Aero Service, in conjunction with Litton Aero Products, will be introducing the Mini-Mac, a compact lightweight hybrid C/A-code carrier phase 'squaring' receiver system. Not much else is known about it at this time.

Macrometer II™ and Mini-Mac™ are trademarks of Aero Service Division, Western Geophysical Company of America.

T-SET

MANUFACTURER: Magnavox

APPLICATION: Low dynamics navigation

FEATURES:

- 5 channel L1 C/A-code continuous tracking
- GPS receiver card to fit in DEC VT-103 terminal including PDP-11/23 computer
- Controlled environment operation
- Receiver physical specs defined by VT-103
- Antenna: -40 °C to +70°C (land or marine configuration available)
- Position, pseudo-range, ephemeris can be output to an RS-232 port for recording, printing, etc.

AVAILABILITY:

$US 50 000

T-SET

Manufacturer: Magnavox
                  2829 Maricopa Street
                  Torrance, California 90503
                  U.S.A.

Magnavox has been involved in the military GPS program for about 20 years. The first GPS receiver which they offered commercially was the Magnavox T-set GPS Navigator. The initial versions were sequencing receivers; now they are a 5 channel continuous tracking L1 C/A-code system. The GPS receiver itself is contained on one card made to fit in a DEC VT-103 terminal with a PDP 11/23 computer. Thus, environmental, physical, and electrical characteristics are defined by the VT-103 terminal specifications, which means that the operation must be confined to controlled environments with conventional AC power. The land or sea antenna/preamp units (1.3 kg or 4.5 kg, respectively) operate at -40°C to +70°C.

Four of the five channels are designed to continuously track satellites, while the fifth is used for inter-channel bias calibration, ephemeris data gathering, and locking onto new satellites. Positions and speeds are output to the display, while processed and measured pseudo-ranges and Doppler and ephemeris data are available for output on RS-232 ports.

The T-set is intended for users interested in gaining GPS experience.

MX 1100
GPS NAVIGATOR

MANUFACTURER: Magnavox

APPLICATION: Marine low dynamics navigation

FEATURES:

- Combined GPS/Transit receiver system
- 2 channel, 4 satellite, L1 C/A-code tracking
- Sequences through 4 satellites and updates position every 1.6 seconds
- Physically similar to MX 1100 series navigator
    Transit receiver systems
       MX 1100 Transit systems
          can be retrofit with GPS addition
- Combination Transit/GPS antenna or two antenna configuration available

AVAILABILITY:

- New $US 45 000
- Retrofit $US 25 000

© Canadian GPS Associates, April 1986

MX 1100 GPS NAVIGATOR

Manufacturer: Magnavox
                     2829 Maricops Street
                     Torrance, California 90503
                     U.S.A.

The MX 1100 GPS Navigator combines GPS and Transit capability (at least until GPS is fully operational) in the familiar MX 1100 Transit receiver package. The two receivers operate concurrently displaying navigation results, with the system picking the optimal one. On the GPS receiver card, one of the two L1 C/A-code channels sequences through each of four satellites every 1.6 seconds, while the other searches for new satellites and gathers data. Positions are updated every 1.6 seconds.

The MX 1100 series navigators can be retrofitted with the additional GPS receiver system. A configuration of either a combination Transit/GPS antenna or two separate antennas is available.

Until the full GPS constellation is available, the combination GPS/Transit receiver provides better accuracy than a Transit-only system, and more continuous navigation than a GPS-only system.

MX 4400

MANUFACTURER: **Magnavox**

APPLICATIONS: **Positioning and navigation at sea, on land and in the air**

FEATURES:

- **2 channel, L1 C/A-code**
- **Output of selectable groups of processed and raw GPS data; 2 RS-422 input/output ports**
- **8-state Kalman filter**
- **Automatic best constellation selection**
- **Position updated every 1.2 s**
- **May be interfaced to Transit or Loran-C receiver and/or heading and speed sensors for dead reckoning**
- **Receiver: 10 - 28 VDC (20 W); -20°C to +50°C; waterproof; 35 x 33 x 11 cm; 7.2 kg; rack-mount option**
- **Antenna: -40°C to +50°C; 33 x 21 cm; 4.5 kg**
- **Demonstrated accuracy: 15 m r.m.s**
                        static: 5.1 m (half hour avg.)
                  velocity: 0.05 m/s

AVAILABILITY:

- **1986**
- **$CAN 25 000**

MX 4400

Manufacturer: Magnavox
                          2829 Maricops Street
                          Torrance, California 90503
                          U.S.A.

The MX 4400 GPS Positioning and Navigation System is Magnavox's dedicated, self-contained GPS positioning receiver. It shares the technology that has been developed for other receivers in the Magnavox GPS product line. The MX 4400 is a 2 channel, L1 C/A-code tracking receiver similar to that in the MX 1100. It has been designed to meet the needs of a broad spectrum of scientific, military, and commercial positioning and navigation requirements.

The receiver is housed in a compact, rugged, waterproof enclosure and is available in a self-supporting or rack-mounted configuration. The front panel has a two-line back-lit display and a simple, straightforward keypad for receiver control. The receiver can display position updates every 1.2 s. Two RS-422 input/output ports are provided. These may be used to output selectable groups of processed and raw data and in the future to input differential pseudo-range and delta pseudo-range corrections in RTCM 108 signal formats. A 5 MHz signal from an external atomic frequency standard may be supplied for positioning with fewer than four satellites.

The MX 4400 has software for waypoint navigation and may be interfaced to heading and/or speed sensors for dead reckoning during GPS outages. An advertised future option is a capability to interface to a Transit or Loran-C receiver.

EAGLE MINI-RANGER

MANUFACTURER: **Motorola Inc.**

APPLICATION: **Air, land, and sea static, kinematic, and relative positioning**

FEATURES:

- **4 channel, L1 C/A-code/carrier tracking sensor**
- **1 second update rate**
- **RS-232 for CDU (DCE)**
- **RS-232 for relative positioning data link (DTE)**
- **18-32 VDC or 10-17 VDC (30 W max)**
- **Receiver: 1/4 ATR, 30 x 18 x 6 cm; 4.5 kg;**
  -20°C to +55°C
- **Antenna/preamp: 11 x 11 x 5 cm; 1.4 kg;**
  -40°C to +85°C
- **Options:**
  1 sec time mark
  429 ARINC interface

AVAILABILITY:

- **November 1986**
- **$US 19 000**

EAGLE MINI-RANGER

Manufacturer: Motorola Inc.
2100 E. Elliot Road
Tempe, Arizona
U.S.A.

Motorola is producing a 4 channel, L1, C/A-code sensor for ground, sea, and air, and static, kinematic and relative positioning applications [Motorola Inc., 1986a; 1986b]. The compact receiver (30 x 18 x 6 cm) comes with two RS-232 ports to facilitate differential operations. Relative positioning data, including satellite identification, satellite correction factors, measurement quality, and time, is updated for output every second through the data link port.

The 4.5 kg receiver comes with two DC power supply options and is operable at -20°C to +55°C. The 1.4 kg antenna/preamp unit operates at -40°C to +70°C.

NORSTAR 1000

MANUFACTURER: **Norstar Instruments Ltd.**

APPLICATION: **Point and relative kinematic or
                        static positioning**

FEATURES:

- **5 or (optional) 7 channel L1 C/A-code operation**
- **1 sec update rate**
- **> 1000 waypoints, > 1000 events**
- **Mass memory unit stores up to 8 hrs of
      30 second data**
- **4 lines of 40 character display (menu driven)**
- **4 configurable serial I/O ports**
     **Phase, pseudo-range, positions, etc. output
          to any or all ports**
- **13 x 35 x 30 cm;**
- **24 VDC, 110/220 VAC optional**
- **-40°C to +60°C**
- **8 kg**

AVAILABILITY:

- **Mid-1987, 7 channel end of 1987**
- **$CAN 79 950**
- **plus $13 995 for 7 channel set**

NORSTAR 1000

Manufacturer:

Norstar Instruments Ltd.
Second floor, 319 - 2nd Avenue S.W.
Calgary, Alberta
Canada T2P 0C5

By the end of 1986, Norstar Instruments Ltd. expects to have completed development of the NORSTAR 1000, a ruggedized, compact, and portable (or optionally rack mountable) 5 (or optionally 7) channel, C/A-code receiver for point or relative (dynamic and static) positioning [Norstar Instruments, 1986]. One feature of this system is that it is menu driven and that it allows inspection and modification of many parameters including, for example, the standard deviation of the navigation filter parameters. As well, the three I/O ports can each be configured for data logging various raw and processed values to several peripherals, such as mass memory units, simultaneously.

The receiver allows for the recording of code, carrier phase measurements, and broadcast ephemeris to either the mass memory unit (8 hours of data at 30 seconds) or to any I/O port for post-processing applications, such as precise geodetic relative positioning.

PS 8400

MANUFACTURER: Prakla-Seismos AG

APPLICATION: Low dynamics navigation and
relative positioning

FEATURES:

- 1 channel 4 satellite multiplex C/A-code
- Waypoint navigation functions to local or remote displays
- Accepts input from log, gyro, modem
- Output capability to print, plot, or record devices
- Position averaging for static
- Manual or automatic relative mode operation
- Consists of
    Antenna unit: 20 x 40 cm, 4 kg;
    -20°C to +70°C

    Receiver unit (not for outside use):   0°C to +55°C

    CDU: 25 x 15 x 18 cm (8 kg)

AVAILABILITY:

- End of 1986

PS 8400

Manufacturer: Prakla-Seismos AG
                   Buchholzer Str. 100
                   D-3000 Hannover 51
                   Federal Republic of Germany

Prakla-Seismos, in a joint venture with Kongsberg Vapenfabrik of Norway, has already developed and tested two PS 8400F (functional) sequential C/A-code receivers for both static and dynamic applications to meet their respective requirements in geophysical exploration and offshore positioning [Stiller, 1985]. Kinematic positioning tests [Gerlach, 1985] yielded typical C/A-code accuracies of better than 30 m. By using relative positioning techniques for static positioning, 2 to 3 m accuracies were obtained in several minutes.

Based on the success of the PS 8400F, the joint venture is in the process of developing the PS 8400 to be available for sale in 1986. The PS 8400 will be an L1, C/A-code multiplexing receiver designed primarily for navigation and thus will be available in either bulkhead mount or 19" rack mount configurations. The 4 kg antenna/preamplifier unit operates at -20°C to +70°C; one or two control display units (25 x 15 x 18 cm) can be connected to the receiver unit; the 26 kg receiver unit (49 x 25 x 27 cm) operates at 0°C to +50°C. Standard navigation and waypoint functions are available. Through an external modem and communication link, relative positioning can be done automatically in real time.

In cooperation with the Geodetic Institute of the University of Bonn, Prakla-Seismos is also developing a GPS receiver for precise relative geodetic positioning.

COLLINS
NAVCORE I™

MANUFACTURER: Rockwell International

APPLICATION: Timing, navigation, relative positioning

FEATURES:

- 4 satellite, 1 channel, L1 C/A-code sequential GPS sensor
- Complete satellite and positioning cycle every 1 second
- Three configurations
  Timing
  Navigation
  Positioning/differential
- Two RS-232 ports
  1 for control/display
  1 for processed and raw data out
- 20 x 19 x 12 cm, 3 kg, 0°C to 55°C
- 12-40 VDC (30 watts)

AVAILABILITY:

- $US 18 000

COLLINS NAVCORE I™

Manufacturer:

Rockwell International
Collins Industrial GPS Products
Cedar Rapids, Iowa 52498
U.S.A.

During the NAVSTAR GPS Phase IIB Full Scale Development program of the Join Program Office, Rockwell-Collins developed a family of user equipment, for a wide range of applications, consisting of one, two, and five channel sets [Krishnamurti et al., n.d.]. One-channel sets were designed for manpack and tank configurations; two-channel sets for helicopters and aircraft carriers; and five-channel configuration for submarines and aircraft, such as the F-16 and B-52. Drawing from these development experiences, Avionics Group of Rockwell International has produced the Collins NAVCORE I™ GPS navigation receiver (sensor) for the commercial market. The NAVCORE I, L1, C/A-code receiver sequences through 4 satellites in one second providing completely updated navigation solutions at up to once per second.

Functionally, three GPS receiver units can be derived from the single GPS sensor hardware module: a timing receiver, a navigation receiver, and a position/differential receiver. The timing configuration outputs static position and time and time mark only (with respect to UTC) once per second. The navigation receiver configuraton outputs navigation solutions once per second, and GDOP information and timing every two minutes. The positioning/differential configuration is the most flexible, able to output everything the other sets do plus raw pseudo-range and delta range measurements and ephemeris data, some at variable rates.

Physically, the sensor is available in one 20 x 19 x 12 cm or two half height modules with interconnect cables, weighing about 3 kg, requiring 12 to 40 VDC (30 Watts) power, and operating at 0°C to +55°C. The two RS-232 ports provide (a) control/display I/O, and (b) output of raw or processed data. A one pulse per second timing signal is also provided. Because the NAVCORE I is a GPS sensor only, necessary peripheral equipment must include a control display unit and antenna. Other commercial GPS products are under development.

TR5S

MANUFACTURER: Sercel-France

APPLICATION: Low dynamics and point positioning

FEATURES:

- 5 channel, L1 C/A-code
- Code, carrier phase measurements, and broadcast data available through 2 RS-232 ports
- 2- or 3-dimensional navigation
- Non-portable configuration

  Receiver: 37 x 53 x 45 cm; 30 kg;
        +9°C to +40°C, 24 DC

  Antenna/preamp: 5 kg, -20°C to +50°C

  Monitor (video): 28 x 25 x 43 cm; 11 kg;
        0°C to +40°C, 220 VAC

  Keyboard: 6 x 37 x 26 cm; 1 kg;
        0°C to +40°C

AVAILABILITY:

- 450,000 FF or $US 67 500

TR5S

Manufacturer: Sercel-France
    Contact: Sercel Electronics of Canada Ltd.
                     Bay 1, 1715 27th Avenue N.E.
                     Calgary, Alberta
                     Canada T2E 7E1

Although the TR5S is not ruggedized or very portable, with its keyboard and video monitor configuration, it is suitable for situations where space and power are not major considerations. The receiver is most useful as a tool to evaluate the GPS capabilities in real time and postmission with the raw code and carrier phase measurements, broadcast data, and recorded processed positioning results. Data are available at a 0.6 second rate.

The TR5S is intended for low dynamics of 100 km/hr with accelerations of 0.5 g. For precise surveying applications, the antenna-preamp assembly includes a ground plane. The 30 kg receiver, of dimensions 37 x 53 x 45 cm, operates on 24 VDC at temperatures between +9°C to +40°C; the 5 kg antenna operates at temperatures between -20°C to +50°C; the 11 kg video monitor (28 x 25 x 43 cm) and the 1 kg keyboard (6 x 37 x 26 cm) both operate at 0°C to +40°C.

GTT-2000

MANUFACTURER: Sony Corporation

APPLICATION: Navigation

FEATURES:

- 4 channel, L1 C/A-code
- GPIB interface (or RS-232 option) for position and ephemeris output
- Auto start and acquisition function
- 15 waypoints navigation functions
- LCD display
- Antenna: 7 x 28 cm; 1 kg; -20°C to +75°C
- Receiver unit: 16 x 21 x 30 cm; 7 kg;
                              -10°C to +50°C
- 9-32 VDC (75 W)

AVAILABILITY:

- Early 1987

GTT-2000

Manufacturer: Sony Corporation
                        4-14-1 Asahi-cho
                        Atsugi-shi, Kanagawa-ken
                        243 Japan

The Sony Corporation has already developed a time transfer receiver and a navigation receiver. Development of a receiver for precise geodetic applications has also begun. The GTT-2000 navigation receiver [Sony Corporation, n.d.] will be available commercially in early 1987.

The 7 kg compact 16 x 21 x 30 cm receiver unit is available with three power supply options: 9-16 VDC, 18-32 VDC, and 9-32 VDC. It operates at -10°C to +50°C. The 1 kg, 7 cm diameter by 28 cm antenna operates at -20°C to +75°C. GPIB or RS-232 interface ports are available for computed position outputs.

SEL GPS RECEIVER

MANUFACTURER: Standard Elektrik Lorenz AG

APPLICATION: Low dynamics navigation

FEATURES:

- 4 channel, L1 C/A-code
- Receiver: 16 x 14 x 40 cm
- Antenna: 10 x 10 x 2 cm plus preamp
- Weight: 8 kg
- Power: 12/24 VDC (15 watts)
- For land navigation, auxilliary sensor package compensates for GPS signal loss

AVAILABILITY:

- 1989
- < $5000

SEL GPS RECEIVER

Manufacturer: Standard Elektrik Lorenz AG (SEL)
                        Lorenzstrasse 10
                        D 7000 Stuttgart 40
                        Federal Republic of Germany

SEL is developing a 4 channel, L1, C/A-code GPS receiver for air, land, and marine applications. Only preliminary specifications are available. The compact, lightweight system is expected to sell for less than $5000 when it is made available in early 1989. For land navigation applications, an auxilliary sensor package will be incorporated to compensate for GPS signal loss due to buildings and trees.

A joint venture between SEL (Germany), TRT/LMT (France), Elmer (Italy), and Magnavox (U.S.A.) is producing an L1/L2 5 channel P-code set for use at high dynamics to be available in 1989.

GPS MONITOR
STATION RECEIVER

MANUFACTURER: **Stanford Telecommunications, Inc.**

APPLICATION: **Collect GPS measurements used by Operational Control System**

FEATURES:

- **Down converter chassis for up to 6 dual receiver chassis, and test transmitter (STI 5012C) in double rack configuration**
- **Each dual receiver can track all L1/L2, C/A- and P-code combinations of measurements for 2 satellites continuously**
- **Supports anti-spoof acquisition and tracking**
- **Performance:**

Measurement	Mode	Resolution (m)	Accuracy (m, L1)
pseudo-range	C/A	2.3	7.5
pseudo-range	P	0.23	1.1
Doppler	P	.0007	.0025

GPS MONITOR STATION RECEIVER

Manufacturer: Stanford Telecommunications, Incorporated (STI)
                             2421 Mission College Blvd.
                             Santa Clara, California 95050
                             U.S.A.

The first commercially available GPS receiver (1980) was the STI-5010, an L1/L2, C/A- and P-code slow sequencing receiver. To cycle through 4 satellites took about 5 minutes. The receiver unit alone required about 30 cm of rack space. The pseudo-range measurements were performed by external counters. The receiver was controlled and the position was computed by an external computer. The 5010 is excellent for experimenting with GPS, providing all raw measurements and data along with intermediate frequencies.

Because of the 5010 performance, STI was awarded the contract to produce the monitor station receivers (MSR) for the GPS control stations. Each MSR consists of two racks of equipment: 1 down converter chassis provides a signal for up to 6 dual receiver chassis; an STI-5012C test transmitter is also included to provide a calibration signal at regular intervals. Each receiver can track L1/L2, C/A-, P-, and future Y-codes to make pseudo-range and Doppler measurements.

Other STI GPS products include the STI-502, a time transfer receiver, the STI-5012C GPS test transmitter and, towards the end of 1986, GPS receiver modules (with configurations containing from 1 to 8 channels) for the OEM market.

PAHRS MODEL 1

MANUFACTURER: Starnav Corporation

APPLICATIONS: Low to medium dynamics navigation
Heading and attitude

FEATURES:

- 5 channel, L1 C/A-code
- Phase, pseudo-range and rate and satellite message output
- Kalman filter for position, velocity, and time
- Least-squares estimator for attitude and heading
- Waypoint navigation and route management
- 3-element antenna: 38 x 38 x 18 cm; 22.7 kg; -40°C to +50°C
- 2-piece receiver: 115 VAC (90 W) or 28 VDC (110 W); -20°C to +50°C
   signal processor: 27 x 23 x 32 cm; 13.5 kg
   display and keyboard: 32 x 22 x 28 cm; 9 kg
- Expected accuracies: position: 30 m worst case
   velocity: 0.1 m/s
   heading: 0.3°
   roll, pitch: 1°

AVAILABILITY:

- Product announcement October 1986
- $CAN 25 000

PAHRS MODEL 1

Manufacturer: Starnav Corporation
                        148 Colonnade Road
                        Suite 201
                        Ottawa, Ontario
                        Canada   K2E 7R4

The Starnav Corporation, founded by a former Canadian Marconi employee, is developing a unique GPS receiver, the PAHRS Model 1. This receiver, in addition to providing the usual real-time position and velocity information, can also determine the attitude and heading of the vehicle, vessel, or aircraft to which the antenna is attached. This capability is achieved through the use of a novel three-element heated antenna which in principle works like an interferometer. The receiver switches between the three elements and code and phase tracks the signals from each element in the usual fashion. By suitably combining the outputs of the trackers, the microprocessor computes the heading, roll, and pitch of the antenna and hence of the vehicle. A Kalman filter is used to improve the raw, real-time estimates. The anticipated heading accuracy is 0.3°, and roll and pitch accuracy is 1°. PAHRS is designed to replace a conventional mechanical gyrocompass.

In addition to the antenna, PAHRS consists of a signal processing unit and a control and display unit. The size of the Model 1 signal processor is 27 x 23 x 32 cm and the weight is 13.5 kg. The control and display unit is 32 x 22 x 28 cm in size and weighs 9 kg. Starnav may reconfigure future models to reduce the size and weight of the units. PAHRS can run off 115 VAC or 28 VDC power and consumes about 100 W.

Software will be provided for waypoint navigation and route management.

TI 4100 NAVSTAR NAVIGATOR

MANUFACTURER: Texas Instruments Inc.

APPLICATIONS:

- Static to medium dynamics single point or relative positioning
- Precise geodetic relative positioning

FEATURES:

- L1/L2, P-code and C/A-code multiplex receiver 8 pseudo-channels: 4 L1, 4 L2
- Pseudo-range, carrier phase and message output
- Real-time navigation functions with 9 waypoints
- Ruggedized; 22-32 VDC (90 W); -20°C to +50°C

   Receiver unit: 37 x 45 x 21 cm; 24.5 kg

   Antenna unit: 30 x 17 cm dia.; 2 kg

   Optional recorder: 21 x 36 x 30 cm; 7 kg

AVAILABILITY:

- $US 120 000
- $US 18 000 dual cassette drive

TI 4100 NAVSTAR NAVIGATOR

Manufacturer: Texas Instruments Incorporated
P.O. Box 405, M/S 3418
Lewisville, Texas 75067 U.S.A.

The TI-4100, available since 1982, is the only commercially available C/A-code, P-Code, L1/L2 receiver. Because of these features and its single channel 4 satellite multiplex design, the TI 4100 is the most versatile receiver available today [Texas Instruments, 1986]. Successfully used and proven applications for the receiver include [Henson and Montgomery, 1984]:
- 3-D navigation with 4 satellites at stationary, low, and medium dynamics in ships, aircraft and on land with position accuracies better than 15 m with L1/L2 P-code and velocity accuracies at 0.15 m/s to 2.00 m/s for medium dynamics.
- 3-D relative positioning (4 satellites) in aircraft, ships, and on land at distances up to hundreds of kilometres with accuracies of 2 to 5 m.
- With 3 satellites and altitude aiding 2-D accuracies of about 15 m.
- With 3 satellites and external clock aiding 3-D positioning at about 15 m.
- With 2 satellites and altitude and time aiding again about 15 m 2-D positioning.
- 3-D geodetic precise relative positioning with accuracies from 1:100 000 to better than 1:1 000 000 depending on software used to postprocess the data and amount and quality of simultaneous data collected.
Currently, when using C/A-code only, accuracies of 20 to 30 m are achieved when ionospheric refraction is minimal.

The ruggedized (-20°C to +50°C) portable or rack mountable TI 4100 system consists of a 24.5 kg, 37 x 45 x 21 cm receiver/processor with hand-held control and display unit (CDU); a 2 kg, 30 cm x 17 cm diameter antenna; an optional 7 kg dual cassette recorder (21 x 36 x 20 cm); and a 22 to 32 VDC power source (90 W) and cables. Both CDU and recorder (replacable by computer) are interfaced through RS-232 ports.

The receiver makes available to the recorder port the time tagged code, carrier beat phase, and carrier phase rate measurements along with satellite navigation messages, and positions and velocities. Various navigation functions are included, such as cross-track error, distance to go, etc., with storage for up to 9 waypoints.

TI also has available SATPLAN™ software which computes and graphically displays satellite rise and set times, geometry, etc., and GEOMARK™ for determining 3-D baselines from carrier phase data for geodetic applications through postmission processsing. Both programs run on the TI PC.

4000A GPS LOCATOR and 4000S GPS SURVEYOR

MANUFACTURER: **Trimble Navigation**

APPLICATION:

- **4000A - low dynamics navigation, time transfer**
- **4000S - plus precise relative positioning**

FEATURES:

- **4 channel, L1 C/A-code**
- **20 kg, 17 x 45 x 48 cm, rack mounted**
  (4000S in protective casing) 0°C to +50°C
- **115/230 VAC or 24 VDC (4000A) or**
  12 VDC (4000S)
- **Outputs ephemeris and positions, etc., pseudo-ranges. 4000S also outputs carrier phase and integrated Doppler**
- **Automatic search and acquisition**
- **1.5 kg compact antenna, -30°C to +75°C**
  4000S includes ground plane
- **Computer control and recording interface RS-232C (option on 4000A)**

AVAILABILITY:

- **4000A - $US 25 000 1 month delivery**
- **4000S - $US 44 000 2 months delivery**
  Includes postprocessing software

4000A GPS LOCATOR,
4000S GPS SURVEYOR

Manufacturer: Trimble Navigation
585 North Mary Avenue
Sunnyvale, California 94086
U.S.A.

As of March 1986, Trimble had more GPS receiver models available to the civilian market at low cost than any other manufacturer. In 1984, Trimble introduced the 4000A, a 4 channel, L1, C/A-code navigator and time transfer receiver; a rack mountable 24 VDC, 115/230 VAC 50 watt receiver with a compact antenna which operates at -30°C to +75°C. Updated positions and velocities are available for output to the integral CDU or RS-232 I/O port at a 10 second rate.

At the end of 1985, the 4000S was introduced. Enhanced, with more powerful processor and software features, the 4000S allows for recording of time tagged carrier phase, pseudo-range, and integrated Doppler measurements and broadcast ephemeris, and can be used for precise relative positioning in either postprocessing (currently available) mode or real time (planned option) [Trimble Navigation, 1985; 1986]. At least two receivers make up a survey system, each consisting of an encased 4000S, a recording system (usually a battery operable personal computer), an external 12 VDC power supply (60 watts), and the antenna and cable. Each receiver system weighs a total of less than 40 kg (without external power supply). For precise three-dimensional relative accuracies of about 1 cm + 2 ppm of the baseline distance of 1 to 100 km, at least 30 minutes of good continuous data from optimal satellite geometry is required. The postprocessing is usually done on the same computer used for recording the data, requiring about 15 minutes of processing for 30 minutes of simultaneous carrier phase data.

The accuracy of relative static positioning from pseudo-ranges is 2 m. The receiver is also capable of dynamic positioning to 200 knots.

Trimble has recently upgraded the capabilities of the 4000S and renamed it the 4000SX.

LORAN-GPS 10X

MANUFACTURER: Trimble Navigation

APPLICATION: Low dynamics navigation

FEATURES:

- LORAN-GPS combination
- 2 channel, L1 C/A-code multiplexed GPS receiver
- Each CDU 25 x 12 x 7 cm
- Receiver/processor: 11 x 25 x 30 cm
- Weight with antenna: 7 kg
- 30 watts at 12 or 24 VDC
- -10°C to +60°C
- 100 waypoint navigation
- 1 second update rate

AVAILABILITY:

- $US 16 000 to $US 25 000, depending on number of CDUs, software, with/without LORAN

LORAN-GPS 10X

Manufacturer:　　Trimble Navigation
　　　　　　　　585 North Mary Avenue
　　　　　　　　Sunnyvale, California 94086
　　　　　　　　U.S.A.

To increase continuous navigation capabilities of stand-alone GPS or LORAN, Trimble has produced a marine navigation system to combine the advantages of both GPS and LORAN in the LORAN-GPS 10X receiver [Braisted et al., n.d.b]. The two channel, L1, C/A-code multiplexed receiver portion of this system provides position and velocity updates at 1 second intervals, whereas the LORAN portion provides an update at 6 second intervals when GPS is not operational. The compact receiver/processor (11 x 25 x 30 cm) and two CDUs (25 x 12 x 7 cm) consume 30 watts at 12 or 24 VDC and weigh 7 kg with antenna.

Trimble Navigation also produces a GPS sensor for low dynamics applications [Braisted et al., n.d.a]. The Model 400, a 2 channel, L1, C/A-code sequential receiver is packaged in a 1/4 ATR short ARINC-sized package for interfacing to existing display and keyboard modules via dual RS-232 or ARINC 429 interfaces.

WM101

MANUFACTURER: WM Satellite Survey Company

APPLICATION:
- Precise relative positioning
- Low dynamics navigation

FEATURES:
- 4 L1 channel sequencing for up to 6 satellites
  C/A-code pseudo-ranges
  Satellite message
  Carrier phase measurements
- 2 pieces—antenna and receiver unit (14 kg)
  includes tape recorder and internal battery
- 50 x 40 x 17 cm waterproof
- -25°C to +55°C operational
- 20 watts average (12 VDC)

FUTURE OPTIONS:
- Meteorological sensor interface
- Modem interface
- L2 'codeless' carrier phase

AVAILABILITY:
- Includes postprocessing software
- $US 80 000/unit
- Spring 1986

WM101

Manufacturer: WM Satellite Survey Company
c/o Wild Heerbrugg
CH-9435 Heerbrugg
Switzerland

Wild Heerbrugg and Magnavox have joined forces as the WM Satellite Survey Company and are offering as their first product the WM101 surveying receiver [Scherrer, 1985]. This is the first commercially available GPS receiver product in which the power supply, recorder, control display unit, and receiver/processor have been combined into a single compact robust unit weighing only 14 kg in a package slightly larger than a briefcase (50 x 40 x 17 cm). This, and the only additional piece required in the field—the 1.5 kg antenna of 20 cm height—makes this system very portable.

Both antenna and receiver are waterproof and operable at temperatures of -25°C to +55°C and -40°C to +70°C, respectively. The antenna cable length options vary from 10 to 120 metres.

The 4 channel, L1, C/A-code GPS receiver can be used for low dynamics navigation but is designed primarily for precise relative positioning by post-processing the data. Up to 6 satellites are tracked from which pseudo-ranges, broadcast ephemeris, and carrier phase data can be recorded on cassette tape. To compute the three-dimensional vector between stations, WM supplies a software package, called PoPS, which runs on a personal computer.

Accuracies of 1 cm plus 2 ppm are expected using the broadcast ephemeris. WM plans to add codeless L2 carrier tracking along with a meteorological sensor interface and real-time baseline determination software as options sometime in the future.

OTHER
GPS RECEIVERS

COMMERCIAL:

- other positioning receivers
- time transfer receivers
- receivers for military use

NON-COMMERCIAL:

- **SERIES, SERIES-X**
- Boojum
- Universities:

    New Brunswick

    Delft

    Bonn

    Stuttgart

    Leeds

OTHER GPS RECEIVERS

Many other manufacturers, not included in this appendix, are also producing commercial GPS products for positioning.

Non-commercial GPS developments include the SERIES and SERIES-X receivers developed by Jet Propulsion Laboratory (JPL), and Boojum receivers developed at the University of Toronto. These codeless receivers provide Doppler, C/A- and P-code phase and carrier phase measurements.

For development and research purposes, receivers have been developed using off-the-shelf components at several universities, including the University of New Brunswick, and Delft, Leeds, Bonn, and Stuttgart universities.

Manufacturers of GPS receivers not represented in this Appendix or those introducing new GPS receivers are invited to send product information to:

Canadian GPS Associates
Post Office Box 3184, Postal Station B
Fredericton, New Brunswick
Canada
E3A 5G9.

The new information will be included in later editions of this publication.

APPENDIX B

GLOSSARY OF
GPS TERMINOLOGY

APPENDIX B
GLOSSARY OF GPS TERMINOLOGY

Ambiguity
   see Carrier beat phase ambiguity

Bandwidth
   A measure of the width of the spectrum of a signal (frequency domain representation of a signal) expressed in Hertz [Stiffler, 1966].

Baseline
   A baseline consists of a pair of stations for which simultaneous GPS data has been collected.

Beat frequency
   Either of the two additional frequencies obtained when signals of two frequencies are mixed, equal to the sum or difference of the original frequencies, respectively. For example, in the identity,

$$\cos A \cos B = (\cos(A+B) + \cos(A-B))/2,$$

the original signals are A and B and the beat signals are A+B and A-B. The term Carrier Beat Phase refers only to the difference A-B, where A is the incoming Doppler-shifted satellite carrier signal, and B is the nominally constant-frequency reference signal generated in the receiver.

Between-epoch difference
   The difference between two complete carrier beat phase measurements made by the same receiver on the same signal (same satellite, same frequency), but at different time epochs.

Between-frequency difference
   The instantaneous difference between (or, more generally, any other linear combination involving) the complete carrier beat phase measurements made by the same receiver observing signals from the same satellite at two (or more) different frequencies.

Between-receiver difference
   The instantaneous difference in the complete carrier beat phase measurement made at two receivers simultaneously observing the same received signal (same satellite, same frequency).

Between-satellite difference
The instantaneous difference in the complete carrier beat phase measurement made by the same receiver observing two satellite signals simultaneously (same frequency).

Binary pulse code modulation
Pulse modulation using a string (code) of binary numbers. This coding is usually represented by ones and zeros with definite meanings assigned to them, such as changes in phase or direction of a wave [Dixon, 1976].

Binary biphase modulation
Phase changes on a constant frequency carrier of either 0° or 180° (to represent binary 0 or 1, respectively). These can be modelled by $y = A(t) \cos (\omega t + \phi)$, where the amplitude function $A(t)$ is a sequence of +1 and -1 values (to represent 0° and 180° phase changes, respectively) [Dixon, 1976].

Carrier
A radio wave having at least one characteristic (e.g., frequency, amplitude, phase) which may be varied from a known reference value by modulation [Bowditch, 1981, Vol. II].

Carrier frequency
The frequency of the unmodulated fundamental output of a radio transmitter [Bowditch, 1981, Vol. II].

Carrier beat phase
The phase of the signal which remains when the incoming Doppler-shifted satellite carrier signal is beat (the difference frequency signal is generated) with the nominally-constant reference frequency generated in the receiver.

Carrier beat phase ambiguity
The uncertainty in the initial measurement, which biases all measurements in an unbroken sequence. The ambiguity consists of three components

$$\alpha_i - \beta^J - N_i^J$$

where

α_i is the fractional initial phase in the receiver

β^J is the fractional initial phase in the satellite (both due to various contributions to phase bias, such as unknown clock phase, circuit delays, etc.), and
N_i^J is an integer cycle bias in the initial measurement.

Channel

A channel of a GPS receiver consists of the radio frequency and digital hardware, and the software, required to track the signal from one GPS satellite at one of the two GPS carrier frequencies.

Chip

The minimum time interval of either a zero or a one in a binary pulse code.

C/A-code

The standard (Coarse/Acquisition, or Clear/Access) GPS code—a sequence of 1023 pseudo-random binary biphase modulations on the GPS carrier at a chip rate of 1.023 MHz, thus having a code repetition period of one millisecond.

Complete instantaneous phase measurement

A measurement of carrier beat phase which includes the integer number of cycles of carrier beat phase since the initial phase measurement. *See* Fractional instantaneous phase measurement.

Correlation-type channel

A GPS receiver channel which uses a delay lock loop to maintain an alignment (correlation peak) between the replica of the GPS code generated in the receiver and the incoming code.

Cycle slip

A cycle slip is a discontinuity of an integer number of cycles in the measured carrier beat phase resulting from a temporary loss-of-lock in the carrier tracking loop of a GPS receiver.

Delay lock

The technique whereby the received code (generated by the satellite clock) is compared with the internal code (generated by the receiver clock) and the latter shifted in time until the two codes match. Delay lock loops can be implemented in several ways, for example, tau dither and early-minus-late gating [Spilker, 1978].

Delta pseudo-range

The difference between two carrier beat phase measurements, made coincidentally with (code) pseudo-range epochs.

Differenced measurements

see Between-epoch difference; Between-frequency difference; Between-receiver difference; Between-satellite difference.

Many combinations of differences are possible. Which differences, and their order, should be specified in describing a processing method (for example, Receiver-satellite double differences).

Differential positioning
  see Relative positioning

Dilution of precision (DOP)
  A description of the purely geometrical contribution to the uncertainty in a kinematic position fix, given by the expression

$$DOP = \sqrt{TRACE(A^TA)^{-1}},$$

where A is the design matrix for the solution (dependent on satellite/receiver geometry). The DOP factor depends on the parameters of the position fix solution. Standard terms in the case of kinematic GPS are:

GDOP	(three position coordinates plus clock offset in the solution)
PDOP	(three coordinates)
HDOP	(two horizontal coordinates)
VDOP	(height only)
TDOP	(clock offset only), and
HTDOP	(horizontal position and time).

Doppler shift
  The apparent change in frequency of a received signal due to the rate of change of the range between the transmitter and receiver. *See* Carrier beat phase.

Dynamic positioning
  See Kinematic positioning

Fast switching channel
  A switching channel with a sequence time short enough to recover (through software prediction) the integer part of the carrier beat phase.

Fractional instantaneous phase measurement
  A measurement of the carrier beat phase which does not include any integer cycle count. It is a value between zero and one cycle. *See* Complete instantaneous phase measurement.

Frequency band
  A range of frequencies in a particular region of the electromagnetic spectrum [Wells, 1974].

Frequency spectrum
  The distribution of amplitudes as a function of frequency of the constituent waves in a signal [Wells, 1974].

Handover word
The word in the GPS message that contains time synchronization information for the transfer from the C/A-code to the P-code [Milliken and Zoller, 1980].

Independent baselines
Baselines determined from independent observing sessions.

Independent observing sessions
Sessions for which any common biases affecting the observations can be ignored.

Ionospheric refraction
A signal travelling through the ionosphere (which is a nonhomogeneous and dispersive medium) experiences a propagation time different from that which would occur in a vacuum. Phase advance depends on electron content and affects carrier signals. Group delay depends on dispersion in the ionosphere as well, and affects signal modulation (codes). The phase advance and group delay are of the same magnitude but opposite sign [Davidson et al., 1983].

Interferometry
See Relative positioning

Kinematic positioning
Kinematic positioning refers to applications in which a trajectory (of a ship, ice field, tectonic plate, etc.) is determined.

Lane
The area (or volume) enclosed by adjacent lines (or surfaces) of zero phase of either the carrier beat phase signal, or of the difference between two carrier beat phase signals. On the earth's surface, a line of zero phase is the locus of all points for which the observed value would have an exact integer value for the complete instantaneous phase measurement. In three dimensions, this locus becomes a surface.

L-band
The radio frequency band extending from 390 MHz to (nominally) 1550 MHz [Bowditch 1981, Vol. II].

Multipath error
An error resulting from interference between radiowaves which have travelled between the transmitter and the receiver by two paths of different electrical lengths [Bowditch, 1981, Vol. II].

Multichannel receiver
A receiver containing many channels.

Multiplexing channel

A receiver channel which is sequenced through a number of satellite signals (each from a specific satellite and at a specific frequency) at a rate which is synchronous with the satellite message bit-rate (50 bits per second, or 20 milliseconds per bit). Thus one complete sequence is completed in a multiple of 20 milliseconds.

Observing session

The period of time over which GPS data is collected simultaneously by two or more receivers.

Outage

The occurrence in time and space of a GPS Dilution of Precision value exceeding a specified maximum.

Phase lock

The technique whereby the phase of an oscillator signal is made to become a smoothed replica of the phase of a reference signal by first comparing the phases of the two signals and then using the resulting phase difference signal to adjust the reference oscillator frequency to eliminate phase difference when the two signals are next compared [Bowditch, 1981, Vol. II]. The smoothing time span occurs over approximately the inverse of the bandwidth. Thus a 40 hertz loop bandwidth implies an approximately 25 millisecond smoothing time constant.

Phase observable

See Carrier beat phase

P-code

The Precise (or Protected) GPS code—a very long (about 10^{14} bit) sequence of pseudo-random binary biphase modulations on the GPS carrier at a chip rate of 10.23 MHz which does not repeat itself for about 267 days. Each one-week segment of the P-code is unique to one GPS satellite and is reset each week.

Precise positioning service (PPS)

The highest level of dynamic positioning accuracy that will be provided by GPS, based on the dual frequency P-code [U.S. DoD/DOT, 1982].

Pseudolite

The ground-based differential GPS station which transmits a signal with a structure similar to that of an actual GPS satellite [Kalafus, 1984].

Pseudo-random noise (PRN) code

Any of a group of binary sequences that exhibit noise-like properties, the most important of which is that the sequence has a maximum autocorrelation, at zero lag [Dixon, 1976].

Pseudorange
   The time shift required to align (correlate) a replica of the GPS code generated in the receiver with the received GPS code, scaled into distance by the speed of light. This time shift is the difference between the time of signal reception (measured in the receiver time frame) and the time of emission (measured in the satellite time frame).

Pseudo-range difference
   See Carrier beat phase

Receiver channel
   See Channel

Reconstructed carrier phase
   See Carrier Beat Phase

Relative positioning
   The determination of relative positions between two or more receivers which are simultaneously tracking the same radiopositioning signals (e.g., from GPS).

Restart capability
   The property of a sequential processing computer program, that data can be processed rigorously in a sequence of computer runs, rather than only in one long run.

S-code
   See C/A-code

Satellite constellation
   The arrangement in space of the complete set of satellites of a system like GPS.

Satellite configuration
   The state of the satellite constellation at a specific time, relative to a specific user or set of users.

Simultaneous measurements
   Measurements referred to time frame epochs which are either exactly equal or else so closely spaced in time that the time misalignment can be accommodated by correction terms in the observation equation, rather than by parameter estimation.

Slow switching channel
   A switching channel with a sequencing period which is too long to allow recovery of the integer part of the carrier beat phase.

Spread spectrum systems

A system in which the transmitted signal is spread over a frequency band much wider than the minimum bandwidth needed to transmit the information being sent [Dixon, 1976].

Squaring-type channel

A GPS receiver channel which multiplies the received signal by itself to obtain a second harmonic of the carrier, which does not contain the code modulation.

Standard positioning service (SPS)

The level of kinematic positioning accuracy that will be provided by GPS based on the single frequency C/A-code [U.S. DoD/DOT, 1982].

Static positioning

Positioning applications in which the positions of points are determined, without regard for any trajectory they may or may not have.

Switching channel

A receiver channel which is sequenced through a number of satellite signals (each from a specific satellite and at a specific frequency).

Translocation

See Relative positioning

User equivalent range error (UERE)

The contribution to the range measurement error from an individual error source, converted into range units, assuming that error source is uncorrelated with all other error sources [Martin, 1980].

Z-count word

The GPS satellite clock time at the leading edge of the next data subframe of the transmitted GPS message (usually expressed as an integer number of 1.5 second periods) [van Dierendock et al., 1978].

APPENDIX C

GPS
INFORMATION SOURCES

GPS INFORMATION SOURCES

This appendix contains sources of information on GPS of interest to those who wish to learn more about GPS or to use it in practice. Sources in three categories are listed:
- publications complementary to this Guide,
- information sources on the current status of GPS, and
- additional GPS services available from Canadian GPS Associates.

OTHER PUBLICATIONS

• *Everyman's Guide to Satellite Navigation*
A booklet designed to acquaint managers with principles involved in using GPS for navigation. August 1985. 66 pages. Single copy free. Available from
> Steven D. Thompson
> ARINC Research Corp.
> 2551 Riva Road
> Annapolis, MD 21401, U.S.A.
> > Telephone: (301) 266-4650

• *The WM GPS Primer*
Information required for basic understanding of GPS satellite surveying, highlighting the WM101 receiver and its postprocessing software, PoPS. 1985. 116 pages. Single copy free. Available from
> René Scherrer (3388)
> WM Satellite Survey Company
> Wild Heerbrugg
> Geodesy Division
> CH-9435
> Heerbrugg, Switzerland

• *Surveying with GPS*
> by R.W. King, E.G. Masters, C. Rizos, A. Stolz, and J. Collins.
Reference book on GPS designed for the surveying community. November 1985. 128 pages. $AUS 20. ISBN 0-85839-042-6. Available as
> Monograph No. 9
> School of Surveying
> The University of New South Wales
> P.O. Box 1
> Kensington, NSW, Australia 2033

• *Global Positioning System*
Collections of papers published in *Navigation.*
Volume I, 1980, 246 pages, ISBN 0-936406-00-3, $US 10
Volume II, 1984, 257 pages, ISBN 0-936406-01-1, $US 10
Volumes I and II can be obtained for $US 18 the set
Volume III, in preparation, $US 12
Available from

> The Institute of Navigation
> 815 Fifteenth Street, Suite 832
> Washington, DC 20005, U.S.A.
> Telephone: (202) 783-4121

• *Positioning with GPS — 1985*
Proceedings of the first international symposium on precise positioning with GPS, Rockville, Md, April 1985.
Volumes I and II, 946 pages. $US 24 the set. Available as

> Publication N/CG 17X2
> National Geodetic Information Center
> National Ocean Service, NOAA
> Rockville, MD 20852, U.S.A.
> Telephone: (301) 443-8316

• *Proceedings of the Fourth International Geodetic Symposium on Satellite Positioning*   Austin, Tx, May 1986.
Volumes I and II, 1510 pages. $US 50 the set. Available from

> Attn: Ms Barbara Becker
> Applied Research Laboratories
> University of Texas at Austin
> PO Box 8029
> Austin, TX 78713-8029, U.S.A.
> Telephone: (512) 835-3466

• *Federal Radionavigation Plan*
Official U.S. plan describing the impact of GPS on other publicly supported radionavigation systems, and specifying the civilian availability of GPS. Issued approximately every two years. 1984 edition available as

> DoT-TSC-RFPA-84-8
> Accession number AD-A151 295
> National Technical Information Service
> Springfield, VA 22161, U.S.A.

STATUS OF GPS

- **GPS satellite status and health**
  NAVSTAR/GPS Operational Control System
  Attn: Rufus N. Biggs, 2SCS/DOO
  Falcon Air Force Station
  Colorado Springs, CO 80914-5000, U.S.A.

  Recorded daily operations report (303) 550-2099
  Mission operations controller (live) (303) 550-2363 or 2477
  Telexed or mailed satellite status/health reports (Notice Advisory to
  NAVSTAR Users (NANU)) sent to those on
  AIG 5825 distribution list

- **GPS satellite clock behaviour and related GPS information**
  U.S. Naval Observatory
  Washington, DC 20392-5100, U.S.A.

  Dial-up on-line computer files
  Requires terminal/computer/modem set to full duplex, 7 data
  bits, even parity, upper case.
  300 or 1200 baud: (202) 653-1079; international CCITT.21:
  (202) 653-1095
  2400 baud or CCITT.21 or CCITT.22 bis: (202) 653-1783.
  Files of interest:
  @GPS: GPS status information
  @GPSSY: GPS system description and more permanent
  information

  USNO Series 4 bulletins contain information on the status of GPS including
  GPS time steering.

- **Approximate GPS orbit information** (can be in error by tens of km)
  NASA Prediction Bulletin subscriptions
  Control Center Support Section
  Code 513.2
  Project Operations Branch
  NASA Goddard Space Flight Center
  Greenbelt, MD 20771, U.S.A.

  Request should specify NASA satellite identification numbers (see our
  Figure 4.02, column 5) of satellites for which prediction bulletins are
  desired.

- **Accurate GPS orbit information**

  NGS: Precise orbital positions and velocities for GPS satellites are available to the U.S. public from the U.S. National Geodetic Survey. Satellite ephemerides are scheduled to be available within four weeks after the orbital data are collected. Contact

  > Chief
  > National Geodetic Information Center, N/CG17
  > National Geodetic Survey
  > National Ocean Service, NOAA
  > Rockville, MD 20852, U.S.A.
  > > Telephone: (301) 443-8775

  Litton Aero Service: Aero Service, a division of Western Geophysical and a member of the Litton Resources Group, offers a commercial orbit data service utilizing data obtained at its tracking network stations in the United States. Contact

  > Mr. Jim Cain
  > Manager, GPS Services
  > Aero Service
  > 8100 Westpark,
  > Postal Box 1939
  > Houston, TX 77251, U.S.A.
  > > Telephone: (713) 784-5800

- **Civil access to the GPS Precise Positioning Service**

  > Assistant Secretary of Defense, Command, Control,
  > > Communications and Intelligence
  > Attention: Colonel Phillip J. Baker
  > The Pentagon
  > Room 3D174
  > Washington, DC 30201-3040, U.S.A.

- **Performance of GPS geodetic receivers**

  > Larry Hothem, Test Coordinator
  > Federal Geodetic Control Committee
  > 6001 Executive Boulevard
  > Room 305/C1
  > Rockville, MD 20852, U.S.A.
  > > Telephone: (301) 443-8171

- *Interface Control Document ICD-GPS-200*
  Official description of the GPS signal structure and specifications.
  September 1984. Available from
  > Mail Code SN-65
  > Rockwell International Corporation
  > Satellite Systems Division
  > 12214 Lakewood Boulevard
  > Downey, CA 90241, U.S.A.

CANADIAN GPS ASSOCIATES

- **Courses tailored to specialized audiences**
  Presented anywhere in the world

- **8.5" x 11" transparencies of figures from this volume**
  $CAN 500 per complete set of 262.

- **Contact**
  > Canadian GPS Associates
  > Box 3184
  > Postal Station B
  > Fredericton, New Brunswick
  > Canada
  > E3A 5G9

APPENDIX D

BIBLIOGRAPHY

APPENDIX D
BIBLIOGRAPHY

anon. (1986). "FCC resolves issue of satellite position fixing technology." *Aviation Week and Space Technology,* Vol. 124, No. 24, p. 115.

Ayers, H. and M.D. Gonthier (1986). "JMR SatTrak GPS receiver." GPS seminar, 13-14 March, Québec City, Quebec, Canada.

Bauersima, I. (1983). "NAVSTAR/Global Positioning System (GPS) III: Erdvermessung durch radiointerferometriche Satellitenbeobachtungen." Miteilungen der Satellitenbeobachtungstation Zimmerwald Nr. 12, Druckerei der Universität Bern, Switzerland.

Beck, N. (1985). "Practical aspects of satellite positioning." Presented at seminar on Impact of GPS on Surveying Practice in Ontario, Erindale College, Mississauga, Ontario, Canada, November.

Beutler, G. (1984). "GPS carrier phase difference observation software." Department of Surveying Engineering Technical Memorandum TM-2, University of New Brunswick, Fredericton, N.B., Canada.

Beutler, G., D.A. Davidson, R.B. Langley, R. Santerre, P. Vaníček and D.E. Wells (1984). "Some theoretical and practical aspects of geodetic positioning using carrier phase difference observations of GPS satellites." Department of Surveying Engineering Technical Report No. 109, University of New Brunswick, Fredericton, N.B., Canada

Bomford, G. (1980). *Geodesy.* 4th ed. Oxford University Press, Oxford.

Bossler, J.D., C.C. Goad and P.L. Bender (1980). "Using the Global Positioning System (GPS) for geodetic positioning." *Bulletin Géodésique,* 54, pp. 553-563.

Bowditch, N. (1981). "Useful tables, calculations, glossary of marine navigation." Vol. II, *The American Practical Navigator,* Publication No. 9, DMAHTC, Washington, DC, U.S.A.

Braisted, P., R. Eschenbach and R. Sutherland (n.d.a). "$1,000 GPS receiver technology — A fifth generation GPS receiver." Trimble Navigation, Sunnyvale, Ca, U.S.A.

Braisted, R., R. Eschenbach and A. Tivori (n.d.b). "Combining LORAN and GPS—The best of both worlds." Trimble Navigation, Sunnyvale, Ca, U.S.A.

Broughton, D.W., R.I. Essai and P.J. Farrow (1984). "Principles of satellite orbits." In: *Global Civil Satellite Navigation Systems,* Collected papers of NAV'84, Royal Institute of Navigation, London, U.K., May, pp. 3-6.

Brouwer, D. and G.M. Clemence (1961). *Methods of Celestial Mechanics.* Academic Press, NY, U.S.A.

Buennagel, L.A., P.F. MacDoran, R.E. Neilan, D.J. Spitzmesser and L.E. Young (1984). "Satellite Emission Range Inferred Earth Survey (SERIES) project: Final report on research and development phase, 1979 to 1983." Jet Propulsion Laboratory Publication 84-16, Pasadena, Ca, U.S.A., March.

Buffett, B.A. (1985). "A short-arc orbit determination for the Global Positioning System." M.Sc. thesis, Division of Surveying Engineering, The University of Calgary, Calgary, Alberta, Canada.

Canadian Marconi Company (1985). "CMC capabilities and experience." CMC document No. 1162-1042, December, Kanata, Ontario, Canada.

Cannon, M.E., K.P. Schwarz and R.V.C. Wong (1986). "Kinematic positioning with GPS—An analysis of road tests." *Proceedings of the Fourth International Geodetic Symposium on Satellite Positioning,* University of Texas at Austin, Austin, Tx, U.S.A., April, pp. 1251-1268.

Clark, T.A., B.E. Corey, J.L. Davis and others (1985). "Precision geodesy using the Mark-III very-long-baseline interferometry system." *IEEE Transactions, Geoscience and Remote Sensing,* Special Issue on satellite geodynamics, Vol. GE-23, No. 4, pp. 438-449.

Clynch, J.R. and D.S. Coco (1986). "Error characteristics of high quality geodetic GPS measurements: Clocks, orbits and propagation effects." *Proceedings of the Fourth International Geodetic Symposium on Satellite Positioning,* University of Texas at Austin, Austin, Tx, U.S.A., April, pp. 539-556.

Collins, J. (1986). "Measuring platform subsidence using GPS satellite surveying." *Proceedings of Colloquium IV, Land, Sea and Space — Today's Survey Challenge,* CPA, CHA, Lake Louise, Alberta, Canada, April, pp. 377-382. Available from the Canadian Institute of Surveying and Mapping, Ottawa, Canada.

Counselman, C.C. and S. Gourevitch (1981). "Miniature interferometer terminals for earth surveying: Ambiguity and multipath with Global Positioning System." *IEEE Transactions, Geoscience and Remote Sensing,* Vol. GE-19, No. 4, pp. 244-252.

Davidson, D., D. Delikaraoglou, R. Langley, B. Nickerson, P. Vaníček and D. Wells (1983). "Global Positioning System differential positioning simulations." Department of Surveying Engineering Technical Report No. 90, University of New Brunswick, Fredericton, N.B., Canada, March.

Degnan, J.J. (1985). "Satellite laser ranging: Current status and future prospects." *IEEE Transaction, Geoscience and Remote Sensing,* Special Issue on satellite geodynamics, Vol. GE-23, No. 4, pp. 398-413.

Delikaraoglou, D. and R.R. Steeves (1985). "The impact of VLBI and GPS on geodesy in Canada." *Proceedings of the First International Symposium on Precise Positioning with the Global Positioning System,* Rockville, Md, U.S.A., April, Vol. II, pp. 743-752.

Delikaraoglou, D., D.J. McArthur, P. Héroux and N. Beck (1986). "Improvements in the second generation GPS software of the Canadian Geodetic Survey." *Proceedings of the Fourth International Geodetic Symposium on Satellite Positioning,* University of Texas at Austin, Austin, Tx, U.S.A., April, pp.821-839.

Dixon, R.C. (1976). *Spread Spectrum Systems.* John Wiley, New York, U.S.A.

European Space Agency (1985). "A global civil navigation satellite system concept." ESA submission to ICAO and IMO working groups on navigation systems.

Fruehauf, H.J. (1982). "Precision oscillators and their role and performance in navigation systems." *Proceedings of IEEE PLANS '82,* pp. 289-301.

Gerlach, B.E. (1985). "Positioning with a GPS pseudorange receiver—Functional model test results." *Proceedings, Inertial, Doppler and GPS Measurements for National and Engineering Surveys,* Munich, F.R.G., July.

Goad, C.C. (1985). "Precise relative position determination using Global Positioning System carrier phase measurements in a nondifference mode." *Proceedings of the First International Symposium on Precise Positioning with the Global Positioning System,* Rockville, Md, U.S.A., April, Vol. I, pp. 347-356.

Goad, C.C. and B.W. Remondi (1984). "Initial relative positioning results using the Global Positioning System." *Bulletin Géodésique,* Vol. 58, No. 2, pp. 193-210.

Gold, R. (1967). "Optimal binary sequences for spread spectrum multiplexing." *IEEE Transactions on Information Theory,* pp. 619-621.

Goldfarb, J.M. and K.P. Schwarz (1985). "Kinematic positioning with an integrated INS-differential/GPS." *Proceedings of the First International Symposium on Positioning with the Global Positioning System,* Rockville, Md, U.S.A., April, Vol. II, pp. 757-772.

Golumb, S.W. (1967). *Shift Register Sequences.* Holden-Day, San Francisco, Ca.

Hatch, R. and K. Larson (1985). "MAGNET-4100 GPS survey program processing techniques and test results." *Proceedings of the First International Symposium on Precise Positioning with the Global Positioning System,* Rockville, Md, U.S.A., April, Vol. I, pp. 285-298.

Hellwig, H. (1979). "Microwave time and frequency standards." *Radio Science,* Vol. 14, No. 4, pp. 561-572.

Henriksen, S.W. (ed.) (1977). *National Geodetic Satellite Program.* Vols. 1 and 2, NASA SP-365, American Geophysical Union, Washington, DC, U.S.A.

Henson, D. and B. Montgomery (1984). "TI 4100 Navstar Navigator test results." Presented at the 40th Annual Meeting of The (U.S.) Institute of Navigation, Cambridge, Ma, U.S.A., June.

Hothem, L.D. (1985). "Proposed revisions to geodetic survey standards and preliminary specifications for geodetic surveys using relative positioning GPS techniques." National Geodetic Survey, version of 27 October, Rockville, Md, U.S.A.

Hothem, L.D., C.C. Goad and B.W. Remondi (1984). "GPS satellite surveying—Practical aspects." *The Canadian Surveyor,* Vol. 38, No. 3, pp. 177-192.

Japan Radio Corporation (1985). "JLR-4000 GPS navigator instruction manual." Tokyo, Japan.

Johnson, C.R., P.W. Ward, M.D. Turner and S.D. Roemerman (1981). "Applications of a multiplexed GPS user set." In: *Global Positioning System.* Papers published in *Navigation,* reprinted by The (U.S.) Institute of Navigation, Vol. II, 1984, pp. 61-77.

Jordan, E.D. (ed.) (1985). *Reference Data for Engineers: Radio, Electronics, Computer, and Communications*. 7th ed., Howard W. Sams and Co., Inc., Indianapolis, U.S.A.

Jorgensen, P.S. (1980). "NAVSTAR/Global Positioning System 18-satellite constellation." In: *Global Positioning System*. Papers published in *Navigation*, reprinted by The (U.S.) Institute of Navigation, Vol. II, 1984, pp. 1-12.

Kalafus, R.M. (1984). "RTCM SC-104 progress on differential GPS standards." Presented at the 40th Annual Meeting of The (U.S.) Institute of Navigation, Cambridge, Ma, U.S.A., June.

Kalafus, R.M., J. Vilcans and N. Knable (1983). "Differential operation of NAVSTAR GPS." *Navigation*, Vol. 30, pp. 187-204.

Kaula, W.M. (1966). *Theory of Satellite Geodesy*. Blaisdell, Waltham, Ma, U.S.A.

King, R.W., R.I. Abbot, Y. Bock and C.C. Counselman (1985). "Deformation measurement by radio interferometry with GPS." *EOS, Transactions of the AGU*, Vol. 66, No. 46, p. 854 (abstract only).

Kleusberg, A. (1986). "Kinematic relative positioning using GPS code and carrier beat phase observations." *Marine Geodesy*, 10, pp. 167-184.

Kleusberg, A., S.H. Quek, D.E. Wells and J. Hagglund (1985a). "Comparison of INS and GPS ship velocity determination." *Proceedings of the Third International Symposium on Inertial Technology for Surveying and Geodesy*, Banff, Alberta, September. Division of Surveying Engineering, UCSE Report No. 60005, University of Calgary, Calgary, Alberta, Canada, 1986.

Kleusberg, A., S.H. Quek, D.E. Wells, G. Lachapelle and J. Hagglund (1986). "GPS relative positioning techniques for moving platforms." *Proceedings of the Fourth International Geodetic Symposium on Satellite Positioning*, University of Texas at Austin, Austin, Tx, U.S.A., April, pp. 1299-1310.

Kleusberg, A., R.B. Langley, R. Santerre, P. Vaníček, D.E. Wells and G. Beutler (1985b). "Comparison of survey results from different types of GPS receivers." *Proceedings of the First International Symposium on Positioning with GPS*, Rockville, Md, U.S.A., April, pp. 579-592.

Krishnamurti, G., S.A. Harshbarger and T.N. Smith (n.d.). "The design and performance of GPS Phase II user equipment navigation software." Rockwell International, Cedar Rapids, Ia, U.S.A.

Lachapelle, G. (1977). "Estimation of disturbing potential components using a combined integral formulae and collocation approach." In: Collected Papers of the Geodetic Survey of Canada, Surveys and Mapping Branch, Ottawa, Ontario, Canada.

Lachapelle, G. (1979). "Comparison of Doppler-derived and gravimetric geoid undulations in North America." *Proceedings of the Second International Geodetic Symposium on Satellite Positioning,* Austin, Tx, U.S.A., April, pp.653-670.

Lachapelle, G. (1986). "GPS—Current capabilities and prospects for multi-purpose offshore surveying." *Proceedings of FIG XVIII International Congress,* Toronto, Ontario, Canada, June, Commission 8, pp. 86-101.

Lachapelle, G. and E. Cannon (1986). "Single and dual frequency GPS results for baselines of 10 to 500 km." *The Canadian Surveyor,* Vol. 40, No. 2, pp. 173-183.

Lachapelle, G. and R.L. Wade (1982). "NAVSTAR/GPS single point positioning." Technical papers of the 42nd Annual Meeting of the American Congress on Surveying and Mapping, Denver, Co, U.S.A., March, pp. 603-609.

Lachapelle, G., J. Lethaby and M. Casey (1984a). "Airborne single point and differential GPS navigation for hydrographic bathymetry." *The Hydrographic Journal* (U.K.), 37(2):200-208.

Lachapelle, G., J. Hagglund, H. Jones and M Eaton (1984b). "Differential GPS marine navigation." *Proceedings of the IEEE PLANS '84,* San Diego, Ca, U.S.A., November, pp. 245-255.

Lachapelle, G., J. Hagglund, W. Falkenberg, P. Bellemare, M. Casey and M. Eaton (1986). "GPS land kinematic positioning experiences." *Proceedings of the Fourth International Geodetic Symposium on Satellite Positioning,* University of Texas at Austin, Austin, Tx, U.S.A., April, pp. 1327-1344.

Langley, R.B., G. Beutler, D. Delikaraoglou, B. Nickerson, R. Santerre, P. Vaníček and D.E. Wells (1984). "Studies in the application of the Global Positioning System to differential positioning." Department of Surveying Engineering Technical Report No. 108, University of New Brunswick, Fredericton, N.B., Canada, September.

Leeman, R.W. and L.B. Fletcher (1985). "GPS—A user's critique." *Proceedings of the First International Symposium on Precise Positioning with the Global Positioning System,* Rockville, Md, U.S.A., April, Vol. II, pp. 613-624.

Lerch, F.J., B. Putney, S. Klosko and C. Wagner (1981). "Goddard earth models for oceanographic applications (GEM 10B and 10C)." *Marine Geodesy*, No. 5, pp. 145-198.

Levitus, S. (1982). "Climatological atlas of the world ocean." NOAA Professional Paper No. 13, U.S. Department of Commerce, Washington, DC, U.S.A.

Lindlohr, W. and D.E. Wells (1985). "GPS design using undifferenced carrier beat phase observations." *Manuscripta Geodaetica*, Vol. 10, No. 3, pp. 255-295.

Lisitzin, E. (1974). *Sea Level Changes*. Elsevier Scientific Publications Co., Amsterdam, The Netherlands.

MacDoran, P.F., J.H. Whitcomb and R.B. Miller (1984). "Codeless GPS positioning offers sub-meter accuracy." *Sea Technology*, October. Also in CSTG Bulletin No. 7, December, pp. 192-194.

MacDoran, P.F., R.B. Miller, L.A. Buennagel and J.H. Whitcomb (1985a). "Codeless systems for positioning with NAVSTAR-GPS." *Proceedings of the First International Symposium on Precise Positioning with the Global Positioning System*, Rockville, MD, April, Vol. I, pp. 181-190.

MacDoran, P.F., J.H. Whitcomb, R.B. Miller and L.A. Buennagel (1985b). "Codeless GPS systems for marine positioning and navigation." 17th Annual OTC, Houston, Tx, U.S.A., May (OTC 4994).

Mader, G.L. (1986). "Decimeter level aircraft positioning using GPS carrier phase measurements." *Proceedings of the Fourth International Symposium on Satellite Positioning*, University of Texas at Austin, Austin, Tx, U.S.A., April, pp. 1311-1326.

Marsh, J.G., A.C. Bremner, B.D. Beckley and T.V. Martin (1984). "Global mean sea surface based on the SEASAT altimeter data." Preprint.

Martin, E.H. (1980). "GPS user equipment error models." In: *Global Positioning System*. Papers published in *Navigation*, reprinted by The (U.S.) Institute of Navigation, pp. 109-118.

McArthur, D., N. Beck, K. Lockhead and D. Delikaraoglou (1985). "Precise relative positioning with the Macrometer V-1000 interferometric surveyor: Experiences at the Geodetic Survey of Canada." *Proceedings of the First International Symposium on Precise Positioning with the Global Positioning System*, Rockville, Md, U.S.A., April, Vol. I, pp. 521-532.

McDonald, K.D. and R.L. Greenspan (1985). "A survey of GPS satellite system alternatives and their potential for precise positioning." *Proceedings of the First International Symposium on Precise Positioning with the Global Positioning System,* Rockville, Md, U.S.A., April, Vol. I, pp. 457-472.

McPherson, W.R. (1981). "SARSAT applications." *Canadian Aeronautics and Space Journal,* Vol. 27, No. 2, pp. 118-126.

Merrifield, J.T. (1985). "Fifth-generation GPS receiver aims at commercial market." *Aviation Week and Space Technology,* 19 August, pp. 123, 125.

Mertikas, S. (1985). "Differential Global Positioning System navigation: A geometrical analysis." Department of Surveying Engineering Technical Report 95, University of New Brunswick, Fredericton, N.B., Canada.

Mertikas, S.P., D. Delikaraoglou and R. Santerre (1986). "Alert program for NAVSTAR Global Positioning System, Transit, LAGEOS, and Starlette satellites." Department of Surveying Engineering Technical Report No. 85, University of New Brunswick, Fredericton, N.B., Canada

Milliken, R.J. and C.J. Zoller (1980). "Principle of operation of NAVSTAR and system characteristics." In: *Global Positioning System.* Papers published in *Navigation,* reprinted by The (U.S.) Institute of Navigation, Vol. I, 1980, pp. 3-14.

Moreau, R. (1986). "The Quebec 1985 TI 4100 test." *Proceedings of the Fourth International Geodetic Symposium on Satellite Positioning,* University of Texas at Austin, Austin, Tx, U.S.A., April, pp. 1059-1072.

Moreau, R., J.G. Leclerc, B. Labrecque, G. Beutler, R.B. Langley and R. Santerre (1985). "The Quebec 1984 Macrometer test." *Proceedings of the First International Symposium on Precise Positioning with the Global Positioning System,* Rockville, Md, U.S.A., April, Vol. II, pp. 557-566.

Morgan, V.G. (1983). "The challenge of precisely positioning a 3D seismic survey." *Navigation,* 30(3):261-272.

Motorola Inc. (1986a). "Preliminary specification GPS Core receiver (Rev. C)." March.

Motorola Inc. (1986b). "Eagle Mini-Ranger Global Positioning System receiver." Equipment brochure.

Nakiboglu, S.M., B. Buffett, K.P. Schwarz, E.J. Krakiwsky and B. Wanless (1984). "A multi-station approach to GPS orbital improvement and precise positioning." Proceedings, *Proceedings of IEEE PLANS '84,* San Diego, Ca, November, pp. 153-162.

NATO (1983). "Method of expressing navigation accuracies." North Atlantic Treaty Organization Standardization Agreement 4278.

Norstar Instruments (1986). "Norstar 1000 operational executive summary (preliminary)." Calgary, Alberta, Canada, March.

O'Neill, G.K. (1984). "The Geostar system." In: *Global Civil Satellite Navigation Systems,* Collected papers of NAV'84 conference, Royal Institute of Navigation, London, U.K., May, pp. 339-345.

O'Toole, J.W. (1976). "The CELEST computer program for computing satellite orbits." U.S. Naval Surface Weapons Center TR 3565, Dahlgren, Va, U.S.A.

Radio Technical Commission for Marine Services (1985). "Recommendations of Special Committee 104 [Chaired by R.M. Kalafus] differential NAVSTAR/GPS service." RTCM, P.O. Box 19087, Washington, DC 20036, U.S.A.

Rapp, R.H. (1982). "A global atlas of sea surface heights based on the adjusted SEASAT altimeter data." Department of Geodetic Science and Surveying Technical Report No. 333, The Ohio State University, Columbus, Oh, U.S.A.

Rapp, R.H. (1983). "The development of the January 1983 1° x 1° mean free-air anomaly data tape." Internal Report, Department of Geodetic Science and Surveying, The Ohio State University, Columbus, Oh, U.S.A.

Remondi, B.W. (1985a). "Performing centimeter accuracy relative surveys in seconds using GPS carrier phase." *Proceedings of the First International Symposium on Precise Positioning with the Global Positioning System,* Rockville, Md, U.S.A., April, Vol. II, pp. 789-798.

Remondi, B.W. (1985b). "Performing centimeter-level surveys in seconds with GPS carrier phase: Initial results." NOAA Technical Memorandum, NOS-NGS 45, Rockville, Md, U.S.A. Also in *Navigation,* Vol. 32, No. 4, pp. 386-400.

Remondi, B.W. (1985c). "Modeling the GPS carrier phase for geodetic applications." *Proceedings of the First International Symposium on Precise Positioning with the Global Positioning System,* Rockville, Md, U.S.A., April, Vol, I, pp. 325-336.

Remondi, B.W. (1985d). "Using the Global Positioning System (GPS) phase observable for relative geodesy: Modeling, processing, and results." Ph.D. dissertation, Center for Space Research, The University of Texas at Austin, Austin, Tx, U.S.A., May. Available from National Geodetic Information Center, N/CG17X2, Rockville, Md 20852, U.S.A.

Rockwell (1984). "NAVSTAR GPS space segment/navigation user interfaces." Interface Control Document ICD-GPS-200, Rockwell International Space Systems Group, Satellite Systems Divison, dated 9/25/1984.

Russell, S.S. and J.H. Schaibly (1978). "Control segment and user performance." In: *Global Positioning System.* Papers published in *Navigation,* reprinted by The (U.S.) Institute of Navigation, Vol. I, 1980, pp. 74-80.

Scherrer, R. (1985). "The WM GPS primer." WM Satellite Survey Company, Heerbrugg, Switzerland.

Schwarz, K.P. (1983). "Kalman filtering and optimal smoothing." In: Papers for the CIS Adjustment and Analysis Seminars, ed. E.J. Krakiwsky, Canadian Institute of Surveying, Ottawa, Ontario, Canada.

Schwarz, K.P. (1986). "Geoid profiles from an integration of GPS-satellites and inertial data." Paper presented at the International Symposium on the Definition of the Geoid, Florence, Italy, May.

Schwarz, K.P., C.S. Fraser and P.C. Gustafson (1984a). "Aerotriangulation without ground control." International Archives of Photogrammetry and Remote Sensing, 25, Part A1, Rio de Janeiro, Brazil, June.

Schwarz, K.P., M.G. Sideris and R. Forsberg (1985). "Orthometric heights without levelling." Presented at the Annual Meeting of the Canadian Institute of Surveying, Edmonton, Alberta, Canada.

Schwarz, K.P., R.V.C. Wong, J. Hagglund and G. Lachapelle (1984b) "Marine positioning with a GPS-aided inertial navigation system." *Proceedings of the National Technical Meeting of the Institute of Navigation,* San Diego, Ca, U.S.A., January.

Scott, V.D. and J.G. Peters (1983). "A standardized exchange format for NAVSTAR GPS geodetic data." Applied Research Laboratories, The University of Texas at Austin, Austin, Tx, U.S.A., March.

Scott, V.D., J.R. Clynch and J.G. Peters (1986). "A proposed standardized exchange format for NAVSTAR GPS geodetic data." Preliminary paper, Applied Research Laboratories, University of Texas at Austin, Austin, Tx, U.S.A.

Service Argos (1978). "Argos user's guide." Centre National d'Etudes Spatiale, Toulouse, France.

Smith, D.E., D.C. Christodoulidis, R. Kolenkiewicz, P.J. Dunn, S.M. Klosko, M.H. Torrence, S. Fricke and S. Blackwell (1985). "A global geodetic reference frame from LAGEOS ranging (SL5.1AP)." *Journal of Geophysical Research*, Vol. 90, No. B11, pp. 9221-9233.

Sony Corporation (n.d.). "Instruction manual for GTT-2000 GPS receiver." (Preliminary.)

Spilker, J.J. (1978). "GPS signal structure and performance characteristics." In: Global Positioning System. Papers published in *Navigation*, reprinted by The (U.S.) Institute of Navigation, Vol. I, 1980, pp. 29-54.

Stansell, T.A. (1978). *The Transit Navigation Satellite System*. Magnavox Government and Industrial Electronics Company, Torrence, Ca, U.S.A.

Steeves, R.R., D. Delikaraoglou and N. Beck (1986). "Development of a Canadian Active Control System using GPS." *Proceedings of the Fourth International Geodetic Symposium on Satellite Positioning*, University of Texas at Austin, Austin, Tx, U.S.A., April, pp. 1189-1203.

Stiffler, J.J. (1966). "Telecommunications." Vol. V of Space Technology, NASA.

Stiller, A. (1985). "Development of civilian GPS receivers for the Federal Republic of Germany for different applications." Deutsche Forschungs- und Versuchsanstalt für Luft und Raumfahrt, E.V.

Sturza, M.A. (1984). "Commercial aviation GPS navigation set architecture." The National Technical Meeting of The (U.S.) Institute of Navigation, San Diego, Ca, U.S.A., January.

Swift, E.R. (1985). "NSWC's GPS orbit/clock determination system." *Proceedings of the First International Symposium on Precise Positioning with the Global Positioning System*, Rockville, Md, U.S.A., April, Vol. I, pp. 51-62.

Texas Instruments (1986). "Product specifications for TI-4100 Navstar Navigator." Lewisville, Ky, U.S.A., January.

Thompson, S.D. (1985). *Everyman's Guide to Satellite Navigation.* ARINC Research Corp.

Thornton, C.L., W.G. Melbourne and T.H. Dixon (1986). "NASA GPS-based geodetic program in Mexico and the Caribbean." *Proceedings of the Fourth International Geodetic Symposium on Satellite Positioning,* University of Texas at Austin, Austin, Tx, U.S.A., April, pp. 1003-1018.

Tomioka, G. and K. Yamada (n.d.). "GPS navigator." Japan Radio Corproation, Tokyo, Japan.

Trimble Navigation (1985). "Trimble 4000S GPS surveyor." Rev. 11/27/85, Sunnyvale, Ca, U.S.A.

Trimble Navigation (1986). "GPS surveyor system." Sunnyvale, Ca, U.S.A., February.

U.S. Department of Defense/Department of Transportation (1982). *Federal Radionavigation Plan.* Vols. I-IV, March.

U.S. Department of Defense/Department of Transportation (1984). *Federal Radionavigation Plan.* Final report: March 1982-December 1984. U.S. Department of Defense document #DoD-4650.4 and U.S. Department of Transportation document #DoT-TSC-RSPA-84-8. Available from NTIS, Document AD-A151 295.

U.S. Federal Geodetic Control Committee (1986). "Proposed geometric geodetic survey standards and specifications for geodetic surveys using GPS relative positioning techniques." Version of 1 September, Rockville, Md, U.S.A.

University of Texas (1986). *Proceedings of the Fourth International Geodetic Symposium on Satellite Positioning.* University of Texas at Austin, Austin, Tx, U.S.A., April, 2 volumes.

van Dierendonck, A.J., S.S. Russell, E.R. Kopitzke and M. Birnbaum (1978). "The GPS navigation message." In: *Global Positioning System.* Papers published in *Navigation,* reprinted by The (U.S.) Institute of Navigation, Vol. I, 1980, pp. 55-73.

Vaníček, P. and E.J. Krakiwsky (1986). *Geodesy: The Concepts.* 2nd rev. ed., North-Holland, Amsterdam, The Netherlands.

Vaníček, P., R.B. Langley, D.E. Wells and D. Delikaraoglou (1984). "Geometrical aspects of differential GPS positioning." *Bulletin Géodésique,* 58, pp. 37-52.

Vaníček, P., G. Beutler, A. Kleusberg, R.B. Langley, R. Santerre, and D.E. Wells (1985). "DIPOP differential positioning program package for the Global Positioning System." Department of Surveying Engineering Technical Report No. 115, University of New Brunswick, Fredericton, N.B., Canada.

Vaníček, P., D.E. Wells, A. Chrzanowski, A.C. Hamilton, R.B. Langley, J.D. McLaughlin and B.G. Nickerson (1983). "The future of geodetic networks." *Proceedings of the International Association of Geodesy Symposia,* Symposium d, The Future of Terrestrial and Space Methods for Positioning, Hamburg, FRG, August, Vol. 2, pp. 372-379.

Vaníček, P., A. Kleusberg, R-G Chang, H. Fashir, N. Christou, M. Hofman, T. Kling and T. Arsenault (1986). "The Canadian geoid." Final contract report for the Geodetic Survey of Canada; Energy, Mines and Resources Canada, Ottawa, Ontario, Canada.

Vessot, R.F.C. (1976). "Frequency and time standards." In: *Methods of Experimental Physics,* Vol. 12, Pt C, ed. M.L. Meeks, Academic Press, N.Y., NY, U.S.A.

Wanless, B. (1985). "A prototype multi-station, multi-pass satellite data reduction program." M.Sc. thesis, Division of Surveying Engineering, The University of Calgary, Calgary, Alberta, Canada.

Ward, P. (1981). "An inside view of pseudorange and delta pseudorange measurements in a digital NAVSTAR GPS receiver." Presented at the ITC/USA/'81 International Telemetering Conference, San Diego, Ca, U.S.A., October.

Wells, D.E. (1974). "Doppler satellite control." Department of Surveying Engineering Technical Report 29, University of New Brunswick, Fredericton, N.B., Canada.

Wells, D.E., P. Vaníček and D. Delikaraoglou (1981). "The application of NAVSTAR/GPS to geodesy in Canada: Pilot study." Department of Surveying Engineering Technical Report 76, University of New Brunswick, Fredericton, N.B., Canada.

Wells, D.E., A. Kleusberg, S.H. Quek, J. McCullough and J. Hagglund (1985). "Precise ship's velocity from GPS: Some test results." *Proceedings of the First International Symposium on Precise Positioning with the Global Positioning System,* Rockville, Md, U.S.A., April, Vol. II, pp. 799-808.

Wong, R.V.C. and K.P. Schwarz (1983). "Dynamic positioning with an integrated GPS-INS." Division of Surveying Engineering UCSE Report 30003, University of Calgary, Calgary, Alberta, Canada.

Yiu, K.P., R. Crawford and R. Eschenbach (1982). "A low-cost GPS receiver for land navigation." *Navigation*, Journal of The (U.S.) Institute of Navigation, Vol. 29, No. 3, pp. 204-220. Also in *Global Positioning System*. Papers published in *Navigation*, reprinted by The (U.S.) Institute of Navigation, Vol. II, 1984, pp. 44-60.

Ziemer, R.E. and R.L. Peterson (1985). *Digital Communications and Spread Spectrum Systems*. Macmillan Publishing Co., N.Y., NY, U.S.A.